LEE

Otterman J. Hermen

LEE

Otterman J. Hermen

Rutledge Books, Inc. Danbury, CT

31630

Books by Otterman J. Hermen

Remembrance Past and Present: A Story

The Gift

Rutledge Books, Inc.
107 Mill Plain Road, Danbury, CT 06811
1-800-278-8533

Manufactured in the United States of America

Cataloging in Publication Data
Hermen, Otterman J.
  Lee

  ISBN: 1-887750-62-2
    I.   Title.
813   97-66793

All the names in this book have been deliberately changed, except where full names are used, to protect the living and the families of the deceased.

This story is based on the actual life of a woman. It is set at a time not unike our own. Fiction is always, however obliquely, about the time and place in which it was written.

For her children and grandchildren.

"The glory of ancestors sheds
a light around prosperity; it
allows neither their good or
bad qualities to remain in obscurity."

Caius Sallustius Crispus Sallust

Contents

Chapter	Title	Page
1.	Once	1
2.	Family	9
3.	Kin	31
4.	San Andres	41
5.	Education	47
6.	University	55
7.	Teaching	59
8.	Meeting	67
9.	Courtship	81
10.	Serenade	95
11.	Wedding	135
12.	Marriage	145
13.	Lester	165
14.	Riot	189
15.	Robert	201
16.	Separation	209
17.	War	227
18.	Apart	237
19.	Kam	251
20.	Judy	287
21.	Hugo	315
22.	Deathblow	333
	Epilogue	343

1.

ONCE

I once knew a man and his wife Lee, and their children, for more than thirty-two years, that endured in their love and support of each other, despite what I and others that knew them felt was their overabundance of misfortunes in their lives, yet they carried on in the wisdom according to an Arabic proverb.

.Life is composed of two parts:
That which is past — a dream; and
that which is to come — a wish.

Lee's husband had saved my life during the Korean War in 1950 under extremely dangerous conditions to his own. We were both members of the first American outfit to meet the enemy in Korea. Task Force Smith, composed of the 1st Battalion of our Infantry Regiment, met a strong enemy force at Osan on July 5, 1950, and we were very quickly forced to retreat. During the retreat, I was hit by intense incoming small arms fire in both of my arms, legs, and chest as I was directing my squad rearward in our panic to escape the certain death of remaining in our present position. When I went down, I was conscious but in a great deal of pain as my cries of "Medic," went unheeded in everyone's mad rush to make their getaway — except for Lee's future husband.

LEE

The North Koreans had a habit of once they downed an individual they ceased directing fire on him if they saw that he was just wounded (which was my condition), and waited; knowing that someone, or a team of medics would come to his aid, increasing their kill! As Lee's future husband's platoon passed through the position that my squad had previously held, he saw me, still conscious, weakly, painfully calling "Medic!" He waved his platoon rearward, and in a low crouch position left the road and ran to where I was half laying, half sitting in the rice paddy. That's when all hell broke loose—the North Koreans opened up with every small arms weapons they had! The incoming rounds were coming in so fast and furious (I still don't know how we were not hit) that it appeared that raindrops were striking the rice paddy around us! Without saying a word, nor attempting to dress my wounds, Lee's husband picked me up, threw me across his left shoulder, and still in his low crouch position, ran toward the road running aside the rice paddy to safety. That's when I passed out.

I awoke three days later in a ward at Tokyo General Hospital, Tokyo, Japan. The Korean War was over for me. The round that struck me in the chest had come to rest in my lung. The doctors removed it, and I was immediately shipped via an United States Air Force airplane ambulance back to the ZI (Zone of Interior) for two years of convalescing at a VA Hospital near my home. As soon as I was able, December 1950, I began to search, via correspondence with the Department of Army, Washington, DC, for the name and location of the individual that had saved my life. I knew that he was a member of the 1st Battalion of our Infantry Regiment because we were the first and only "Ground Pounders" in Korea in July of 1950. It was also known that he was a "Platoon Sergeant" by virtue of the six strips I saw on his fatigue jacket just before I passed out. I was motivated by such a

2

profound sense of gratitude for this total stranger that had saved my life while endangering his own, I knew that I had to find him to thank him — even if it took the rest of my life! As I laid in that rice paddy that sunny afternoon in July of 1950, wounded, hurting, in pain, and afraid; with no one heeding my calls for help, I just knew that I was going to die. To be snatched from the jaws of death leaves you with a deep-felt appreciation for life that those who never had this near death experience can never comprehend. You have been given another chance!

The Department of the Army (DoA) responded to my queries about Lee's future husband while I was still hospitalized in a VA Hospital near my northeastern home, informing me that the war in Korea was so fluid that there was no way they could provide me with the information requested. The units fighting in Korea were never in one place long enough. In January 1952, my former unit returned to Japan, making it's headquarters at Camp Schimmelpfenning, near Sendai. I wrote the Personnel Officer at Sendai, and learned that my Sergeant's name was Jones, and that he had been killed in action in August of 1950. By this time, 1952, I had been discharged from the United States Army, becoming a disabled veteran, while obtaining employment as a night guard at one of the numerous banks in my city. Over the years of being a night bank guard, I rose through the ranks to Sergeant, Lieutenant, Captain, and finally appointed to the position of Security Officer with the responsibility for the security of the entire institution. With the information I had received from my old outfit in Sendai about Jones' death, I still refused to believe that Jones was dead. I told myself, that you did not do what he had done concerning my rescue, then go off and get yourself killed!

Over the years, I continued to keep in contact with my old unit via the Department of the Army, while at the same time tracking them in the media. Anything that I heard about my former unit on the radio, television, or read in the print media, I entered in a journal that I diligently maintained. In late 1952, my former unit returned to Korea and moved north of the 38th Parallel with it's division, where it remained until the armistice. When the North Koreans finally exchanged their Prisoners of War (POW) list on December 18, 1951 of the 3,198 Americans, there was Jones' name listed. I knew that he had not died. He had survived the ordeal of North Korean/Chinese imprisonment which included mass deaths of allied POWs from starvation, medical neglect, brutality, and more vicious atrocities. During the first nine months of the Korean War, Pyongyango radio had broadcast official communiqués claiming capture of 65,000 allied troops. If the sample figures were representative, more than 70% of all allied prisoners had died or disappeared during captivity! On August 5, 1953, the first POWs started coming home. The first days brought most of the sick and wounded, on litters or hobbling on twisted limbs with makeshift crutches. This included Jones, for both of his kneecaps had been broken by the Camp Commandant while being held captive. The scene was repeated daily at Panmunjom trough August and the first week of September. Ambulance convoys carried the released POWs to a processing center near Munsan, and helicopters took the seriously ill or wounded men, including Jones, to hospitals in Korea and later on to Japan. At the hospital in Japan, Jones' kneecaps and other health related conditions arising from his captivity as a POW of the North Koreans/Chinese were successfully treated.

Once the Department of the Army had notified me (which I requested) that Jones was a patient at Tokyo General Hospital, I immediately mailed him a one page letter. It included my name, address, and telephone number, and informed him that I was the individual whose life he saved in July of 1950. I asked if we could meet once he returned to the States so I could thank him for what

no one else had done—heeded my cries for help! While convalescing at Tokyo General Hospital until March 1954, Jones was
also being debriefed by Army Intelligence about personnel that
had been declared Missing in Action (MIA) whom he might have
seen or come into contact with while a captive. During this time,
Jones answered my letter and agreed to meet with me. This is
when I discovered that we were from the same city and state but
different neighborhoods. Subsequent letters mentioned that he
was without any family that he knew about, and was raised in a
state institution for parentless children. He did not mention any
of his experiences as a POW or the inhumane brutality of his
North Korean/Chinese captors. Nor did he mention his hospitalization to repair what had been done to him as a POW. He only
spoke of his desire to come home, stating that he never doubted
that he wouldn't survive the camps. I was intrigued when I first
read of Jones' conviction that he would survive. How did he
know? I have since learned from my long friendship with Jones,
that there are survivors amongst us; individuals who will go to
their graves unbroken by life's blows because they have courage
— fortitude. According to Webster's Dictionary, the word fortitude is defined as "courage and strength to hold fast against danger, pain, and stress." Jones belonged to this small group of survivors and courageous men.

Sergeant Jones returned to the United States in March of
1954, but we did not meet until February of 1955, as he was on
his way out of the country to a volunteered overseas assignment—Newfoundland; mentioning that he was distressed by the
unjustified disdain that the majority of Americans had for their
soldiers. I could see the sadness in his face and hear the question
in his voice: Why did the American public feel the way they did
about their military? As he continued, he mentioned that he had
to get away from Americans and their negative attitudes about

him (being a professional soldier), and from others with their comments that soldiers were lazy, uneducated, good-for-nothing, and worse, depending upon what part of the country you where in. Jones said that if he did not leave the country, he knew that he would eventually react violently to the undeserved disrespect the American public directed toward him and others if they dared to wear their uniforms when traveling in public transportation. He had no desire to become involved with the law enforcement establishment of this country, no matter the rightness of his offense—he would lose before the so-called Bar of Justice just because he was poor!

After his tour was over in Newfoundland, Jones immediately volunteered for another overseas tour of duty. He was doing all he could to stay out of the United States, and possible trouble, because of his equally acquired disdain of the American public. Whenever he did come stateside between assignments or on leave, we would have our dinners, do the town together with our dates, and talk about our dreams. Even when Jones was away, we continued to correspond. I was one of nine living children—five girls and four boys—and my family became Jones' family, and I, his younger surrogate brother. I was fortunate in that I had an abundance of nieces and nephews to lavish with my affection and attention as they grew to adulthood, their children once they married, and Lee's children. Over the years I have had my share of ladies of the night, girlfriends, and my family leaving me with the belief that here was no physical or emotional need for me to marry. I was afraid that I would be in the middle of my life with a wife and children, and my damaged lung would just stop functioning—a fear I had ever since I was wounded in 1950. I did not want to put another human being through that daily fear that I have lived with since the Korean War: "What if this is the last day that I have to live and didn't know it?"

After he returned from Newfoundland, and a thirty day leave home, Jones was assigned to San Jose, Costa Rica (1958) as part of an Organization of American States (OAS) Geological Mapping Mission as their military advisor. When assistance was required with regard to transportation of equipment like trucks, jeeps, airplanes, and helicopters to their mapping sites, it was Jones' job to acquire them from the United States Central Command, Panama, Canal Zone. Jones was a natural born linguist, speaking five languages; German, French, Italian, Portuguese, and Spanish. It was his fluency in the latter two languages that landed Jones his assignment with the OAS mapping mission. Portuguese and Spanish were the languages that the mapping members spoke amongst themselves, and they spoke English only when conducting official business. After his detached duty with the OAS, Jones returned to the United States for a short in-country assignment, a thirty day leave, then on to another duty assignment to the Canal Zone, Republic de Panama.

While on leave before his redeployment to the Canal Zone, we did all the things that mature, single men of that time did: date, eat out, attend live stage shows and concerts, travel via train/automobile to events in neighboring states, reading hardcober books, discuss current affairs (I am a conservative and Jones a liberal), and continue our male bonding. In public, Jones was a very withdrawn person who said very little, but when he placed pen to paper, it was as if a floodgate has been opened! Because of his extensive and varied reading ever since he was able to hold a book, there was no topic that he could and did not hold forth—history, philosophy, politics, anthropology, poetry, science, the Almanach de Gotha, warfare, law, business, social issues, and religions. It was not uncommon to receive two envelopes as part of one letter, each envelope containing eight pages of single-space type-written sheets, that I responded to in

7

kind. Neither in our letters nor in person did we ever discuss Jones' experiences in the Korean War or as a captive of the Chinese/North Koreans. There are few Americans today who choose to remember that it was originally North Korea that we went to war with in June of 1950, but it was the so-called Chinese "volunteers" that captured the bulk of allied prisoners in December 1950, and originally maintained the camps that held them.

While on leave before reporting to his new duty station in the Canal Zone, Republic de Panama, after dinner and a play we returned to my parents home — two in the morning. Sitting on the top step to the front porch, smoking cigars (which I should not have been doing — but did anyway, because death is permanent no matter how it comes to you) I asked Jones what it was he wanted out of life. He thought a minute, drew on his cigar, exhaled the smoke in rings that glowed in the early morning light, and replied, "To find a women who would love me, have our children, and see in me what she could bring to our love that would make me the person she would want to spend her remaining years with. I know that if I had been loved and cared for differently (not in a state institution) as a child, I could have been a better person. I still have a lot of bitterness in me because of my life-style before joining the army." I made no reply to Jones' comments as we silently continued to smoke our cigars into the early morning hours, never realizing that he was to meet such a woman — Lee, and that she would change both of our lives forever.

> "Whatever may happen to thee, it
> was prepared for thee from all
> eternity."
>
> *Marcus Antoninus*

2.

FAMILY

I am writing this narrative about Lee because I realize that her children have no idea who she was, other than "Mom"—never once realizing that she was a person with dreams, disappointments, heartaches, personal tragedies, and the everyday fears that we all live with. I have been in Lee's home when she and Jones would try to tell them a little about their past, and in unison they would respond, "There go Mom and Dad talking history!" Over time, Lee and Jones stopped telling their children about their history. Jones would never undertake this endeavor to place Lee on paper, because he is comfortable with her place in his life, and her support and love for him from the very first moment they met. I do not take issue with Jones' view, but only contend that Lee, like all of us, was more than the sum of her actions and words. The children aside. Why do I take up this undertaking? Because when Jones and I die, there will be no one left to tell Lee's story! In my opinion, Lee's story is worth telling, for she meets Lamartine's definition of a woman:

> "There is a woman at the beginning
> of all great things."
> *Alphonse Lamartine*

Another reason for my effort is to document that a man and a woman can be friends and maintain their friendship even when the woman is married and the man is not. Women routinely make many lasting friendships during their lifetime with women that transcend marriage, rarely are they just friends with men (not including some brother and sister friendships). But Lee and I had a relationship for over thirty-two years as friends — for life. For me, my friendship with Lee brought on the knowledge of how uncompromising love and trust worked like the love between Lee and Jones. Just to be included in Lee's circle of those she loved and trusted, was for me, life rewarding. I knew that my biological family loved me, but with Lee I mattered as someone who might be overlooked without a family of his own. I was never forgotten for any family event or holiday—I was automatically included. Over the years, we never discussed the basis of our enduring friendship. We each accepted it as the natural course of our lives because of the importance of Jones to us.

Lee's parents were of French and Spanish ancestry respectively. Her mother and father were from the island of San Andres which is located on the far side of the Caribbean, approximately 250 miles southwest of Jamaica about half that distance from the eastern coast of Nicargua, and 480 miles west of Colombia to which it belongs, along with its sister island of Providence. Lee's parents were as ill-matched as man and wife as two people could be. Her mother was industrious, passive, and easily intimidated. Her father was lazy, vain, and physically abusive to his wife. When Lee's mother announced to her parents that she was going to marry a Palmer, her mother scolded her, saying, "Those Palmers are just no good!" There were sixteen Palmer brothers and sisters living on the island, each with their portion of the land they received after the death of their father. They did nothing with their inheritance but run the property into the ground that their father had worked so hard to make productive in order to leave them something of value when he died. They wouldn't even harvest the bananas or coconuts for a cash crop—they just let them rot on the trees and ground!" She continued that if Lee's mother went ahead and married into that "no good Palmer family," she would never speak to her again and would never do anything to help her! Lee's mother went ahead and got married, and until her death in 1954, they never spoke a word to each other although they lived next door and Lee's mother repeatedly called to her mother, asking for forgiveness. Lee's grandmother never replied to the pleas of her daughter.

Lee's parent's marriage produced four children—three boys and herself. The first son died after three days, the second son grew into an adult but died in the interior of Columbia in 1979, and the third son remained on San Andres Island and died there in 1981. Lee's father placed all of his hopes and dreams in his oldest son—lavishing attention, money, education, and love on him to the neglect of the other children in the family. But the boy, and later the man, was a true Palmer—lazy, vain, abusive, and violent. Lee's father attempted to teach the boy the basic rudiments of managing his income-producing property, which he never bothered to do himself. When and how to harvest the bananas and coconuts. Daily checking the rat guards on the coconuts trees to assure that they were secure. When to cutback the undergrowth around the trees, and how much to pay Machete Men (men and boys who hired themselves out as day laborers), and etc. Because they were alike, their arguments grew more violent as he matured. They fought over his absolute refusal to work with his father towards making a living for the family from the crops on the property. He would say to his father, "It's your land—you work it! I have other and better things to do with my time then to stay outside all day in the hot sun!" He was not only vain about his looks but also his clothing. All clothing—shirts, trousers, dresses, blouses, and skirts were handmade on the island by individuals with manual foot peddled sewing machines which Lee's father purchased for her oldest brother after sending him to school to become a taylor. Lee's oldest brother would never wear a shirt or trousers more than once, so he would go to his father for money to have another made.

When Lee's mother repeatedly protested to her husband for his support of their oldest son in his conceitedness, his only shouted reply would be: "Mind your own business! It's my money and he's my son!" In the Spanish speaking societies of Lee's day, it was the desire of most males to have at least one son to carry on their name (although when daughters married they retained their family name)—Lee's father was no exception. Lee's mother attempted to correct her oldest son on some matter of his behavior many times, but only received verbal abuse of some perverted type. As Lee grew, and attempted to come to her mother's defense, she would receive the same disrespectful abuse.

The final break between her father and oldest brother came during a violent argument that resulted in Lee's father being knocked to the ground. Her father got up, and ran into the house for his machete. Returning-shouting, "You dare to strike your father! I will kill you!" Lee, her mother, and younger brother, all encircled the boy, crying and screaming, "Don't do it! Please don't kill him," as their father threatened them all with his raised machete. Her brother moved out of their home that same day, and moved in with a local prostitute, greatly distressing his mother and embarrassing his family. It was as if: Lee's brother wanted to put their "family's face in the dirt" by publicly embarrassing them through his actions.

Lee's father's wealth originated from commercial deep sea fishing. He started out with one ocean-going boat and a crew of six, fishing the waters of the Caribbean Sea for three months each trip. If his daily catch was large, he would put into ports in Costa Rica, Nicaragua, Republic de Panama, and Cartagena, Columbia to sell it. If he had a small catch, he returned to San Andres Island to sell his fish, using the proceeds to buy provisions and to refurbish his boat for another trip. The money for Lee's father's original fishing boat came from his father who once owned Negro slaves, and was a wealthy owner of properties on San Andres and Providencia Islands, and mainland Republic de Colombia (in what is now the Republic de Panama and the Canal Zone.) With sixteen children, Lee's grandfather attempted to provide for their future by arranging the marriages of his daughters with other wealthy families on the island and mainland Colombia. He sent one son to Harvard University, and started the others in their own businesses—Lee's father chose deep sea fishing. After selling his catch of fish and paying his expenses, Lee's father at first plowed back the profit into the business planning to extend the number of boats he would own, training the captains in the utilization of navigational charts and the sextant, allowing them half of every catch. Turning his original boat over to one of his trained captains, he now had three boats fishing in the Caribbean Sea. He operated out of San Andres Island, received a parcel of land from his father, built a spacious house on it, and began to live the life of the idle rich. Raising cocks for fighting, increased his gambling, drinking, and womanizing throughout the island as he ran his deep sea fishing business into the ground by not paying his bills or taxes. The profits were used to maintain his chosen life-style. It was during this downward spiral that the islanders began to see Lee's father's true nature, and saw that he was a man with little moral strength when it came to his behavior, engaging in any activity that gave him pleasure. Lee's father was a strikingly handsome man—six feet four, straight bright reddish-brown hair, bushy eyebrows, light blue eyes, straight nose, thin lips, and a very thin-muscular physique. In fairness to Lee's father, there were many residents of the island who were more than willing to help him spend his money as they laughed at his antics and made insulting remarks about him behind his back.

The bulk of the Palmer's holding in Columbia before 1903 lay in that strip of land 10 miles wide across the isthmus that the construction of the Panama Canal was built through and Panama City. An agreement was made with Columbia, known as the Hay-Herran Treaty, by which Columbia was to be paid for the concessions outlined in the treaty the sum of ten million dollars in cash and an annuity of 250 thousand, once their government approved the treaty. The United States ratified the treaty in March of 1903, but the following August the Colombian Congress rejected it, to the great chagrin of President Theodore Roosevelt, who preferred Panama to the Nicaraguan route for the canal and was impatient to have the affair settled.

The deadlock was solved by a revolution in Panama. A group (the five prominent families) in Panama desired the canal project to be put through and suggested to the United States that it seize the strip of land by force, or countenance a revolution. The United States man-of-war, the Nashville, arrived at Colon November 2, 1903. On November 3, an uprising occurred in Panama City, November 4, American Marines disembarked at Colon, and bribed the Colombian troops to leave the next day. The United States recognized the Panama government on the 13th, and on the same day Bunau-Varilla (a French citizen) was received at Washington, DC as an representative of the new government. On November 18, a treaty was signed by the two countries which contained the following points: the United States guaranteed the independence of Panama; paid them 10 million in cash and an annuity beginning nine years after ratification of 25 thousand; and in turn received a strip of territory 10 miles wide across the isthmus. Work on the canal began in 1904, and on 15 August 1914, it was opened to the commerce of the world.

That is where the rub comes in, the "ten million in cash" that was paid to the Panama government by the United States—none of it was ever paid to the owners that lost property in the 10 mile wide strip of land that the canal was built through. It was this lack of compensation for lost land that is the root cause for a large number of Panamanians' anti-American feelings—they blame the United States for the loss of their countrymen's property. They believe that the United States should have paid the individual property owners, and not given the money to the new government. With the loss of the Palmer's properties in the new Republic de Panama (except one parcell in Panama City), Lee's father's financial positions rapidly deteriorated after the death of her grandfather. She was told growing up by other family members. He father could no longer keep up the cost of maintaining three fishing boats, so he sold them to the individual captains that he had trained for a quarter of their value. Lee's father only received a sixteenth of her Grandfather's land holdings upon his death, which could not maintain his previous life-style of the ideal rich, and he absolutely refused to attempt anything else to make a living, even with the encouragement of his siblings and other family members. There was a degree of delight amongst a great many of the islanders to see Lee's father brought so low so quickly, and it was this knowledge of his neighbor's delight (which he resented) that prevented him from ever getting along with anyone on San Andres Island when Lee was growing up. It was then that Lee's father noticed and began to pursue Lee's mother with the aim of making her his wife.

The Wookers were also an original family of San Andres Island, but were never large landowners. They owned the land

15

their homes were constructed on and little else. Over the years, the family males—from 10 years of age onward—hired themselves out as crew members on the many fishing boats operating from the island (some had been crew members on Lee's father boat) or as machete men. The one thing that everyone on the island agreed and would attest to was that all the Wooker family members were devout Roman Catholics and lived their Christian faith. This was the type of clan which Lee's mother came out of. Lee's father never made any overtures toward Lee's mother when he was living the life of the idle rich even though the species house that he had built for himself was next door to her family's which enabled him to see her everyday quietly, going about her daily chores. Lee's father knew that her mother's family would never allow her to keep company with a man that, as their religion taught, was living in sin. After his great comedown, he began to look at Lee's mother with new interest, with the view of making her his wife and mother of their children. Lee's mother, by her own admission, was not an overly attractive woman, admitting to Lee that she was flattered by the attention of one of the handsomest men on the island. The only two photographs Lee had of her mother were an old black and white passport picture and one of her laying in a wooden coffin just before her burial in 1954. The passport picture shows a sad looking woman with her head tilted to the side, with hair appearing to be black, downcast eyes, flat nose, and full lips. The picture of her mother in her coffin shows an older, sad looking woman who's hair is entirely white—at thirty-nine years of age. Lee's mother was the only girl, with four brothers who, along with their mother, did not approve of Lee's father. They knew of the type of life he lead and about his uncontrollable drinking and womanizing throughout the island, but would not stand in her way if that was what their sister wanted. The adamant opposition to the match of Lee's mother and father came from her mother, who repeatedly told her, "You know that I am a Christian woman, who speaks ill of no one, but those Palmers are just no good, and if you get involved with them, you will come to a bad end!" But Lee's mother would not listen to anyone, and married him anyway, moved into his house to live a life of suffering until she found peace in death.

Lee would often say when reminiscing about her mother, that the only reason she believed her father married her mother, was because he knew that was the only way he could ever has his way with her. As close as Lee said she was to their mother, she never told her why she defied her mother and family. When asked, would reply, "You make your bed, you lie in it." Because Lee's father refused to work his land for income to support his family, it fell to Lee's mother to become the breadwinner even before there were children. Her industriousness came into play very early in her marriage when she acquired a 100 pound bag of flour on credit, and used it to bake bread that she sold door to door with the children's help but crying because her own mother would never buy any. Over time, from the profits of her bread sales, she opened a one-room store in the front of her home that she operated with Lee's help until her death, selling her and Lee's baked goods, as well as neighbor's handicrafts for a percentage of the asking price. To feed her family she would go into the serf with a net to catch fish, taking the catch to her husband for him to pick out which fish she was to cook for him. This infuriated Lee, and she would tell her mother, "He does nothing, yet he gets to pick the largest fish for himself. That's not right!" Lee's mother never responded to her daughter's indignation. Lee also helped her mother raise chickens for their eggs, which left Lee with a disdain for all chicken as a source of eatable food. They also raised pigs in the wild to buy Lee's shoes, uniforms, and books for school. Lee's mother literally worked herself to death without protest. Lee's older brother was just like his father when he was young—drinking and womanizing throughout the island. And although her younger brother attempted to help, he was just too sickly, and suffered from shortness of breath whenever he attempted to do anything physical.

When Lee's mother died in 1954, Lee's father was in Bogota, Columbia having his right leg amputated below the knee due to gangrene. He had treated himself for a cut that did not respond to treatment, and he never knew he had a medical problem until he lost the sight in his right eye. Once he reported to the Health Station on the island, he was immediately flown, via seaplane, to a hospital in Bogota. Because of national health insurance, the government provided him with a wooden leg and a glass eye — free of charge!

Although the middle child, she was the only one living home. One morning, her mother never got out of bed as Lee was preparing to go to work while home from the University for the summer, and complained that she was so tired. Unknown to Lee, she slipped into a coma. When her mother did not respond to her pleas to wake up, Lee frantically bicycled to get the nurse at the Health Station. Lee quickly bicycled home with the nurse and found her mother still unconscious. After the nurse had examined Lee's mother, she told her that her mother had experienced a massive heart attack and there was nothing anyone could do there or in Bogota. All Lee should attempt to do was to keep her mother clean, comfortable, and pray as she waited for the end. She thanked the nurse as she left to return to the Health Station. The government of Colombia maintained on San Andres Island, a Health Station staffed by two highly trained government employed nurses (what we would call today Nurse Practitioners) whose job was to administer to the health needs of the islanders.

The Health Station was equipped with a short-wave radio, which enabled the nurses to air evacuate to mainland Colombia those needing more skilled medical services than they could provide. Lee did not go to work, but sat beside her mother's bed crying. She sent for her brothers who did not respond—for reasons they took to their graves—to her call to come to their mother as she lay dying.

The next day, Lee arranged for the burial of her mother after notifying her brothers that their mother had died. She took care of all the arrangements. She washed the body (a duty of daughters in her country), fixed her hair, and dressed her in good underclothing and her best going to church dress. She picked the spot on their land where the grave was to be dug, arranged and paid for the unfinished pine coffin to be delivered to the house, cut the wild flowers to be placed around the coffin, and sent for a priest and a photographer to take a picture of her mother in the coffin for her father to see when he returned from Bogota. Lee had already notified her father of his wife's sudden death, via wireless. After the grave-side service, both families and friends left the burial site, leaving only Lee and her younger brother and his family to see the grave closed. Her oldest brother returned to the house ahead of Lee and ransacked it looking for money. When Lee did return home, alone and emotionally drained, she found her older brother waiting for her, enraged! Before Lee could speak, she was grabbed by the neck of her black mourning dress with his left hand, while he made threatening gestures with his fist in her face. "Where's the money? I know Ma had money because she ran that damn store out front as long as I remember! You better give it to me or I will bust your face in!" Struggling to get out of his grip, she kicked between his legs, clawing with her fingernails at his face that she could not reach, and his arm that was holding her in a straight-arm grip of steel, imploring him to let her go. "There's no money!" she shouted. "There never was! Ma bought everything on credit! You know that! What money I had all went to bury her." With a rage that exploded in his voice, Lee's brother shouted, "You bitch!" punching her right in the center of her face, breaking her nose. When the blow struck, blood splattered over her face and dress along with the accompanying pain like someone sticking a hot poker in her face. As he releases his grip on the neck of her now torn dress, Lee fell to the floor on all fours, as blood mixed with saliva flowed from her nose, lip and mouth: she painfully shouted to her brothers back as he was leaving the house, "You are some man to do this to your defenseless sister on the very day that we have buried our mother. You will get yours! I will pray for you!" In 1954, Lee's brother was six feet, five inches tall and weighted 290 pounds, with Lee weighting in at just a thin 110 pounds.

After returning to University at the beginning of the school year, it was another year before Lee again returned home for vacation in 1955, the same year that Lee's father returned from Bogota, Colombia minus a leg and an eye. Lee never told her father what had happened to her nose because she knew that he would attempt to kill her brother for what he had done and with one leg and eye, Lee was afraid that he might be the one killed. She never went to the Health Station the day she was brutalized by her brother (embarrassed), and told everyone that asked that she fell face forward, on a piece of coral one night while going to the outhouse without a flashlight. Until she left San Andres Island for good, she never spoke to or confronted her older brother again. When he saw her coming, he went the other way. If Lee went into a store and he was already there, he would immediately leave without saying a word, his head hung low. Lee once stated that he did not want to look at the handiwork of his fist. It was then that Lee told herself that no man would ever hit her again, and that she would never marry a Spaniard (condemning herself to die as an Old Maid), because when she was growing up it was commonplace for men on the island to strike their women with their fist.

Lee had never told anyone what her brother had done to her until she told Jones. He held her close and attempted to kiss away her tears as he told her, "Never again! You have me now and I will go to my grave before I will allow anyone to ever put their hands on you!"

In 1978, fourteen years into their marriage, Jones convinced Lee that the entire family should take a trip to The Republic de Panama, in order for the children to see where their parents met, fell in love, courted, married, and lived. This included a visit to San Andres Island, Colombia, to see where their mother grew up, lived, and went to school. They also wanted to locate her mother's grave in order to place a monument on the site so that its location would not be forgotten. Nine years earlier, Lee and Jones sent money to what was believed to be a family friend on the island, with instructions for her to purchase a monument and have it placed on Lee's mother's grave. They received a reply that their instructions had been followed, and that the grave site was now permanently marked. Lee and Jones thanked the woman with relief, assured that her mother's grave would not become overgrown with vegetation. Two years later, a distant relative from Panama visited the island and went to Lee's mother's grave site, and upon returning to her home in Panama City, informed Lee that there was no stone her mother's grave! This news greatly distressed Lee because of her constant fear of a lost grave site which is why she agreed to return to San Andres although she often commented, "You do not go back!"

Before they left, Jones told me in the strictest of confidence, that the real reason he suggested the trip to San Andres Island,

Colombia, was that he was going to seek out Lee's older brother and bust both of his kneecaps for what he had done to her in 1954! Jones is the most vindictive person that I have ever known. He would die and go to Hell in an attempt to get even for a wrong (actual or perceived) done to him. In 1969 sixteen years after being released from the POW camp while visiting a friend in New York City, he saw a former POW hut member after they had been released, that he claimed betrayed him, going down the iron subway stairs. The man did not see Jones behind him, and Jones pushed him down the remaining steps. As he walked past him, laying crumpled with a broken leg at the bottom of the steps, he could see the pain in his face and smiled at him as he passed on his way. Just then, Jones said, the man remembered who he was as their eyes met, and Jones said that he saw and smelled his fear, and was glad. Again, in 1975 (twenty-two years after being releases from the POW camp) while attending a Pops Concert in Boston, Massachusetts, (Lee always gave Jones a ticket as one of his birthday presents), he saw another former hut member from the camp that attempted to have him court-martialed once they were released in 1953. When the concert was over, Jones followed him to his car which was parked on a poorly lit street near the concert hall. His former hut member had a women with him, that Jones took to be his wife, and just as he was about to put his key in the door, he called his name. He stopped what he was doing and looked at Jones with a puzzled expression on his face. Jones said that he could see from the expression on his face and in his eyes, for by then he was standing body close to his former hut member, that he really did not remember who he was until he mentioned that he was his former Hut Leader from the POW camp during the Korean War. The color drained from his face as he realized that his life was in danger, as he remembered Jones promise to find him for the lies he told, even if it took him the rest of his life. Jones took great delight in looking into the face of his former hut member, seeing and smelling his fear as he beat him bloody about the face with his fist. As Jones administered the beating, the woman he took to be his wife was screaming at the top of her lungs for help, from the other side of the car, but none was forthcoming. The beating took less than five minutes, for his victim made no attempt to defend himself. This lead Jones to believe that the victim knew he had it coming because of his lies about him. Jones walked away from this battered man crumpled on the ground alongside his car and his still screaming women, please with himself. Wondering as he walked away while buttoning his suit coat to hide his bloody white shirt, what story would this man tell his women to explain the beating and why he did not attempt to defend himself? Jones was sure that he would not tell his women that he had lied about the man who had saved his life during captivity and that that man had found him. In any other person but Jones, I would not believe this revengeful disposition. Jones has been unable to accept some situations, as they pertain to people when they lie and betray you for no reason — as just part of life but Jones claims that he lives the only way he knew how— Don't get mad, get even. Once he arrived home and Lee saw his bloody shirt and suit coat, she screamed because she thought he was hurt. After Jones explained that he was not injured and that it was the other fellow's blood, he then explained what had happened. She looked at him with fire in her eyes, telling Jones, "You could have been killed!" That was the end of his birthday Pops Concert tickets.

When they returned from their trip, Jones informed me that they never reached San Andres Island. They all had an enjoyable two weeks in The Republic de Panama, and at the beginning of their third week, they took the train across the isthmus to Colon where they were to book passage on a boat for the twenty-four hour trip to the island. After arriving in Colon, they walked the docks with the children, talking to boat captains about passage to San Andres, when Lee turned to Jones and told him, "I am not going back! It's been over twenty years and with no stone, we will never find my mother's grave again."

With all of Jones' persuasive skills and pillow talk, he could not get Lee to change her mind. He told me it was as if Lee had read his mind and knew what he planned to do to her older brother if he was still on the island, and was afraid for him to go.

Lee's attitude about men hitting women and wanting no part of that in her adult life was not an overnight conversion on her part, but it was because of her brother's attack on her, and witnessing her mother's passivity when her father often struck her for come perceived malefaction. Compounding the dangerous living conditions Lee's mother lived with was the added condition of her husband's continuous drinking and womanizing throughout the island and the Republic de Panama. The drinking was financed by any money that he could steal out of her store's cigar cash box. Lee's mother then had her daughter carry all the surplus cash around her neck (inside of her dress) in a cloth drawstring bag she made. When Lee's father could not steal money from his wife's store, the owners of the bars would allow him unlimited drinks just to see him drink himself into a stupor while making an ass of himself, allowing the customers to laugh at his antics. When he was sloppy drunk and Lee's mother would hear him coming up the road to their house at night, shouting his profanities about his wife, her family, his family, and the world in general, she would hurriedly wake the children and send them, in their bed clothes, four houses down the road to their great grandmother's until morning. When the children returned home the next morning, they could not help but to notice that their mother had been beaten again by their father—black eye, broken lip, swollen jaw, and limping when she walked. If their father was home when they returned from their great grandmother's they dared not go and attempt to comfort their mother, for to do so would result in another beating, with their father raining the blows upon their mother as he screamed at her, "You are turning my children against me!" All they could do was to go to their rooms (the two boys shared a room), get in their beds, pull the covers over their heads, and cry over the pain that they knew their mother was suffering.

If it was daylight when Lee's father was about to beat up on his wife (she always knew)) she would tell all of the children to go down to the beach and remain there until she came for them. Lee said that when they had to go to the beach they all sat huddled, hugging each other as they continuously cried because they knew what was happening to their mother at home. Sometimes they had to remain at the beach until nightfall before their mother came to take them home, and when they arrived, their father would sure to be absent. Then Lee and her brothers would all cry, hugging their mother wherever they could get a arm hold as they asked why. Their mother never answered.

Upon returning from the beach once, Lee and her brothers noticed that their father had hit their mother in the mouth with such force that it had knocked out two of her upper front teeth. For the balance of her life Lee said that her mother was so embarrassed by her missing teeth because everyone on the island knew how it happened, for her father bragged about beating his wife, and that thereafter, whenever she spoke, she placed her hand in front of her mouth to hide the gap.

It was from her pigs in the wild that Lee's mother obtained hard currency (most of the commerce on the island was barter), for emergencies, such as shoes for the children when they were small. Lee's father vehemently objected to Lee attending the Catholic school because they had to pay. He often told his wife, in Lee's presence, "That is too much money to spend for nothing, when all she's going to grow up to be is a whore!"

Lee was well aware from a very early age, the disdain her father felt for her just because she was female. The islanders also never let her forget how her father reacted when he returned from Colon, Republic de Panama, with his healthy baby daughter. Her father filled his canoe with cases of whiskey, rowed out into the bay in front of their home, and for three days drank the whiskey until it was gone, cursing his newborn daughter for not being male, his wife for giving birth to a girl, and God for allowing his daughter to see the light of day.

Lee's mother knew her husband was wrong about their daughter, and placed Lee in the Catholic school in order for her to obtain an education and leave the island once she became an adult. Her brothers attended the free Protestant and missionary schools, which provided a cursory education to all comers. The only organized educational institution recognized by the Colombian Government was the Catholic school. Whenever Lee's mother had to kill one of her pigs to defray the cost of her daughter's education, Lee's father would be sure to make his displeasure known to them both, saying, "She's only going to end up being an educated whore!"

During these encounters, Lee's mother would always be sure to remind her husband, "I was a virgin when you married me. I was no whore, nor will our daughter ever be one!"

Lee's father never struck her growing up, although he frequently became angry with her as a teenager, because she would not do as he demanded concerning dating, wanting to go to college and to travel, and to leave the island once she was out on her own. He was afraid of his wife's reaction if he ever struck any of their children, especially their daughter because she knew that he despised her. Lee's mother had made her father a solemn promise (told Lee) that if he ever made the mistake and hit one of their children for any reason, she would poison him. Lee's father had reason to heed his wife's warning, for it was the woman of each household that prepared the daily food. There were cases in the island's history according to Lee, that husbands had been poisoned by their wives for some great transgression, such as incest, rape and sodomy.

By the time that Lee's mother had died, it was too late for her father to ever think about striking her, because she was a young woman on her own. After Lee's father returned from Bogota, Colombia, and she returned from The Republic de Panama a year later, Lee confronted him as to how their lives would now be lived.

She told her father, "I am not your wife! I will never take the physical and verbal abuse you inflicted upon my late mother, but I will attempt to take care of you because I can't hire anyone to care for you when I am away at University due to your history of confrontation with everyone on the island. This may mean you will have to come to Panama, for that is where I plan to live once I obtain my degree. I could never live on this island after all the horrible things you did to my mother. I have constantly been reminded by you and others of what you thought of me because I was female and I don't care anymore. But you are wrong, and always have been wrong about what I would grow up to be and do with my life. Now it is your turn to do as I say and if you ever cross me I will walk out on you and leave you to die all alone!"

He listened to his daughter in silence and didn't utter a word when she had finished. And that is the way Lee and her father lived together until Jones came into their lives.

Lee's mother only overcame her passivity only once during

Lee's childhood. A prostitute had confronted Lee's mother as they both were leaving a Sunday morning mass, telling her very descriptively in a voice that carried, what a good time she had with her husband that Saturday night. Their father was not with them—he was at home sleeping it off—and her mother was so embarrassed by that was described to her, that Lee said it appeared that she was going to faint from shame. When they arrived home her mother woke her husband and proceeded to tell him what had transpired at the church and asked him what he was going to do about it. He looked at his wife, standing beside their bed in her best going to chuch dress—mortified, laughed, said nothing, and turned over on his side to go back to sleep.

Very calmly, Lee's mother replied, "I will not have my face publicly placed in the dirt by one of your low class women," then left the bedroom. Two months passes and one Sunday morning after mass, Lee's mother told her and her brothers to remain at the church (something she had never done before), and play with the other children until she came for them. Long after that Sunday Lee learned why her mother had left them there and what had happened to her father when her mother arrived home alone. Lee's father had "hung one on" that Saturday night so badly that he had to hold his eyelids open with his fingers. This is what her mother had been waiting for. He was laying in their bed on his stomach with nothing on but a pair of white boxer shorts. Lee's mother told her that she took a fishing net and tied her husband to the bed—from his neck to his ankles—then proceeded to beat him the length of his body with a tied bundle of switches that she collected one each day over a period of two months, without saying a word. When Lee's father passed out from the blows, her mother threw buckets of ocean salt water on his body to revive him, then proceeded her silent beating. Lee's father's screams and struggle to free himself only entangled him more as he pleaded with his wife to stop. Lee's mother did not heed her husband's screams or pleas to stop, nor answer his questions of why. She just continued to beat her now semiconscious husband until she became too exhausted to life her bundle of switches. Lee's mother cut the fishing net with her husband's machete in order for him to care for his bloody body, once he regained complete consciousness, then went to retrieve the children who were waiting for her at the church. When they neared home, they all saw their father just coming out of the bay in his bloody boxer shorts with a wet, bloodstained bed sheet wrapped around him as he walked very painfully and slowly down the road past them toward the Health Station without saying a word. Lee nor her brothers never asked their mother what had happened to their father as he went by.

The Sunday of his beating was when Lee's father completely stopped his drinking, and it was two years before he was completely recovered from his injuries. According to Lee, he never hit her mother again.

Long after her mother had died, Lee often reflected upon why her mother stayed with a man that did not respect or love her, and was physically abusive to her. Lee said that after much thought, that it was more than intimidation and her children that kept her mother with her father, but it was the simple fact that her mother had no place to go if she left him. She could not return to her home because her mother had warned her not to marry a Palmer and disowned her. Her brothers, with families of their own, would not assist her with her pleas of help when she had been beaten by her husband, for it was felt in those days that it was a man's "right" to control and "discipline" (read hit) his wife. Even with family's of their own, and their belief in men's "rights, remained unquestioned even when it involved their sister. Lee's uncles would not dear go against the edict of their mother," their sister had married a Palmer, after being told not to, so was no longer a member of their family."

It took money to get off the island, via boat or seaplane, which Lee's mother had none of. What money she earned from her store and pigs went to take care of her children. Suicide was not an option because she was a Roman Catholic, and that faith declares that suicide is a sin for which there is no forgiveness. So Lee's mother endured and suffered in the marriage to her father until her death in 1954. Lee often mentioned that she was devastated because she not only had lost her mother, but also her best friend. It was not until she had a family of her own that Lee came to look upon the death of her mother as a blessing from God—he took her mother out of her suffering, enabling no one to ever hurt her again.

> "How many hopes and fears, how many
> ardent wishes and anxious apprehensions
> are twisted together in the threads that
> connect the parent with the child."
> *Samuel Griswold Goodrich*

3.

KIN

There were large clans of Palmers and Wookers inhabiting San Andres Island, Colombia as long as the island was known to have been inhabited. Equally, as long as any inhabitant could remember, the Palmers were known for their sluggishness and the Wookers were known for their piety and compassion. This folklore about both families as well as all the families on the island, was passed from generation to generation by word of mouth and entries made to their family Bibles.

Lee's father's oldest brother was sent in 1920, by his father, to Harvard University to obtain a degree in economies with the aim of returning to San Andres Island to assist his father in managing his holdings. When their father died, he would be able to advise his fifteen brothers and sisters on the profitable management of their inheritance. While at Harvard, the oldest son lived the life of the privileged rich. He did well in his studies, and upon graduation, he moved to New York City, never to return to his island home and family. No amount of threats or pleading by his father, siblings, and other family members could convince the oldest son to return home, even after repeatedly being informed about the distress he was causing his father and other family members, especially Lee's father, who idolized his older brother. Their father died, never seeing his firstborn again. Lee's father continued to correspond with his older brother over the years, with no thought of ever seeing him again. But the desire was always there.

After World War II, many of the inhabitants of San Andres Island, Colombia, began to emigrate to the United States of America after making money during the war in the Canal Zone off-loading and loading ships as part of the war effort. There was nothing in Colon, Panama City, or in the Canal Zone, or the island to spend their money on, so it was saved by most families (gambled or drank away by others), so they could go to America and live the good life as was pictured in the American motion pictures they saw and magazines they read. Everyone on San Andres Island knew that Lee's father's oldest brother had attended Harvard and was living in New York City, which was then the port of entry for those emigrating from the island. Naturally, after arriving in the United States, they would find Lee's father's older brother and attempt to get his advice about networking, and the location of others from San Andres. That was when they discovered that Lee's father's older brother had never used his Harvard education to make it in America, and was working at a Mom and Pop corner store as a clerk with a wife and six children ever since he graduated. He was unable to advise the many that came to see him. Lee often mentioned that the apparent Palmer's sluggishness was at work.

Over a period of more than forty years, Lee's father's adoration for his older brother never diminished, no matter what the San Andres islanders in the United States passed on to their family members when they telephoned home. They often said that he was nothing, or that he had all that high priced education and had done nothing with it. "Any asshole could be a store clerk without a college education," some would say. "He was no help to anyone looking for advice on how they could adjust to

American society. He never knew anything, even after living in the country all those years."

After fleeing the Panama riot of 1964 and arriving in the United States in February of that same year, Lee, her father, and Jones settled into their new home full of sadness (they had experienced a death before the riot), injured (Lee and her father had been attacked by their countrymen during the riot), depressed (neither of them had ever planned to come to or live in the United States), and penniless (all of their funds were frozen in Panama City banks due to the riot). With the mental baggage they carried, they went about the task of adjusting to their new situation.

Eight months after untangling the family's finances in The Republic de Panama, Lee said they began anew to build in the United States, the life they had planned for in Panama. Unknown to Lee and Jones, Lee's father confessed that he had always had a desire to come to America. Now, in 1964, his dream had been fulfilled after sixty-seven years. Lee's father immediately wrote his oldest brother in New York City to inform him that he was in the country, residing in Massachusetts with his daughter and son-in-law, and would like to come to visit after so long of a forced absence. Lee wrote her father's letters, for his spoken English was better then his written. She included in his letter that a day never went by during their separation that he did not think of him. Jones mailed the letter in April. May passed, with no answer from New York City. June came and went, and still no response from the older brother. In July, Lee's father wrote another letter to his brother, repeating the contents of his first letter, inquiring if he had received it. August and September passed without a reply from New York City. Lee's father became very frantic and perplexed as to why he could not hear from his older brother.

Then, in a fit of depression because his letters had not been answered, he accused Jones of not mailing the letters. Lee angrily told him, "You apologize right now, for that is just not so! Jones would never do anything like that!"

Before Lee's father could apologize, Jones took offense at his father-in-law's accusation and replied, "I did mail your letters! You have not heard from your older brother because he just does not want anything to do with you or us, for he knows that we are refugees from the riot in Panama, and believes that we will ask him for some type of financial help. Remember, Dad, this is America, and after so many years here, he is an American. They help no one—think back to our situation when we got off the plane last winter in the middle of a snow storm, penniless. We lived off the forty-two dollars I had in my pocket for a month. Until my next payday, you didn't see any American offering us a food basket, not even our church, after I explained our need. Did you? You bet your life you didn't! I will prove to you that I am right and have mailed your letters to your brother. Have Lee write another letter for you and I will mail it Certified Mail, Return Receipt Requested. That way your brother will have to sign for it. You will receive a receipt showing who signed for the letter and the date when it was delivered."

In October, Lee's father had her write another letter to his brother, pleading with him to reply. The certified receipt was returned with his brother's signature as the person who received the letter. No reply came until December, and in the letter Lee's father brother told him that he had received all of his past letters, yet had not bothered to answer them because he wanted nothing to do with him. He also told him to please stop writing because he would never reply. Lee told Jones when he came home from the base, how the color had drained from her father's face after he had read his brother's letter, and went upstairs to his bedroom in a state of shock over what he had read. She was worried. She looked in on her father periodically, but only saw him lying on his back on the top of his bed with his arms at his sides and eyes wide open, looking at the ceiling. After receipt of the letter from his brother, he stopped his daily walks around the neighborhood, going to the library to check out hard cover books for reading, and stopped his everyday reading of the local newspaper, and became very silent around the house. On December 16, 1964, Lee's father was admitted to the hospital with a stroke, and died on New Year's Day 1965. He was sixty-eight years of age and was buried that same day in the local cemetery, as was the custom on San Andres Island, Colombia.

Although throughout her life, Lee had her share of difficulties with her father's overbearing attitude and his attempts to control her as a teenager. She was still devastated by his unexpected death. Overbearing. After Lee graduated from the University of Panama, she took a teaching position in Panama City, and being unable to hire anyone on San Andres Island to care for her father (cook, wash has clothes and clean the house) she sent for him to come live with her in the house she had rented. When Lee's father came to her in Panama, she included instructions for him to bring her personal effects that were still in the house—her 78 RPM record collection, and six photograph albums containing pictures of her as a child, other members of the family and childhood friends, and of trips she had made throughout Central and South America. But when his boat arrived from the island at dockside, Colon harbor, her father told Lee that he had broken all of her records and burned all of her photograph albums, saying, "You don't need them!"

After hiring luggage handlers to load the suitcases and boxes on the train to Panama City, purchasing the tickets, and boarding the train, the trip across the isthmus was made in profound silence—Lee never uttered a word to her father. Lee was devastated and angry with her father over the loss of her records and photograph albums. When talking about the instance to me many years later with tears in her eyes, Lee mentioned that she knew the only reason her father did what he did, was because he knew how very much the things he destroyed meant to her and wanted to hurt her—and he did. When they finally arrived home, and before her father even had the opportunity to sit down, he received an angry tongue lashing from Lee about destroying her property. When Lee had spent her outburst, she proceeded into the kitchen eating area, knowing that nothing had changed. The fact still remained that some very sentimental personal items had been indiscriminately destroyed by her father, for no other reason than spite, and were lost to her forever.

When Lee and Jones began courting, her father attempted to break it up by telling Lee, "If you marry, who will take care of me? Gringos are no good—especially soldiers! It's your duty to take care of me because I have only one good eye and one leg. You are my only daughter!"

Lee told him, " I am not my mother, and you will never rule me the way you did her! Nor will I ever take the abuse she did. I love and trust Jones, something I thought I could never do growing up watching the way you mistreated my mother. If Jones ever asks me to marry him, I will in a minute! Why? Because I truly love him and just know that he loves me too even in the short time we have known each other, for he has a dream that I can share with him—a home with children. If you have a problem with anything that I have said, you know where the door is!"

From that instant after finding out who had the handle and who had the blade of the knife neither of them ever had any type of problems concerning Jones. In fact, Jones and Lee both had expected her father to be around to give them advice and to know his grandchildren. Jones never knew of his father-in-law's objections to him courting and marrying his daughter until after his death, for he genuinely liked and got along with Lee's father and was as devastated as she over his untimely death.

Neither Lee nor Jones ever speculated as to what part of that only letter from his oldest brother might have played in Lee's father's sudden death because no one can really know what is important in a person's life that enables them to live or die. Upon the death of her father, as was the custom in her country, (Columbia and the Republic de Panama), Lee went into deep mourning for one year, wearing only black clothing, participating in no social activities except attending mass. With the death of Lee's father, all contact was lost with the Palmers and Wookers in this country and on San Andres Island, Colombia and in the Republic de Panama.

And then there was Auntie, a member of the Wooker clan who was Lee's grandmother's sister and lived in Panama City for as long as anyone on San Andres Island could remember with her husband (who was a Panamanian) and had no children. Auntie was a living example of the Wooker's clan's credo of piety and compassion, and it was to her home that everyone went day or night, being assured that they would be fed, and if necessary, have a place to stay until they could straighten out what had sent them to Auntie's in the first place.

I had the pleasure of meeting Auntie when Lee and Jones brought her to this country for a month's vacation in July of 1972 and immediately liked the very open, positive attitude she demonstrated by her very presence. She was then five feet, eight inches tall, seventy years old, weighing over 300 pounds, with graying, long brown hair that fell to her waist, very light gray laughing eyes, a small nose, and lips that you often see on paintings of Cupids. She had an abiding love for Lee, who she called her "Baby," that knew no bounds.

During Auntie's visit in 1972, laughing, at a small dinner

with friends given by Lee and Jones in their home, Jones recited the story of the first time Lee took him to Auntie's home on the night of their second date:

Lee and Jones arrived at Auntie's home via taxicab and entered the courtyard through an arched gateway to be greeted by Auntie and her husband. Lee had telephones ahead telling them that she was bringing someone by that she wanted them to meet. Jones only knew that Auntie was a relative of Lee's, but not of the strong attachment between the two women nor that Lee was looking for Auntie's approval of him. Jones continued his story by saying that it took him two years for Lee to agree to marry him yet he knew after two months that he loved Lee and wanted her to be his wife and have their children, and so did Lee. Loud laughter!

Auntie fed them, as she did everyone that came to her home, and for four hours, the four of them had an enjoyable, meaningful conversation in English on many topics. All during that first visit, as with the many that were to follow, Jones commented that he could not help but to notice that Lee generally contributed very little to the conversations between Auntie, Auntie's husband, and him. Jones also noticed that she was watching the body language between her aunt and him, and apparently was satisfied with the results of her observations because she had a smile on her lips during the entire visit.

After telephoning for a taxicab to pick them up to return them to the center of Panama City, they made their good-byes and walked to the cab. Auntie spoke to Lee in Spanish not knowing of Jones' fluency in the language, "Baby, wait a minute. I have something to tell you."

They stopped and Lee and her aunt removed themselves a few steps behind Jones, but were still within hearing distance. Auntie again spoke to Lee in Spanish, "Marry him, Baby. He's an angel!"

38

Jones mentioned that he heard everything Auntie told Lee, and Lee did not respond to what she had been told. She only smiled as she kissed her aunt on the cheek while hugging her, before returning to Jones' side as they got in the cab. Thus ended Jones story of his first meeting with Auntie, and for a few moments there was silence around the dinner table, as we each thought about what Auntie had told Lee. What did she know?

On subsequent visits, Lee would relaxingly sit back in her chair in silence, with a smile on her face as she watched her Aunt feed and happily fuss over Jones. No matter who was in her home at the time of Lee and Jones' arrival, or came in later, Jones was attended to first. Auntie loved Jones as she loved her Baby, with a love that bordered on adoration. In 1972, as I watched Auntie's interaction with Jones, I arrived at the conclusion that she was very thankful that her Baby had found someone she could completely love and trust despite the physical and verbal abuse she witnessed her father afflict upon her mother while growing up.

After Lee and Jones married and returned to the United States, whenever they had an inextricable problem that they could not resolve by their usual method of talking the problem through until they arrived at a solution that they both could agree on, Jones would telephone Auntie in The Republic de Panama, telling her to tell Lee that he was an angel.

Listening to her husband's and Auntie's conversation on the other telephone extension, Auntie would tell Lee, "Baby, be nice to Jones. You know he's an angel."

They would all laugh loudly, and what was thought of as an inextricable problem would prove otherwise, thanks to Auntie's eternal belief that Jones was the best thing that had ever happened to her Baby.

When Lee and Jones married in 1963, it was to Auntie that

Lee turned to as a surrogate mother for advice and guidance as to the duties of a wife to her husband, until the riot of 1964 forced them to flee The Republic de Panama and her Aunt's loving hands. Auntie died suddenly in December of 1982, at eighty years of age. Lee and Jones had no opportunity to make it to Panama City for her massive heart attack took her in two days despite her doctor's valiant efforts to save her life. The first day that Auntie was admitted to the hospital, her husband called Lee and Jones and held the telephone to his wife's ear while she lay in her hospital bed as Lee and Jones told Auntie that they were on their way to her. The next day, Auntie died. For many months after her aunt's death, Lee was devastated. She kept repeating, over and over, that she was the last living person from her mother's and father's ancestry. I believe and have accepted as fact that you have to be Latino to fully comprehend what it meant to Lee to live with the daily knowledge that she was the last of their family's lines. And with the death of Auntie, she was without her best friend.

> "We forget that there is no hope
> of joy except in human relations."
> *Antione du St. Euxpery*

4.

SAN ANDRES

Lee's formative years were spent on San Andres Island, Colombia, that she did not leave for any length of time until she attended the University of Panama, Republic de Panama. Her father used to make frequent trips by boat to Colon on the Atlantic side of the Republic of Panama to pursue what he told his wife were "men's activities," without ever defining those activities. Lee's mother suspected that her husband had another woman in Colon, and the day after he left San Andres for Panama, she would follow on another boat. After arriving in Colon, Lee's mother would seek out the location of her husband, and once she found him, would confront him, no matter the locale, demanding that he return home. She reminded him that he had no right to leave his family and fool around with other women. She had sometimes, embarrassingly, found him without his outter clothing, in other women's homes. Whenever Lee's mother could find her husband, although he would attempt to hide, he would return with her to San Andres while raising no objections to her indignation over the issue of the embarrassment of having to bring him home.

It was during one of Lee's mother husband retrieval missions that Lee was born — October 18, 1934, in Colon Hospital, automatically making her a Panamanian citizen. After five days in the hospital, the entire family returned to San Andres Island, which Lee referred to as the best place to grow up. Few people have ever heard of the island which is precisely the reason why it still was an unspoiled tropical paradise.

Shaped like a seahorse, San Andres is seven and a half miles long, a mile and a half wide, with a coral base overgrown with graceful coconut palms. It lies on the far side of the Caribbean, 250 miles southwest of Jamaica, about half that distance from the eastern coast of Nicaragua, and 480 miles west of Colombia to which it belongs. The islanders speak French, Spanish, and English, and are descendants of French Buccaneers, Spanish soldiers, New England sailors, and African slaves. The islanders are a fiercely independent breed, too, so that while no less then eight nations have laid claim to their remote archipelago since it was sighted by Columbus in 1492, and each have ruled only nominally. The real voice has always come from the San Andres itself.

Since Columbia took over the island in 1822, coconut exporting has been San Andres' main industry. Although U.S. dollars have always been acceptable, the island's official currency is the Colombian peso. Back in 1906, the United States alone was importing approximately seven million coconuts from the island. When Lee was growing up, there were four harvests a year with a yield of about eight million coconuts per harvest.

Men, women, children, and entire families all help to care for the coconut trees, peel the coconut husks with a machete, select the better grade coconuts for exporting, and place the coconut meat on palm leaf-woven mats in the sun to dry into copra. But due to the lack of shredding and processing equipment, a central harvesting organization, capital and oceangoing vessels for shipping out the copra, many more millions of coconuts were left to rot on the ground (which the many pigs eat). And at the same time during Lee's childhood, many of the islanders were emigrating to the United States, Panama, Columbia, and Nicaragua looking for work and a better life than the island offered them. The Colombian Government wished to reverse this trend (fear of depopulation) by building a 7,000 foot runway on the island which could service four-engine propeller-powered planes from Barranquilla, Columbia; some half-dozen hotels, gambling casinos, and a bustling free port which attracted visitors from Columbia and Central and South America to take advantage of the duty free prices.

Since the program to stop the emigration of inhabitants from San Andres, real estate in the island has appreciated 1,000%. Land sells by the square meter or the acre and varies according to it location. When Lee left the island for school, she said that it would be difficult to find any undeveloped land on San Andres selling for less than $800 an acre, which was more than some people on the island made in a lifetime. Along with the appreciation, there was the accompanying increase in tax payments by holders of real estate, forcing many of the landowners to lose their land to the government. The government then sold the repossessed land to the developers for huge profits for all those who were connected with the process. Very soon, all of the islander landowners were complaining to each other and to Bogota that the government's entire Anti-Emigration program was no more then a land grab to deprive them of their ancestral land. Lee was able to keep her family's ancestral holdings in tact throughout her life, despite the increases in property taxes, numerous offers from developers to purchase her land — because she was earning "dollars" from her teaching position in the Republic de Panama in which to pay the taxes, and once married, Jones added his financial support.

The island that Lee grew up on, its inhabitants were open in their daily relationships, friendly to starngers, so trustworthy that San Andre's two policemen had little to do other then to warn bicyclists to slow down! There was so little crime, that it was not uncommon for family's visiting outside the island, which they did for months at a time, that they didn't even bother to lock up their homes.

The original settlers were Puritans who landed on San Andres in 1629, naming it Henrietta in honor of the wife of King Charles the first of England. They had such names as Wooker, Wilkins, Hawkinson, Archbold, and Robinson. Today's islanders still carry the same monikers but with Spanish surnames so that you get combinations like Don Juan Wooker, Diego Hawkinson, or Don Archbold. Experienced travelers have compared the San Andres islanders to those on Pitcairn Island in the South Pacific. The natives of Pitcairn are the descendents of mutineers of the BOUNTY and their Tahitian wives who settled there in 1790. Like them, their skin is dark from the sun, but their eyes are often blue, gray and green, their hair red and blonde.

Lee's hair was naturally "Red," until she arrived in this country, and became very annoyed by everyone asking her, to include total strangers, "Did you dye your hair that color?" She then dyed her hair black and kept it that color for the rest of her life — to stop the questions. Lee often mentioned that she thought American's were the rudest people she had ever met, to ask a total stranger such a personal question — about their hair. She had travelled throughout Central and South America, and never been questioned about the color of her hair.

From the few pictures that I have been priviledged to view in the one photograph album that Lee's father was unable to destroy, before joining his daughter in the Republic de Panama, because she had taken it with her when she left the island to attend University. The San Andres women pictured in Lee's album, appear to be particularly attractive. Tall (Lee stood five feet, ten inches), slim, and exquisitely proportioned.

When reminiscing about her island home, Lee's first comments are always about it's breathtaking natural beauty — a South Sea paradise isle with graceful coconut palms and reef — locked lagoons. Offshore, the surf line of the great barrier reef protected the pink, granular beaches from rough seas. A cool trade wind sways the palms, driving away mosquitoes, and the temperature hovers at a comfortable year round 80 degrees. The warm, shallow seas off nearby Serrana and Roncador shoals are host to unusually beautiful coral gardens and tropical fish life, and the underwater visibility was unbeatable. Langosta (rock lobster) were in abundance and very easy to catch. There were no laws or restrictions against sparefishing since all forms of marine life where plentiful. There were also no restrictions on surface fishing either. Kingfish, Jack, sailfish, tarpon and marlin were all plentiful and caught by all. In addition, there were broadbil, swordfish, red snapper, roosterfish, bonita, cobia, amberjack, blus runner and many varieties of fishes abound around Lee's San Andres Island home. The island's largest town, also called San Andres, was bustling and progressive. Where Lee and the majority of islanders lived was residential and quiet.

> "Pleasure is the flower that fades; remembrance is the lasting perfume."
>
> *Louis Francios de Boufflers*

5.

EDUCATION

Lee's elementary and high school education was all received at Saint Carmen's Parish/Convent and School, run by priests and sisters of various religious orders sent from Spain and Colombia to San Andres Island to administer to the religious needs of the Catholic population. The school was for girls only, who boarded at the school Monday through Friday. Their parents could visit their daughters at the end of the school day to bring them home cooked food, clothing, or pocket money. The girls went home for the weekend, returning to the school at five o'clock Monday morning for another week of very intense educational instruction. According to Lee, the education that she and the other seventy-nine girls received loosely covered five major groupings; liberal education; general education along with some vocational training; the place of moral training in one's life; wisdom as the goal of learning; and the importance of manual work in the learning process.

The liberal education Lee received had very little resemblance to the traditional liberal arts education we Americans are familiar with . It focused on scientific disciplines such as mathematics and physics, with the aim of training individuals in the skills her country needed. Lee's educators attempted to connect a liberal education with scientific creativity. The liberal part of her curriculum embraced Latin, Catholic Religion, Catholic Philosophy, logic, and history, while the scientific part was exclusively devoted to mathematics and physics. In tandem with the government of Colombia, it was the educational aim of the Catholic Church run schools throughout the country, not to produce scientists or free-thinking humans who knew how to use their minds to question, but individuals who would use their learned skills, unquestioning in support of those in positions of authority. Lee said she constantly ran into trouble throughout her education on the island because she was always asking, why?

The priests and sisters knew that a general education, leading to university, was good for some of their students, and vocational training was best for others. By the time the students reached the fifth grade, it was determined through a series of tests and their grade level, which path their education would be focused toward. Based upon her test scores and grade level, Lee said that she was selected for the general path, even with what the priests and sisters called her "troubles" — a rebellious attitude toward those in positions of authority. I asked Lee, if she ever thought that her troubles in school might have anything to do with having red hair — the then prevailing wisdom was that "red heads" had tempers. Laughing, Lee replied, "I have also heard that story about temper. The color of my hair had nothing to do with it! I have also heard the story about temper. My troubles were no more then the priests and sister (except one), were always mean to me." By being on the general path, all of Lee's subjects of instruction were related to what would be required for her to enter university (which was free and included a stipend), and become an elementary school teacher. Throughout her pre-university education, Lee performed exceptionally in all her subjects, except one — penmanship. To all that have attended Catholic Parochial schools in this country, you know of the sisters preoccupation with neat penmanship, and how failure to produce the same resulted in having the offending hand struck by a wooden ruler. This always happened to Lee throughout her education at Saint Carmen's school. The result of this penmanship trouble left Lee with an eternal disdain for writing that she somehow passed on to all of her sons, but not to her only daughter who enjoyed writing as much as her father.

The teachers spent a great deal of their time developing the student's intellectual powers towards accepting in their daily life the moral capacity to judge rightly according to Catholic doctrine, and the proper means to achieve God's intended ends. Everytime the tray of life's pleasures is placed before you, does not mean you must partake from it. Her Catholic educators knew that it was easier to teach the educational basics than to teach the concepts of Catholic justice, moderation, and patience when the real world does not operate within these values. Lee's educators readily admitted to their students that learning to be good and to do right in one's daily life is quite different from teaching them to read, write, and think before responding to what the "tray of life" offers. Moral virtue was not intellectual perception nor a practical skill. Character was a quality of the whole person, and knowing that, it also seems that moral virtue cannot be taught directly — they took the indirect way with the example of their lives dedicated to God's work.

Lee often wondered if her school on San Andres was not in reality a recruitment station for the Catholic Church, with young girls encouraged to become nuns for service in that part of the world. Lee's example in developing her own moral character was an Indian nun from the South of Colombia's Jungle rain forests of the Amazon basin. Her name was Sister Leocadia whom had been converted to the Catholic faith and sent to Spain by the Catholic Missionaries with the aim of completing her training in Spain then returning to educate her people. After being sent to a convent in

Spain for her training she was constantly in trouble with the Mother Superior of the order for always asking why she was the only novice to clean all of the slop jars everyday, clean up after each meal in the dining room and kitchen, wash (using a scrubboard) and iron (using a flatiron) the bedding. It was this repeated questioning that made the Mother Superior brand her as strong willed, stubborn, trouble maker, and an ingrate. Even with the unequal treatment she received while in Spain, Sister Leocadia completed her studies, took her vows and the name "Leocadia," and like her namesake, she often told Lee; "She prayed daily that God would not prolong her exile, but soon unite her with the heroic souls that had gone before her." Sister Leocadia was sent to Saint Carmen's on San Andres Island by her order to break what her Mother Superior in Spain said was her very "strong will," performing exactly the same duties in the convent of Saint Carmen as she was doing as a novice in Spain. She was not allowed to teach although she was qualified. When telling the story of Sister Leocadia, Lee often mentioned that her order did not want her but had to accept her because the missionaries in Colombia sent her to them for training.

Throughout her education at Saint Carmen's, Lee was also in trouble with the priest and nuns for constantly asking why. Because Lee would not eat wormy bread, she was told that she had to remain sitting at the table without food until she was prepared to obey Sister. After putting a fork of food into her mouth, and discovering that it was spoiled, would not swallow it but was not allowed to leave the table to spit it out. A Sister stood behind Lee's chair, striking her on her shoulders with a wooden ruler and with each blow—her voice raising until she was shouting, "Swallow it! Do you hear me? Swallow it, I say!" As the blows rained down upon her shoulders, Lee would continue to hold the spoiled food in her mouth with her cheeks puffed out. It was usually these instances that caused Lee to be sent to assist Sister Leocadia in her daily manual chores. In a very short time, Lee and Sister Leocadia's relationship changed from troublesome student and detail nun to friends, for they quickly recognized in each other a kindred spirit. They were both individualists. They worked well together performing their daily tasks, in half the normal time, then they would go into the cool church and spend the rest of the day talking about their families, dreams, home, and how the priest/nuns at Saint Carmen's and the Church proclaimed one thing as an act of faith for them, while they did the opposite.

Lee has often told me, when reflecting upon her school years, that Sister Leocadia was like the older sister she never had. Lee would never fail to give Sister Leocadia credit for help in developing her character by living by her example. Even if she was cleaning out the slop jars, Sister Leocadia knew she really was a trained teacher of children, and not a domestic!

When Lee left San Andres Island for university in the Republic de Panama, she kept in contact with Sister Leocadia through letters, and upon obtaining her first teaching position in Panama City, Lee opened a bank account in Sister Leocadia's name with instructions that a specified amount be sent to her each month. This money was so the sister would not have to beg anyone for the few personal items she needed to make her life a little more bearable, that continued with Jones blessing once they married, although he had never met the nun. In 1978, Sister Leocadia was transferred to Cartagena, Columbia, and died there that same year. She had served for a little over thirty years as a bride of Christ, and had never been able to do that she was qualified to do — teach. She spent all of her time performing menial chores for other nuns and priests. When Lee heard of Sister Leocadia's death, she cried for days. Afterward, when Lee thought of her friend, she would often say that her friend would have been "better off if the missionaries had left her in her rain forest home and unconverted to the Catholic Religion."

Since it was a religious school, Saint Carmen's priests and sisters placed a high value on wisdom — that man can love or seek wisdom but he can not possess it. The wisdom that was expounded was related to the prudent and righteous conduct in everyday affairs. God is the teacher, and wisdom is obtained by listening to his teachings and not by intellectual inquiry alone. The staff of Saint Carmen's school taught that the fear of God is the beginning of all wisdom. When the girls misbehave, talking back to a priest or nun, not making their bed properly, failing to remain on their back when sleeping, and showering without their smock, they should always seek God's forgiveness.

Since her time at Saint Carmen's, Lee retained a strong belief in God (although Jones did not) even when He failed to answer her prayers in such a way that she could understand. As Lee and Jones were confronted with one tragedy after another, Lee began to doubt God's ability to protect them in their lives, telling me once that God has no power, only the devil. To retain her sanity, Lee took to proclaiming, "Nothing in life happens in a vacuum. There is a reason for everything that happens to you, even when you don't understand why." After coming to the United States, Lee could never come to grip with the "wisdom" learned growing up, and what she called the evils she found in most Americans. Evils, like the abuse of children and babies; the treatment of the poor in the society; the racism toward those different than themselves, and the brutally afflicted by men on women. When Lee use to ask Jones or I, why, after reading in the newspaper, or hearing on the radio, or seeing on television some committed evil, we never seemed to be able to effectively answer her concerns — because she never stopped asking; "Why?" Through the reading of books Lee had not been exposed to at Saint Carmen's school, and conversations with others who were not Catholic she began to accept that the Catholic faith was not the One True Revealed Religion only to Saint Peter, but just one of among many religious myths invented by man in the long history of development. Even with the newly acquired knowledge that the Catholic Religion was just one of many, Lee retained her belief that there was a God and that he was good. I once asked Lee why she still believed in God after all of the negative things that happened to her? Lee gave me one of her half smiles, and replied, "It's my anchor in life. If I did not have my belief in God to sustain me, I would lose my mind!" All of the instruction Lee received at Saint Carmen's School, linked the dignity of manual labor with the holiness of learning. The staff held that manual labor is man's divinely appointed destiny in life, and that it teaches humility, patience, industriousness, and self-reliance with God. Their teaching manifested itself in each of the girls being responsible for washing—on a scrub board, and ironing— using a flat iron that was heated over a wood fire, their school uniforms and personal cloths. Helping the kitchen nuns in preparing the meals. Sitting the tables in the eating area—a outdoor covered, open on all four sides, where everyone took their meals. Serving the meals—priests and nuns first at the head table. After the meals, clearing away the residue, while cleaning the eating area and kitchen. Cleaning their living area in the dormitory, which was inspected daily by the nuns—and if it did not pass their instruction—had to be cleaned until it did. In addition to their academic studies, each girl had to also learn—all taught by the eighteen nuns—how to saw from scratch various female and male wearing apparel; to make knitted items; maintain the vestment items (less the crosier) of

the nine priest, along with mending their non-vestment clothing, and crochet items for the church alter. The priest and sisters of Saint Carmen's School were always mindful of the
Spanish proverb;

> "The busy man is troubled
> with but one devil; the idle man
> by a thousand."

6.

UNIVERSITY

U pon completing her high school education at Saint Carmen's, San Andres Island, Colombia, Lee applied to and was accepted by the University of Panama in their elementary teaching program (Colombia and Panama had a long-standing agreement that college bound students could attend each other schools). Lee left San Andres Island after bidding her family, friends, and classmates farewell with a sense of adventure and freedom. The adventure would come from living in the country of her birth, meeting other students from Central and South America, and seeing the Panama Canal that she had heard so much about. Each time that a ship was released from the locks into the Atlantic Ocean, they would experience waves on the beaches of San Andres. Also, Panama City was the place to be in the fifties because of its prosperity, and a healthy place to live due to the eradication of yellow fever and modern sanitation. Pan-Americanism was agitated by the facility of the University of Panama and its students, claiming that the Monroe Doctorine was only a mask for United States imperialistic ambitions. Those advocates for Pan-Americanism were branded by the American Government and its media, as communists. I had once asked Lee about those (students and professors) involved with "Panama for only the Panamanians," if they really were Communist as my government claimed? Her reply was that a few were, but not the majority as reported by the U.S. government and it's media. She further explained, "Remember, we have the same guaranteed freedom of speech clause in out constitution as you have in yours." It was while she was a student at the University of Panama, observing American civilians living in the Canal Zone and American military personnel and how they treated Panamanians that Lee became vocally anti-American. She told me, in some heat, of the contempt and downright hostility she saw and heard the Americans directed toward Panamanians. For example, the United States Canal Zone was run by the Canal Zone Government like a mainland deep southern state — with the full force of its Jim Crow laws aggressively enforced by its police and courts. All Panamanians resented the Jim Crow laws and the Canal Zone Police who enforce them, because that have no concept or laws relating to race in their culture. Freedom, Lee was now the master of her own destiny. She could wear any type of clothing she chose , wear her hair out rather than in a bun at the back of her neck like when she was in school, wear makeup and nail polish, date boys, attend parties, go dancing until the wee hours of the morning at any of the many rooftop dance clubs throughout the city, and spend the stipend she was receiving from the government anyway she liked. Lee said that she enjoyed her life as an educated single woman living in a cos-mopolitan area like Panama City, a city she grew to love.

When Lee moved to the Republic de Panama, she lived with Auntie. Auntie took care of Lee, becoming the mother she no longer had. She prepared Lee's meals before she left in the morn-ing and when she returned in the evening, washed and ironed her clothing, gave her advice — solicited and unsolicited — loaned her money when she ran short and scolded Lee for not doing what she knew to be right. Lee would readily admit that the time she spent living with Auntie was the happiest (before Jones) in her entire life. Lee would often say that she was loved and taken care of by Auntie and her husband just because she was Lee.

Auntie had one ironclad rule while taking care of Lee — whenever her Baby went partying, or dancing, she had to have a date who would pick her up at home and return her there. Lee was not allowed to attend any party or go dancing by herself, nor would she be allowed to meet her date at any other place except at home. Auntie claimed that what she was not allowing her Baby to do concerning dates, was what loose women (read prostitutes) did, and her Baby was no loose woman. Lee said that she had no objections to anything that Auntie told her, for she knew where Auntie was coming from. As a young woman of marrying age, she had to be very careful of her honor, and that she did nothing that would put her's, her Aunt's or her husband's face in the dirt.

All of Lee's dates were young men attending the same school who knew up front that they were only her chaperone for that specific event and nothing else. Early on in her life Lee had already made up her mind that she would never marry a Spaniard, and that message seemed, somehow, to have been conveyed to all her dates. Ruling out Spaniards as a partner Lee laughing, recalled, "I was resolved that once my father died I would become a nun!" If Jones was present when she said this, she would give him a mischievous glance that contained a sparkle in her eyes, and with a smile on her lips, she would say, "Little did I know that there was an along-come-Jones' out there just waiting to grab me!" We would all laugh loudly at her comment including Lee and Jones. Later in the course of the evening, Lee's eyes would meet mine, or as we were standing/sitting together, she would mouth these words for my ears only, "Thank

LEE

God for Jones, I love him with all my heart and soul — even more than life itself! I never knew that there were caring men like him. Above all, a Gringo!" And we would both quietly laugh together at Lee's shared secret of the importance of Jones in her life.

"Either you struggle and
learn, or you lose ground.
You never get to stand still."
Janet Inglis

7.

TEACHING

After graduating from the University of Panama that her father did not leave San Andres Island to attend, Lee was immediately hired by the government of Panama to teach in their elementary education system at the fourth grade level. Although a republic, "a government in which supreme power resides in a body of citizens entitled to vote and is exercised by elected officers, and representatives responsible to them and governing according to law." There was an added twist to the definition of "Republic," as it applied to Panama. Their constitution recognized the Catholic religion as that of the majority of its people, introduced a regime of separation of church and state but allowed religious instruction in the public schools, and also provided state employed lay teachers for the Catholic Church parochial schools. Having state employed lay teachers teaching in the parochial schools, was turning the concept of "separation of church and state" on its head. What Lee could never seem to understand was why the United States government did not provide the same type of assistance to the parochial schools here as Panama. As often as Jones and I attempted to explain to Lee why she never appeared to understand that we as a free people look upon religion as a totally personal experience and commitment, and that the government should not be involved.

Lee chose to teach in a parochial school located in the center of Panama City that was part of the Church of San Jose. Lee taught her fourth graders English, spelling, mathematics, the Catholic religion, social studies, penmanship, and history. The history of Panama that Lee taught her fifty fourth graders of 25 boys and 25 girls (with each gender seperated to a different side of the classroom), was that:

Panama from colonial days had been a province of New Granda (Colombia). At the end of the independence movement on 28 November 1821, a cabildo abierto declared independence from Spain and for a continued union as a province of what was Greater Colombia. When the latter broke up just before Bolivar's death in 1830, Panama again decided to stay by what had reverted to Colombia. Next, Panama rebelled in 1840, and for two years, was an independent nation and went by the name of Isthmus Nation. Many other revolts followed. During the liberal uprising in Colombia in 1885, Colon, on the Caribbean coast, was invaded and burned. Panama was now an autonomous province of Colombia, but this was a misnomer, for it continued to be governed from Colombia, whose officials looted the province. Then, because of heavy taxes and oppressive measures, the country rose again in 1895 in another futile revolt against the Colombian Government. Panama was now divided into four provinces and governed directily from Bogota.

Such were the conditions until independence came in 1903 in connection with the canal question. The Theodore Roosevelt regime aided and abetted the revolt that made the country free. United States warships kept the

Colombian troops from landing while the people of Panama imprisoned the Colombian officials and proceeded to formulate a constitution modeled after the United States. The revolt broke out on 2 November 1903. On 13 November Theodore Roosevelt recognized the new republic, with France following suit 18 November. The first President of Panama was conservative Amador Cuerrero (Fort Amado in the Canal Zone is named after him,) who was inaugurated in January 1904, while the following month a constitution was adopted and the canal treaty with the United States was ratified. Philipple Bunau-Varilla (a french engineer) a chief promoter of independence, became the first minister to the United States.

The curriculum was the same in San Jose School, as on San Andres Island, Colombia, and the subjects Lee taught were familiar ground being revisited, but with one difference she was the teacher. Lee, in the broadest sense possible, attempted to teach her students how to discern, evaluate, judge, and recognize the truth. Lee did not require or impose a fixed content of ideas and doctrines (other than religion) that her students must learn by rote when seeking their "truths." She taught them to always ask why, and how to reason and think for themselves — and to read everything they could get their hands on! Even though Lee knew that teaching was a humble, helping art, she discovered that she really enjoyed it, and was good at it. She had a love of all children and was patient with every one of her varied students — some very poor, some middle class, and a few that were from wealthy households. Lee mentioned that the maxim she always followed in teaching her students was that given the factor of time, anyone can learn anything.

Lee was the only lay teacher at San Jose School, and she and the Sister Principal (who was ten years older than her) of the elementary school quickly related to each other in a positive way — they were both deeply committed to educating what they called "their Children." When Lee interviewed for the position, she told the principal the story of her life growing up on San Andres Island, and that she was caring for her disabled father, and that when he died — she would enter a novitiate and become a nun. Lee mentioned that she also told the Principal of her decision to become a Nun was based in part upon a desire to serve God, and what she had saw her father had done to her late mother, and her oldest brother to her — hitting women! Adding, "that no man will ever strike me again with his fist, for I am going to remove myself from their world." The principal silently listened to Lee's life story and told her in a calm voice that she too had a very unhappy childhood, and her heart went out to Lee for what she witnessed and suffered growing up. But Lee's adult life need not necessarily be unhappy if she had a husband that truly loved her and a family of her own. "Often," the Sister continued, "a lot of life's misfortunes are sometimes preparing us for some unknown betterment, and when we experience that 'betterment' I advise you to embrace it completely." She also told Lee that she did not believe that Lee's destiny was to become a Nun — even with the suffering she had witnessed growing up, she was just too young to give up on the world and the happiness it can and does offer. But she decided to hire Lee for the fourth grade teaching position, and they both would see. Lee joyfully thanked the principal, telling her that she would never disappoint her or misplace the trust that was being extended. Lee had never been happier.

The Sister Principal then began to explain to Lee what made up the San Jose Church complex, and how she would fit into it. There was the main church; the chapel — open twenty-four hours;

the rectory — housing the Archbishop, eight priests and four housekeepers to care for them; the orphanage — with sixty children (40 girls and 20 boys) that can contain 100; the infirmary — staffed by four nursing Sisters; the old persons' home — with 40 residences and space for 50, staffed by 10 retired sisters; the elementary and high school — with 20 teaching Sisters; and their 40 room convent with individual cells, each containing their own bathroom and shower. Since Lee had expressed a desire to become a nun once her father passed, she was welcome to stay at the convent because she lived in the outskirts of Panama City. This would save her from making that long bus trip each day, plus she could experience firsthand what religious life was like for the sisters, although there would be some restrictions if Lee chose to stay. Lee immediately accepted the offer. The principal then outlined what those restrictions would be. Lee would live by the same rules and regulations that the nuns did — she could not wear any makeup, nail polish, jewelry except the pierced earrings she was wearing, a religious medallion and/or crucifix and a wrist watch; she must wear the required ankle length, long sleeve gray cotton beltless smock, and black low heeled shoes; and would not have to cut her red hair, but would have to wear it in a bun at the back of her neck. Lee readily agreed to all that the principal had told her.

Then they then went on a tour of the school's facilities. The school complex was a wooden two-story, three-sided structure with the main church being the fourth side, enclosed onto a cobblestone paved courtyard that was entered through the back of the church and three archway doorways at the courtyard level. The orphanage living quarters were located on the first floor of the school complex — individual two person rooms with two community bathrooms at either end of the courtyard. A railed wooden balcony running the entry three sides of the building with two wooden staircases per side, to the twelve classrooms above. After climbing the stairs, Lee and the Sister Principal visited each of the classrooms, being warmly received by the sisters teaching their classes as well as the students. As they went from classroom to classroom, Lee was given general information about the curriculum, different students. She was also told that each teacher had complete autonomy in their classroom, and that the very few disciplinary problems (mostly uniform violations), were handled by her, and that they boarded no students as they ended their tour back in the courtyard. Returning to her home that afternoon, Lee said that she felt as if she was on cloud nine, because after twenty-four years, she was at least beginning to live a meaningful life, and doing something good with her education. She honestly believed that she had something to give as a teacher — helping her students in their pursuit of knowledge.

Over dinner that night, Lee told her father that she had obtained a teaching position, and would be living at the convent under their rules, Monday through Friday, returning home after the last class on Friday for the weekend. She said she would hire two day help women to come in during the week to clean the house and wash and iron his clothes. During the weekend, she would cook a week's worth of food for him and place it in the refrigerator for him to heat up on the stove at meal time. Neither Lee nor her father were comfortable with strangers preparing their food, claiming, that something could be put in the food to make them sick or cause their death—and they would never be the wiser. Lee's father listened in silence until Lee had finished proclaiming her good news, then asked his daughter one question, "Are you sure that this is what you want your life to be? You haven't lived! You are young, beautiful, educated, and you have your entire life ahead you, yet what you have described to me, seems to limited and a waste of your life! And if the way I treated your late mother when you were growing up is any way responsible for this decision of yours to give up on all men, then I am truly sorry for what I have done." Without any anger in her voice, Lee replied, "Yes, you share a great deal of responsibility for my decision through your repeated beating of my mother, but there is no way to erase memories — good or bad. I can live the life I have planned for myself." She did this successfully until Jones entered her life two and a half years into her teaching career. What I have laid out for you the reader as a continuous narrative has been like all my recollections about Lee—fragmented, over the many years that it was my pleasure to know and call her friend. When I heard for the first time where Lee taught, why, and what she planned to do with her life upon the death of her father, I once asked Lee if she really intended to give up on men and the peoples of the world. She answered yes, saying that there was nothing she was looking for in the world. Her entire life was teaching her children and serving God via that effort. I then asked if maybe unfairly, having experienced convent life, now happily married, and with a family of your own—do you now believe, that just maybe, you were attempting to run away from who you really turned out to be? Without hesitation, Lee replied, "No! You must remember, it is my husband who has shown me, through his trusting and supporting love, that I can safely and completely love him back knowing that he will care and cherish it. You must also remember that Jones is the only man that I have known in an intimate way and I have no past history with other men. From our very first date, it was a great leap of trust on my part just to go out with Jones after the negative opinions that I have held all my life about men — no good and they will hurt you!. And from that first act of trust on my part, I quickly learned to love Jones and his company leaving me with the desire that I never wanted to be separated from him. Closing her comments to my question by telling me to remember:

"Man's love is man's life a part;
it is woman's whole existence."

George Gordon Byron

8.

MEETING

In keeping with his often stated policy of remaining outside of the United States of America just as often and long as he could, Jones related that only once in his entire time in the army did an American civilian ever tell him that they appreciated what he and others were doing to maintain and protect all of our freedoms. Jones called in some debts at the Missile Training School in Fort Bliss, Texas, where he was an instructor, for reassignment to one of the many HAWK (Homing All the Way Killer) Air Defense Missile Batteries being organized at Bliss, for deployment overseas, gaining assignment to one being sent to the Panama Canal Zone.

During his time at Fort Bliss, Jones perfected his Spanish along with a reputation at the Missile Schools as a highly effective instructor, even if he was perceived by his peers and students as being cold-blooded, hard-nosed, and uncompromising in demanding that his missile technician students know 100% of what was taught in his courses. Failure to get the instruction "down pat" could result in disasters. Jones repeatedly drummed into his students' heads that the missiles that they would be responsible for had to perform when needed. Now, with his reassignment to a HAWK Battery going overseas, Jones would now be able to determine if he knew 100% what it took to be a Senior

Non-Commissioned Officer In Charge (N.C.O.I.C.) of a section of missile technicians, responsible for keeping their HAWK missile operational.

Upon reporting to his HAWK Battery, Jones discovered that the Executive Officer (X.O.), a then First Lieutenant, was also a former instructor at the Missile Training School that he knew, and had a amiable relationship with. They both spoke the same language when it came to the HAWK missile system — a very good weapon system if maintained correctly. After intense preparations Jones and his battery arrived in the Panama Canal Zone in February of 1960 to take up their duties of defending the canal. A Washington, DC newspaper reported:

> The army has announced that two HAWK Air Defense Missle Batteries would be sent to the Canal Zone. The two units earmarked for the Canal Zone were stationed at Fort Bliss, Texas. Each battery was manned by five officers and sixty-eight enlisted men.

> The HAWK was selected for the canal defenses rather then the Nike family of missles because the area which might be under attack — the Panama Canal — is a fixed, small location. The highly-mobile HAWK units would have maneuverability advantage not requiring permanent installations. Using a special radar technique the HAWK is able to detect and destroy fast moving targets from tree-top level about ten miles.

Jones' HAWK Battery went to the Bay of Panama side of the Canal Zone to an island called Flamenco. Their battalion headquarters gave them two months to have all of their missiles operational, but it was done in one. Thereafter, duty in Panama became "Class A" (easy) for the members of the HAWK Battery on Flamenco Island, including Jones. For the first time in his army career, Jones wrote me of his joy in his new duties and assignment. In his letters he mentioned his love of the country, its varied people, and the life style of the Panamanians, not hurried. Included in one of Jones" letters was the comment that he had only six years to go toward making his twenty years, plus one day, for retirement from the United States Army, and he was seriously thinking about making the Republic de Panama his new home after he retired, with no thought then (1960) of ever returning to the United States. He had found in Panama that he was just another human being and (in America he was held in contempt just because he was a soldier), he enjoyed that new experience. It was in Jones' letters from Panama that I then realized that he had never gotten over his disillusionment with the citizens of this nation, and the way he and other released POW's of the Korean War were treated once they returned to the states — shabbily!

Jones often told the story of how he met Lee, and when he did, she would have a Mona Lisa smile on her lips until he finished. When the story ended, Lee would immediately go to Jones, and along with her kiss, give him a flat, open hand touch in the center of his chest, and they would look with mischievous sparkling eyes into each others faces and laugh softly as they kissed again. I once asked Lee why she did this. She seems surprised by my question and replied, "To assure myself that he is for real and still here." Lee looked upon Jones as her soul mate — they were meant to be together and Lee had to keep reassuring herself that this fact was true.

The first meeting of Lee and Jones occurred due to a memo in November of 1960, from Battalion headquarters that was circulated on Flamenco Island requesting volunteers to help prepare and participate in a Christmas party for the American children living in Balboa, Canal Zone. After reading the memo, Jones suggested to his First Sergeant and Baterry Commander that a Christmas party for the American children living in the Zone made no sense. With the pay scale (more than double the Panamanians and military personnel) of all Americans employed in the Zone, no child of American parents would go without on Christmas day, but that was not the case of the many needy children in Panama City, that Jones told them he saw on his many weekend forays into the city. Jones suggested to his top kick and old man, that the men in the Battery on Flamenco Island organize and give a Christmas party there on the island for some of the needy children of Panama City while volunteering to put it all together. They liked the idea, but first they would have to meet with the Battalion Commander for clearance because the island was a security zone due to the HAWK missile systems.

A week later, the Battery Commander, First Sergeant, and Jones met with the Battalion Commander, and after presenting their case for a party, he consented. The presentation: All members of the Battery would participate by being the companion of one child during the Christmas party. Each enlisted man would be asked to donate $10 and each officer $20 — acquiring $780 to purchase Christmas presents for each child. The Christmas presents would be purchased at the Post Exchange (PX) and/or at commercial establishments in Panama City (asking for and obtaining charitable discounts) with each child receiving three pieces of clothing and two toys.

Every private automobile, including the officer's cars, would be utilized for transportation to pick up the children. Only those children that someone had left for the church to raise, been abandon to the streets of Panama City, or had turned up asking for food and shelter would be invited. After being transported to Flamenco Island, and given a short speech of welcome in

Spanish, by the Battery Commander, the guests would be given a tour of the island. On land, by the tracked vehicles which were used to pull the missle carriers; by water, a boat raid around the island. Not planned. Hung throughout Flamenco, were twenty handmade Pióatas, filled with candy that were made by some of the Panamanian girlfriends of the Battery's enlisted members. All of the Pióatas were broken by the children before Santa gave out his presents. They would play games, with prizes for the winners, like potato shack races, tug-of-war, and pin the tail on the donkey. After the games, the children would have dinner in a beautifully decorated mess hall containing an artificial Christmas tree to be provided and decorated by one of the officer's wives. Accompanying the planned sixty children from the four church orphanages, would be whatever amount of support staff (Sister) necessary to assure that they would not become frightened in unfamiliar surroundings. They also helped in the pronunciation of the children's names when Santa distributed his gifts from his very, very large bag. It would be from the Sisters that we would get the sizes of their clothing, and suggestions as to what type of toys the children would like. After the party, and the children returned to their individual orphanages, those at San Joes, Lee told Jones, "None of the children were disappointed with the clothing and toys they received!" As the children, companions, staff from the churches, and other guests would file into the mess hall to locate their table numbers, they would experience a traditional Panamanian Christmas dinner of sorrel and arroz con pollp, accompanied with desert of ice cream and cake.

The traditional Panamanian Christmas dinner would be prepared by United States Army cooks assigned to the mess hall on Flamenco Island, supervised by cooks from the four church kitchens that were providing the children for the party. All ingredients for the meal would be provided by the mess hall, and what they did not have in stock, the Mess Sergeant purchased at the Big Market in Panama City.

After the meal, and Santa's gift-giving in the mess hall, the children and guest would be returned to their respective four orphanages, bringing an end to the day's activities.

The Battalion Commander, placed one restriction on Jones in planning the Christmas part, "Don't get the army involved with any controversial organization, group, or political party." Jones readily agreed, saying that he understood, and countered with a restriction of his own, "No publicity! The idea of the Christmas party was not an excuse to make the army or Americans look good to the citizens of Panama City. It was for his part, and those he had spoken to, only an attempt to help some needy children during the forthcoming holiday, because we can."

Lee said that was the way the Christmas party on Flamenco Island played out — no official publicity by the army or newspapers in the Canal Zone or Panama City. But after the party, word got out by those that had attended, what the members of the HAWK Battery on Flamenco had done for some of the city's needy children, resulting in the members of the Battery being held in some esteem by the citizens of Panama City. Also, former companions of some children maintained a relationship with them long after the Christmas party was over; visiting then in the orphanages, taking them on outings, recognizing their birthdays with a party, etc. After a week of notifying the members of the Battery, via meetings in the mess hall, what was being planned regarding the forthcoming Christmas party Jones and one of his Missile Technicians, Ruiz, a bilingual Mexican-American, proceeded upon their quest to find the children to invite to their party. Dressed in their best laundered Class "A" Khaki uniforms, they visited three church orphanages in Panama City and received commitments from those in charge, that fifteen children from each would be allowed to attend. Jones already determined that he needed a total 60 children. After leaving the third church, he and Ruiz drove to San Jose Church orphanage for the last 15 children they needed.

After arriving at San Jose Church orphanage, parking Ruiz's automobile, and walking to the only entrance they saw in the seven foot stone wall encircling the complex, the bell cord was pulled aside the very formidable looking oak door recessed in the stone wall, hearing it ring inside. After what appeared to Jones and Ruiz to be a lengthy wait, the bared sliding door built into the door, slid open and they were confronted with the face of who they were to learn was the Sister Principal of the elementary school. She inquired, inhospitably, in Spanish, "What do you want?" After Ruiz explained the purpose of their mission, they were hesitantly invited inside, with the door being locked behind them. They slowly walked, while they both continued to explain (they conversed in Spanish), the details of the party, to the center of the cobblestone courtyard. The Sister Principal replied, "I see," and called out, "Lita!" After a few moments, Lee came out of her classroom to the balcony's rail, answering the Sister Principal and saw Jones for the first time. She had always told me even though there were three people standing in the center of the courtyard looking up at her, her eyes immediately came to rest and remained on Jones. What she also immediately noticed was that he looked nothing like the Gringos she had seen around Panama City, going by bus to her home on the outskirts of the city on weekends. Standing very straight in his clean but ruffled (although she could see that it had been freshly laundered because you could see every crease where it had been folded), looking be-medaled Khaki uniform. The Sister Principal asked Lee to please come down, which she did, then began to explain to Lee why she had interrupted her class, telling her to take the soldiers to her classroom and the others, and identify the orphan children who would attend the Christmas party. The Sister Principal then told Jones and Ruiz in non-accented English, that she had reservations about allowing her children to be in the company of what she felt were uncouth American soldiers. She said she would suppress her reservations because it would bring a little joy into an often unjoyful parentless life. It did not escape her that they and the members of the Battery were only attempting to do something good. We did not have to have a Christmas party for a group of unknown children, who were not even American! In some heat, Jones immediately attempted to counter the Sister Principal remarks by explaining, that most American soldiers were nothing like she imagined — graceless, clumsy, vulgar, and indecent — but were actually decent, likable individuals if she would give herself the chance to know them. The Sister Principal made no reply as she walked toward what appeared to be the door to her office off the court-yard, while Lee, Jones, and Ruiz walked toward the stairs leading to the classrooms on the second level. Lee says that she watched Jones out of the corner of her eyes the entire time they were stand-ing in the courtyard, and he never noticed! She was struck by the "straightness" of Jones' posture, (the other Gringo with him did not stand as straight) which she interpreted as a man that knew who he was!

During the exchange with the Sister Principal, Lee could tell that Jones was educated by the way way spoke, and was not afraid to speak his mind, for the Sister Principal was someone in authority, and she had been conditioned throughout her life, not to question those in such positions. This intrigued her because she had fears about her life, men, people in general (she trusted few), and herself — she had the inclination to speak very little, and often, people misread her silence as weakness, when only she knew how strong she was. Lee noticed during that first meeting, that there was nothing strikingly handsome about Jones, but she did notice that he had very, very small eyes behind his eyeglasses, clear facial skin (no shadow of a beard), neat military haircut that Lee came to learn, Jones had cut every week, was almost six feet tall, and had very large hands. As Lee climbed the stairs, she told me that was when she realized that for the first time in her 26 years of life, she saw and met a man who she was instantly interested in! She wanted to know what he was like as a person, whether or not he could be trusted, and how he treated women.

As Lee continued to watch Jones out of the corner of her eye in the classrooms they visited, she related to me years later how annoyed she was with herself just because she was interested in Jones. After knowing what Lee believed to be true about gringo soldiers (no good), and still finding one of them interesting enough to want to know more about him on a personal level was upsetting! Who was he — really? Where was he from in the States? Why the party? Was he kind? Had he killed in war? Lee's thoughts were troubling, upsetting and disgusting, in view of the way she had planned her life before that first meeting with Jones. Lee then remembered what the Sister Principal had told her 2 1/2 years earlier during the interview for the teaching position, "suffering leading to betterment later in one's life." The fact that Lee could meet a man that she could love was not impossible! From the moment "betterment" entered her mind, Lee searchingly looked, listened, and watched Jones with new interest, while a stream of frightening questions ran amuck through her brain: Could it be true? Is this man my soul mate? Does he know that I am thinking about him; I want him for my own? Does he know that I am watching him? What does he think of me? Does he think that I am attractive? Am I being stupid? What am I thinking and feeling cannot be for real — what I am experiencing only happens in books, right? Why him? Why am I feeling so light-headed?

In 1960, while climbing the stairs to the classrooms on the second level, years later, Jones related to me and others that he had noticed Lee as she cheerfully bounced down the stairs in response to the Sister Principal's call. He said that when he saw Lee coming toward them from across the courtyard, he saw what appeared to be a five foot, nine inch tall, very attractive, young, slim woman, with her red hair in a bun at the back of her neck. She had large, beautiful light brown eyes, a nose that appeared to have been broken, full lipstick free lips, clean white teeth, clear facial skin; wearing an ankle length, long sleeve cotton beltless gray smock (that could not hide the woman it covered), a gold chain with a small Saint Carmen religious medallion attached, what appeared to be gold mounted, one carat diamond earrings in her pierced ears, a gold watch on her right wrist, no makeup, and on her feet a pair of low, black heeled shoes.

Just for a moment, Jones thought that Lee was a nun until the Sister Principal made the introductions including the information that Lee was their only lay teacher, who lived in the convent. Adding, Lee would have to leave them to make a life with the man she would someday married. Lee made no reply. They shook hands all around, and Jones told how he enjoyed that momentary sensation of holding Lee's slender, cool, soft hand in his, as she welcomed them to their school. During the entire time the Sister Principal spoke to Lee in Spanish, Lee stood with her hands in front of her body, one hand holding the other, without a hint of a smile appearing on her lips, and attentively listened to what she was being told. As Jones listened to the conversation, he found the lack of Lee's hint of a smile mystifying and strange, in one so young. The way Lee came down the stairs from her classroom, and greeted Ruiz and him, Jones thought her to be an exuberant type, but now, she appeared a nonsense type. As Jones continued to listen to the conversation between Lee and the Sister

Principal, a smile came to his lips as he realized that this encounter had an element of amusement about it. — The hated, bad gringo soldiers attempting to do something good for a change. — As Jones watched Lee's body move beneath her belt-less smock as she climbed the stairs to the second level, he wondered what had happened in her young life that had removed the smile form her lips. He told himself, that given half the chance, he would make Lee smile just to see her face and eyes light up with merriment from the knowledge that there were still things in the world for her to smile about.

They received the 15 children's names from San Jose Church Orphanage who would attend the Christmas party on Flamenco Island. After saying their good-byes to Lee (with Jones telling her that he looked forward to seeing her again) and thanking the Sister Principal for her cooperation, Jones and Ruiz returned to the island feeling very good about what they had accomplished. The party was going to happen!

The Christmas party went off without a hitch. Jones volunteered Lee to accompany him throughout the day to help with his Spanish as he went to each activity to assure that all was proceeding as planned and to make sure the children were having a good time. Jones later admitted, that having Lee accompanying him, was his way of having her near. Ruiz was performing the same task regarding the flow of the party. The Sister Principal from the San Jose Church/Orphanage accompanied her children to the island (as did Sisters from the other churches), and when Jones realized she was there, he smiled to himself, as he thought it was to assure that nothing unpleasant would happen to her children in the company of what she referred to as "uncouth American soldier." When the Battalion Commander put in his appearance later in the day to observe the festivities, Jones with Lee at his side, introduced the Sister Principal to him. This was the second occasion Jones said that he learned that the Sister Principal spoke flawless English because that was how she and the Colonel communicated during their lengthy conversation as they walked amongst the happy children. After the activities ended, Jones borrowed Ruiz's automobile to return the Sister Principal and Lee to San Jose. Jones had already asked Lee earlier in the day if he could telephone her at the convent and if she could receive calls. She had told him, yes, he could call, and would look forward to hearing from him. As Jones drove, he watched the Sister Principal in the rear view mirror, for she appeared to be deep in thought. Upon reaching the convent, Lee thanked Jones again for what he, Ruiz, and the other members of Flamenco did for the children which she appreciated and would never forget; adding that she truly enjoyed herself and the time she spent in his company — call me! They shook hands, and again Jones had that momentary sensation of holding Lee's slender, cool hand in his. Lee then entered the convent, and closed the door behind her. The Sister Principal also thanked Jones for the days activities. Revealing that she had been thinking in the car how to ask him, after seeing the American soldiers up close with her orphans, why did they bother since the children were not their responsibility. She felt that people only do what they feel compelled to do. You are not a Spaniard nor a Panamanian. She also felt guilty for articulating her strong dislike of American Soldiers when they first met. Jones thanked her for sharing her thoughts and explained why he and the other members of his Battery bothered. It was just something they could do. Jones bid the Sister Principal goodnight and returned to Flamenco Island, and thinking while driving, nonthing enlightens like first hand and experienced knowledge.

Lee readily admits that it was that day spent in Jones' company during the Christmas party that enabled her to stop being annoyed with herself for finding an American gringo soldier interesting after all the negative comments she heard about them growing up. I asked Lee once what she felt when she was with Jones. She instantly replied, "Safe! I knew that the feeling of safety was a major component of love along with knowing that the feelings I had for Jones was definitely love. But I was afraid to admit, even to myself, that the man I could and would love for the rest of my life just walked in off the street." She further explained when she came out of the classroom in response to the Sister Principal's call and looked down from the balcony and saw Jones — Lee recounted that for a second, she could not breathe. Years later, reflecting on that moment in 1960, Lee mentioned that she had no idea what her experience of seeing Jones for the first time meant, except that she knew something had happened that day which would change her life forever!

> "Tis sweet to know there is an eye
> will mark our coming, and look
> brighter when we come."
> *George Gordon Byron*

9.

COURTSHIP

L ee told the story of how once the Christmas party on
Flamenco Island was over, she was momentarily relieved.
She believed that she had seen the last of Jones, although a part
of her was hoping that he would telephone and see her again. She
enjoyed spending the day in Jones' company as she held onto his
arm as they walked about the island. They observed the children
enjoying themselves, greeting members of the Battery, the Sister
Teachers, and participated in the lively head table conversation.
The conversation was in English and Spanish where she observed
that Jones talked a lot, which did not bother her at all for she only
listened to the sound of his voice, and smiled at him when he
looked her way. Being near him was enough.

As the day progressed, their closeness created uncomfortable
questions for Lee that she did not know the answers for: "Why
do I feel safe in his company? Am I instantly in love with a man
that I absolutely know nothing about? What will he say, do, and
think of me if he knew my negative opinions of Americans and,
especially American soldiers? What would my father and the
Sister Principal say about my sudden interest in a gringo with the
view of making him mine for life?"

As Lee prepared for bed, the night after the Christmas party,
she admitted to herself that she was experiencing an longing up

to that point in her life she never thought could apply to her. While being afraid of her own indecision, she told herself, all she had to do was to continue her life as before, forget, and never see Jones again if he called or become involved with him. Even as that thought entered her mind, Lee said that she panicked, "But I do want to see him again!" After she got up from the completion of her prayers, she climbed into bed, then pulled the covers up to her chin and prepared to go to sleep. Turning out the lamp on the night table, Lee remembered the maxim that she had lived by up to that point: "What is meant to be, will be." As she drifted off to sleep, she had by then resolved that she would take on day at a time, make her own decision about Jones and not be swayed by anything said by others. Lee spent a very stressful night, saying that she was constantly tossing and turning in her bed with questions running through her half-awake brain — "What will I say to him if he does call? What if he asks to take me out? What will I wear (Wore her gray school smock everywhere)? What if he doesn't call? Can or do I want to forget about him? — No!" She finally fell asleep wondering why life was so difficult when it came to important personal relationships when, in the end, all she had to trust was her heart.

After hearing Lee's version of how she spent that first night after the Christmas party on Flamenco Island, I made a point of asking Jones, without repeating what had been confided to me by Lee, "How did you spend the night after dropping Lee off at the convent?" He immediately replied, "No problem, I had already made up my mind that Lee was the woman that I had been seeking in my many past liaisons with other women around the world. The only problem I foreseen in courting and making Lee my wife, was to somehow, convince her that I was more than I appear to be." Jones continued, "I had no doubts, given time, Lee will come to see that I love her and that my love was eternal! If she would have me, I would love, care, and protect her against the evils of the world that in just two meetings, I knew she feared. Once together, we would laugh at the amazing wonderment of our married life. I believed that Lee loved me, just by the way she held on to my arm during the party — as if she never wanted to let go."

It was two weeks (January 1961) before Lee received the phone call that half of her soul was longing for while the other half was hoping would never arrive. Leading up to the actual call, whenever the telephone rang in the visitors room of the convent, Lee would physically jump believing that the call was for her and that the long-awaited moment had arrived. The Sister Principal and other residents noticed Lee's nervousness, asking if she was all right. Lee assured the nuns that she was fine, just preoccupied, but appreciated their concern. However, her answer never seemed to truly satisfy the Sister Principal because they were friends and she knew something was wrong. She looked at Lee searchingly while advising her, "Be careful! Be sure you know what you are doing, for it is very easy to make a serious mistake when dealing with a strong emotion such as love." But Lee said she knew exactly what her friend meant; that she had no experience of a personal or physical nature with a man. Since leaving the university, she had lived a cloistered life by choice, she was innocent in the ways of the world outside the convent walls, she had already determined her life's path over two years ago, and regardless what is proclaimed — Americans are different then the rest of the peoples of the world! Most others see situations and say, "Oh well." Americans in the same position attempt to do something about it, even when it's none of their business.

The call arrived on a Thursday night at 6:00 P.M, and when Lee was called to the telephone from her room, she said that she never felt such a relief — Jones had called as he had promised. Lee immediately ran down the stairs to assure that he did not hang up, went into the visitors room and closed the door as she placed the receiver to her left ear and said hello. She then heard Jones' voice, in his schoolbook Spanish, mentioning that he had called as he promised. Lee said that she sat in the chair beside the small table that held the telephone and talked for one and a half hours about what they had been doing since they were last together and about their feelings toward each other.

Lee was finally hearing the voice of the man that she had thought about constantly every day for the past two weeks, and that was enough for her. Jones asked Lee to go out with him (she noticed that he did not say 'date') that coming Saturday, for an afternoon of sightseeing around Panama City, a movie, and dinner. Adding, that he had no automobile, so they would have to use the public transportation system (buses) and their feet to get around. Lee said that the bus was fine with her, for that was how she traveled to her home on weekends. She also mentioned that she had nothing against walking either, but she would not be able to go with him that Saturday. Jones then went through every night of the next week as Lee declined each offer. Then she heard Jones say to someone in the background, "My God, that woman is certainly busy!" She then told Jones that she would go out with him the following Saturday, if he still wanted to take her. She added that he would be able to pick her up at the convent at 2:00 P.M. Jones said, "Good, I will see you then, but until Saturday, will I be able to call you?" Lee warned him, "Yes, you can telephone me, but please make sure it is after 6:00 P.M., for that is when our free time begins until evening prays at 8:30 P.M., then to bed at nine." Jones replied, "Okay, look forward to seeing you Saturday," and after saying good-bye, he hung up. Lee told me that she sat in the chair for another hour after hanging up the phone going over in her mind every word that Jones had spoken while, still savoring the sound of his voice.

As Lee prepared for bed, she realized that she no longer could deny her love for Jones, for the entire time she was listening to his voice coming through the telephone wires, her inside were singing. Admitting the truth of her love for Jones to herself, Lee said that had made her that much more afraid. She had no idea what she was doing being in love while, at the same time realizing that she was a 26-year old, college educated woman, responsible for her actions as an adult — her rational mind told her. Her irrational mind told her, "I don't care! I love Jones and will not lose him now that I have found the only man that I can love and care for the rest of my life!"

The reason Lee gave me why she had refused Jones' offer of a date within that coming week was because she felt that she had no contemporary clothing to wear! Lee said that she wore her ankle-length, long sleeve, beltless, gray smock whenever she left the convent. Intuitively, Lee said that she just knew her gray smock was just not the appropriate apparel for her first (or any other) date with Jones. So she used the week before that Saturday to purchase what she felt was appropriate clothing. White short sleeve blouses. Full, below the knees conservative colored skirts and black gloves, all her life in the United States, Lee was never without her gloves in her handbag (white for summer and colored for winter), saying, "that a woman was not completely dressed unless she had her gloves." Silk stockings, black handbag, and a new pair of low heeled black dress shoes. Lee prepared for her first date through her shopping for new clothing. When she returned to the convent after each of her buying forays into the city, all the residents wanted to see what new items she had added to her wardrobe — coming by her bedroom to view and comment upon them until lights out at 9:00 P.M. The twenty-four Sisters were as excited and happy about Lee's forthcoming date with what they called, her soldier. They bombarded Lee with questions that she could not answer: "How old was he? Was he college educated? Was he rich (everyone knows that all Americans are rich)? Where was he from in America? What type of family did he have? Was he handsome?" During all of the inquiries as to Jones' background, Lee would reply laughing, "I don't even know the answers to your questions! You can see my soldier Saturday and come to your own conclusion." Only the Sister Principal appeared not to share in the excitement of Lee's preparations for her first date since she came to live with them over two years ago — silently watching from the sidelines, with what Lee said she interpreted as an expression of apprehension on her face.

Saturday arrived, with Lee recounting how she was dressed in her new, strange-feeling clothing by noon. While remaining in her bedroom, sitting on her bed with her black, cotton gloves in her hands, and handbag laying on the bed, she waited for the bell outside the courtyard door to be rung by Jones. While slowly dressing herself (watching her slow motion movements in the dresser mirror), after her shower, was when Lee said that all doubts and fears had left her. Somehow, as Lee dressed, she knew there was no need to fear Jones' love (or her love for him), because he would be patient with her. At 1:30 P.M, she heard the bell ring, and knew without waiting to be called, that it was Jones. Lee said that she picked up her handbag from the bed, walked down stairs, out the back door and stood in the center of the courtyard as she watched the Sister Principal going to open the door. When the door opened, there was her clean, still ruffled looking Jones in civilian clothing, short sleeve white shirt worn outside of his dark blue trousers for coolness, dark blue socks, and black loafers on his feet — smiling. After greeting the Sister

Principal, and softly repeating over and over, "You are beautiful, so beautiful!" Jones slowly walked toward her — their eyes met as they continued to smile at each other. The smile of two people sharing the secret of their love for each other. The smiles were to remain on their lips until they left the courtyard. As Jones slowly walked toward Lee standing very straight in the center of the courtyard, while what he feasted his eyes upon was a slim, tall, beautiful woman, who's red hair was no longer in a bun at the back of her neck — but made over into a permanent. No make-up. Dressed in a white short sleeve blouse open at the neck — that left you with no doubt that she was a woman. Wearing a small religious medallion of Saint Carmen that was exposed in the open "V" of her blouse. Gold diamond earring in her perched ears. A knee length green pattern full skirt, with her very attractive legs enwrapped in silk stockings, and on her feet — a pair of black low heeled dress shoes. When he reached Lee, they, in unison said, "Hello." Lee extended her hand for Jones to shake. He took it into his and remembered when they first met in November of 1960. He also noticed that Lee was still wearing her gold watch along with a black handbag slung over her left forearm. Holding Lee's hand just as long as he dared, Jones told her again, "You are truly beautiful!" Lee thanked him, and after a few minutes of meaningless small talk about the weather, Jones asked, "Are you ready to go?" She said yes as he offered her his right arm as they slowly walked toward the courtyard door when spontaneous clapping broke out behind them. They both stopped in their tracks and turned around finding that on the second floor balcony held the Sisters and the children who lived on the premise — all smiling and clapping their hands in delight. Embarrassed, Jones turned to Lee and told her that when he entered the courtyard, he never noticed that the balcony was full of people — he only saw her waiting for him. Lee smiled as she lightly squeezed his forearm as she told him, "Don't be embarrassed they just wanted to see what you looked like. You have to remember that I have lived with the Sisters and some of the children for over two years and never went out on a date, so it's a first for them also." At the courtyard door, Jones told the Sister Principal that he would have Lee back at the convent by 8:00 that night. She replied, "Fine, and please come up to the front door when you return." They passed through the doorway and heard the door lock behind them as they walked together to the bus stop at the corner for the beginning of their first extended time alone together.

Lee and Jones' date consisted of walking around Panama City taking in the sights. Jones took pictures (mostly of her) with his camera. They went to a movie (which Lee always selected), sitting in the balcony and dinner at one of the numerous restaurants (that Jones selected) throughout the city. Lee often mentioned in amazement how Jones would eat anything "just to try something new". That was another myth Lee had grown up with: Americans would not eat Panamanian food, they claimed it was not sanitary. During their date Jones asked Lee if she would help him perfect his Spanish and he would do the same for her English. Lee could read and write English flawlessly and was a better speller than Jones, but limited ability in speaking the language. Lee readily agreed, for that meant she would be seeing Jones again, and he would not be leaving her life.

For the remainder of 1961, Jones picked up Lee in the afternoon and returned her to the convent every Saturday night by 8:00 P.M., and she started returning to her home on Sundays. Lee kept to these arrangements because she was not sure how well Jones could get around Panama City via the public bus system. He also had not automobile, nor could everyone understand the Castilian Spanish he was taught in high school. Lee also did not want her father's hostility toward all Americans to drive Jones away before he had the opportunity to learn how much, and deep, her love for him was. She needed Jones in her life!

When Lee returned home, the Sunday after her first date with Jones, her father asked, "Why didn't you come home Saturday?" Bursting with happiness, Lee told her father all about Jones' attributes and how they met. She told him that they talked on the phone everyday, that he was a gringo American soldier, and treated her nice — was a gentleman. He respected her as a woman — no vulgar language. Physically unattractive — but very intelligent, and was going to help her with her spoken English as she would his Spanish. He seemed genially interested in me, and towards developing a relationship. She also told him that they had another date that coming Saturday, and she was sure that she was in love. Lee said her father hit the ceiling with his wrath, calling her a damn fool. He became angrier by the minute, while shouting at her and hobbled about their living room on his one crutch. Lee sat quietly on the sofa with her hands folded in her lap. "You say that you're in love with a gringo! Gringos are no good, especially soldiers! You know they stole my land when they built their canal! It's you duty as my daughter to take care of me for I am disabled! If your love for your gringo leads to marriage, who will take care of me? I forbid you to see that Gringo again! You know nothing about men and the dogs some of them are! I don't even believe that you have ever been kissed by a man! End it!" Lee said that at first, she listened quietly and dispassionately to her father's expected ranting and raging (she had learned long ago, that he cared for no one or anything except his own comfort). But it was the kissing remark that got to her, and she became angry. From her position on the sofa, Lee told her father in a firm, no-nonsense voice, "Let me tell you something! You are right about never having been kissed by a man, but not because there

were not many who wanted to! I never had the desire to be kissed
by a man just to say that I had experience. At some point in our
relationship, Jones will give me his kiss of love, and I will passionately return it! The reason why I have never allowed myself
to be kissed by a man is because I have never been in love, until
now. Now let me tell you something else, and you listen to me
good! I have experienced in one date, something that I thought I
would never be able to do - love a man! After watching the way
you mistreated my late mother, I wanted nothing to do with any
man! And then, out of the blue, Jones came into my life and I
already love and trust him — completely! I know, and don't think
he knows, how very much I love him! If he ever asked me, I will
I marry him without a moments hesitation or doubt, for I know
that I have found my soul-mate who will love, care, and protect
me with the last breath in his body! Now if you have any problem
with anything that I have said, or plan to do with my life, now or
in the future — you know where the door is! I am not my mother! I intend to live my life in the way I perceive is best for me and
not what is best for you!" That was the end of Lee's father's public display of disapproval over his daughter dating Jones.

Lee's father was not the only person attempting to discour-
age her in the planned, and later continuation, of her relationship
with Jones — the Sister Principal was also concerned. Her objections, Lee said, were partly based on Lee's lack of experience in
what she called, "the real world," but more of a fundamental
down-to-earth reason. Having a lay person living in the convent
enabled the Sister Principal to have things done for her and the
other sisters that they often could not conveniently do for themselves. If Lee was not there, they could not go out after nine at
night, visit a family member of a sister (these visits were restrict-
ed to two a year — each a week in duration), soliciting charitable
assistance for the orphanage from establishments that they were

not allowed to enter (saloons, nightclubs, gambling houses, etc. while they waited outside). On a more personal level, the Sister Principal admitted to herself and Lee, that after more than two years of Lee living with them, becoming friends during that time, she had become accustomed to Lee always being there whenever she needed her. The Sister Principal admitted that it was selfishness on her part (that she had prayed for forgiveness), when the matter involved Lee's future happiness, but she would sincerely miss Lee if she left. The Sister Principal then hugged Lee as they left the visitors room. Walking side by side on the wide staircase, after Lee had returned from her first date with Jones (the Sister Principal waited for her to return), and after telling Lee of her concerns, as they proceeded to climb to the second floor, "Be that as it may, whatever you decide to do with your life my child — you have my blessings."

There was one memorable event that occurred on their first date; Lee and Jones often laughingly talked about with neither of them offering an explanation for their merriment! After getting off the bus at the corner, at the end of their first date — Lee took off running! Jones immediately stopped dead in his tracks, asking, "What the Hell?" By the time he reached the convent door, it was closed and locked, with Lee inside, and somehow, he knew not to ring the doorbell. Jones stood in front of the locked door in total bewilderment as he asked himself, "What just happened?" After a few moments of staring at the closed door, Jones returned to the corner bus stop. After a few minutes wait, Jones took the bus that would return him to the Canal Zone and Flamenco Island in total confusion! He had no idea why Lee had ran from him. To the best of his knowledge, Jones said they had a good time together during their first date. Both of them laughed together, enjoyed the movie, had a good meal, and had an overall great time as they walked in stride throughout the city. Jones said to her that night, "You are the first woman who could ever keep in stride with me, and I like that, because I do not have to keep changing step or walking at a slower stride."

The following Monday after 6:00 P.M., Jones telephoned the convent, asked for Lee, and when she came to the phone, immediately asked, "What happened?" Lee, after saying, "Hi," being very apologetic, told Jones, "I do, sincerely apologize for my behavior Saturday night! Please forgive me? I was stupid for running away from you after we had such a good time together, and if you ever decide to take me out again, I assure you that it will never happen again! I am truly sorry if my stupid actions on Saturday night embarrassed or hurt your feelings, but I promise you, if you will give me another chance, you will come to learn there is nothing in this world that could ever make me knowingly hurt you! You have no idea how very important you and your well-being are to me. I only ask one thing of you, Jones, if you can forgive me for Saturday night, please, never ask me why I ran from you." Jones replied, "It's okay, I thought that I had unconsciously said or done something that offended you. Can I pick you up at 2 P.M. this Saturday?" "Yes, please. I will be ready," with relief in her voice, Lee answered Jones knowing that she had not frightened off the man she loved by her irrational behavior.

Lee has often told me after hearing the story of her running away from Jones, that in their many years together, Jones has never once attempted to question her as to what was going on in her mind that night on their first date. I also knew not to ask why she ran, because it had to be something that made no sense; no matter how you attempted to rationalize the reason.

In recounting memories of Panama City, Republic de Panama, Lee would always include in her narrative the seawall facing the Bay of Panama. The seawall was waist high, ten feet thick, painted white, and built to follow the contours of the bay.

According to Lee, it would take over two hourts to walk the wall end-to-end (she and Jones timed themselves during one of their dates). Approximately six feet from the seawall was a four foot wide concret walking path that ran the length of the seawall. Six feet from the walking path, spaced for privacy, where two person white concrete benches, between every other bench, set back another six feet, where white painted caste iron, upright, globed street lights. It was to those benches that Lee said that she and Jones always ended up, after dinner, on each of their dates, beginning with their second date. It was here, that Lee told Jones her life story, and he his, as they both watched the light from the stars and/or moon play on the waters of the Bay of Panama, as the waves went in and out against the seawall. After dating for three months, it was at the seawall where Jones kissed Lee for the first time while declaring his love for her. With this first kiss, Lee knew that he loved her back in the same way that she loved him. Though that one kiss, she knew the meaning of her life thereafter, to be loved by Jones!

Having never felt the love for a man before, she was definitely not going to lose Jones because he made her feel secure in the knowledge that he was there for her alone. After their first kiss, it became very difficult for Lee to be separated from Jones. She always worried that some mishap would befall him. To reassure her, Jones took to telephoning her twice a day; noon and after 6:00 P.M. and continued to do so for the rest of their life together — Jones calling home twice a day.

> "The heart has reasons
> that reason does not understand."
> *Jacques Benigne Bossuet*

10.

SERENADE

The night that Lee was first kissed by Jones, still sitting on the seawall bench, she took from around her neck a small religious medallion of Saint Carmen and placed it around Jones' neck while telling him, "Wear it always as a visual proclamation of my eternal love for you. As the gold of this chain and medallion shall never tarnish-so never shall my love!" Jones took Lee in his arms again and kissed her lips, thanking her, as he told her that he had nothing to exchange as a token of his love, for he had never worn a religious medallion before, even though she knew he also was a Roman Catholic. Still in Jones' arms while leaning against his chest, Lee told him that he had already given her more than he could possibly ever know — he had found her, when she had never known that she had been lost all of her life. Waiting for him to make his appearance, while never realizing that, "Hell is truth seen too late." Jones gave Lee a squeeze and told her that ever since he was nine years old, after looking at a picture book in the library about the building of the Panama Canal, he has always been fascinated with the Republic de Panama. Originally believing it to be because of the Panama Canal — a truly engineering marvel for its time; now he knows that it was his soul telling him that Panama was where the other half of him was to be found — Lee! They kissed again, and held each other tightly as they silently continued to watch the lights of the city, stars, and moon play on the waves in the Bay of Panama.

When I first heard the story of Lee giving her religious medallion to Jones, I had known Lee long enough to know her seemingly obvious actions had an unannounced, underlining meaning. So, I knew to ask her what giving her Saint Carmen's medallion to Jones meant and this is the story she told me:

There were many young, and not so young, women in Panama City whose sole aim in life was to marry an American (she had heard this type of talk when she had attended the University of Panama and when she graduated, among the citizens of Panama City) and go to what they called: "The Land of the Big P.X." While it was true Jones was not much to look at, he was an American! Also, you could see form the way he stood, walked, and spoke his mind, that he was unique among men. I also saw this uniqueness in Jones, but that was not the reason for loving him (from the first time I saw him standing in the courtyard of San Jose Church) but the assured knowledge that I had found my soul mate. The person that I was preordained to spend the rest of my life with!

In Panama, women's religious medallions are smaller than men's are (theirs often were the size of an American silver dollar or larger) and because of the topical weather, all men wear their shirts with the neck open. So, with my woman's size religious medallion around Jones' neck for all to see, especially those women whose only aim in life was to marry an American-would warn them, "Hands off! He belongs to me!" After finding Jones, I was taking no chances of loosing him to another woman because of lack of vigilance on my part."

After Lee had finished her story, I sat at her kitchen table in stunned silence for several minutes, (I would never imagined that so much was invloved with that Saint Carmen's medallion Jones still wears). Silence for several minutes. Finally saying to Lee, as she went about her task of preparing dinner, "Well, I'll be damned! Does Jones know?" "No, but I plan to tell him some-day," Lee replied. Soon after our conversation in her kitchen, Lee did tell her husband about the religious medallion during a Sunday dinner that I attended. Silence. Then loud laughter, to include the children. Through her laughter, very seriously, Lee told the gathering, as we all stopped eating as we attempted to bring our laughter under control, "I was taking no chances!" There was more loud laughter.

From their first date in January 1961, through July 1962, Jones continued to pick Lee up at the San Jose Convent every Saturday afternoon and returned her there by 8:00 P.M. In July of 1962, Lee and Jones had been seeing each other for eighteen months, and with each meeting, becoming more and more in love with the emotional attachment that brings. Every word, action, gesture, glance, touch, and kiss came naturally between them-as if they had known each other all of their lives! One Saturday in July of 1962, when Jones came to pick Lee up at San Jose Convent, she had decided to take him home to meet her father, and told him when he arrived at 2:00 P.M. Lee still remembered the blow up with her father after her first date when she had told him that she was in love and seeing an American soldier. Now, sometime later, she had no idea how he would react to meeting her man in per-son. At that point in time, Lee said that she did not really care what her father thought! She was in love! After all, she told herself, it was her home also, and she was entitled to bring her friends there. Lee really believed that her father would not make a scene

in front of a total stranger. Just to be on the safe side, she had
warned her father beforehand not to. For all of his many actual
and perceived faults (and there were many) Lee mentioned that
her father, at heart, was a gentleman. The other reason for the trip
to her home, Lee told Jones, was that she planned to move out of
the convent that month and back into her home with her father.
She would commute by bus Monday through Friday, to her
teaching position at San Jose. By her living at home, Jones could
bus out to see her early Sunday morning and spend the entire
day, rather than the six hours they now had together, and leave
whenever time he chose to return to Flamenco Island that night,
for the buses ran twenty-four hours a day.

She would cook for and feed him (Lee said she had very early
in their relationship noticed that Jones was always hungry-later
learning that it was a result of his captivity during the Korean
War). Jones agreed with noticeable pleasure to all Lee had told
him as they strolled hand in hand around Panama City before
later taking the bus to her home-commenting, "Great! Sounds
good, and I like the idea of meeting your father." Later that
Saturday afternoon, they took the bus for the fifteen-mile ride to
Lee's home on the outskirts of Panama City. Jones had already
assured Lee, after she mentioned that she was very concerned
that he would loose his way when he came out to see her
Sundays, that he had the ability, that if he ever went to a place
once, he would always be able to return, so she need not fear that
he would become confused, as to directions to her home once he
started to come out Sunday mornings to see her."

The bus let them off at the corner of her street, and they
walked hand in hand on the sidewalk to her home. What Jones
saw for the first of many times, was a single story, cream painted, concrete house with a red tiled roof, and what was very

noticeable was that none of the houses had chimneys! Completely surrounding Lee's house, sitting in the middle of the plot as was all the houses on the street, was a four-foot concrete wall painted the same color as the house-with a two-foot high dedicative iron worked fence attached to its wall. Three dedicative iron worked gates, two in front-one leading to the front door, the other to an empty carport. In the back was the same type of gate as in the front, leading to the back porch, door and kitchen. Once inside, you entered a foray with a hallway running the length of the house with rooms on either side: living room, diner room, three bedrooms (only two then, being utilized-Lee's and her father's) with their individual baths, wall-to-wall ceiling tiled kitchen/eating area that ran across the back of the house.

Lee recounted as if it was only yesterday, that first meeting between Jones and her father, which was divulged to her afterwards by Jones. Lee and Jones entered her home, closing the front door behind them, while calling to her father, "I have brought someone home for you to meet." "In here." They went into the living room hand in hand, and Lee and Jones found her father sitting in his easy chair with his crutch lying beside it. She gave him a kiss on the cheek and asked, "How have you made it through the week? Any problems with the day help?" To which he replied, "Just fine, no problems. Who's this?" Still looking at Jones form his chair, Lee made the introductions, then left, saying that she was going to prepare something to eat for them-leaving Jones and her father together. This is what Jones told Lee happened when she went into the kitchen:

He stood (was not offered a seat) before her father in silence as Lee's father looked him up and down with an expression of disgust on his face. This slightly frightened him, he told Lee (a new experience-for he claimed that he has never been frightened of anyone or anything in his entire life until he met her father for the first time) as he waited for her father to speak.

Lee's father looked Jones in the eye from his easy chair, and told him, "You are the first man that my daughter has ever brought home for me to meet, and if you mean her no good, then leave her alone! I do not like gringos, especially American soldiers! You people stole my land when you built your canal! If you harm my only daughter, I will come into the Zone on my one leg, and with my one eye, find you, and proceed to chop you to pieces with my machete!"

Just then, before Jones could reply to Lee's father's comments, she called them from the kitchen, "Come to dinner!" They left the living room together and walked side-by-side down the hallway to the kitchen eating area at the rear of the house without Jones or Lee's father saying one word to each other. They took their places (both men at each end of the table) ate their delicious meal of fried chicken, fish, rice, plantain, and tea while Lee, with a worried expression on her face, attempted to maintain a one-sided conversation with herself. Jones and her father, she said, never uttered a word to each other or to her (although she tried to draw them into conversation) during the entire meal. When Lee was telling me the story of the first meeting between Jones and her father, she mentioned that during the silent meal, it was as if they were both afraid to speak out of fear that their individual anger would consume them both! Lee said, as she watched them both eating their meal from her position in the middle of the table, she thought she had an insurmountable problem. If her father were responsible-she would read him the riot act! What really concerned Lee, as she picked at her food, was Jones-what if he did not want to deal with what he perceived as resistances from her father, and left her (she had no solution for that)! But in the end, after hearing the story Jones told of his meeting with her father, Lee realized that her fear (Jones leaving her) was groundless.

After cleaning up the kitchen eating area, Lee and Jones left her home to return to Panama City. Lee bid her father good-bye with another kiss on his cheek as she told him, "I will see you tomorrow." During the bus ride back to the city, sitting very close together in their seat, Jones, with his arm around Lee's shoulder — holding her close to his body, and she leaning against him, told her without rancor, what had transpired between her father and himself. When he had finished, Lee placed both her arms around Jones' waist and pulled her body as close to his as she could and began to softly kiss him on the side of his face and neck while telling him with a pleading for understanding expression on her face and in her voice, "It will be all right honey. My father is only being a parent. He doesn't want me to be hurt-you must remember that you are my first! I know that you would never deliberately hurt me, because I know that you love me as much as I love you (and maybe more)! I love you Honey. as she continued to kiss him about the face and neck!" In the short time Jones was to have a relationship with Lee's father, Lee's assessment of her father as it related to Jones was correct, it was all right between them, for it grew into a loving (Lee's father telling Jones once, "I no longer worry about my daughter after I die-you love her, and I know you will take care of her.") and amiable relationship.

Lee did move out of San Jose convent and back into her home in July of 1962. It was a tearful and sorrowful farewell from the resident Sisters, with Lee, telling them, "There is no need for tears, for I will still be with you all during the day Monday through Friday-it's not as if I am leaving, never to return!" The

Sisters attempted to smile through their tears as they genuinely attempted to be happy for Lee as they each kissed her on the cheek and hugged her that first Monday after school as she was about to begin the routine of commuting to and from her home. As they wished Lee well, they also told her to be careful. They mentioned how they would all miss her at evening prayers, for they had all become accustomed to her always being there for them. They implored Lee not to forget them-for she would always be in their prayers, and above all, "That we have come to love you dearly as one of our own."

That Monday after school in July of 1962, when Lee left San Jose convent to return to her home until the following morning, she also had what she called her last lengthy conversation with the Sister Principal. Sitting behind her desk, with Lee sitting in front, the Sister Principal told her, "I do, sincerely wish you well! While at the same time, I confess to you, that I will miss you profoundly. At this time of temporary parting, concerning your new routine, I also must be truthful with you by letting you know that you are doing the right thing by attempting spending more time with your soldier-he loves you, and I already know that you love him more than life itself! In the beginning, I disliked your soldier, for what I know now, was for no other reason than he was an American. I knew that the negative feelings I held towards him was wrong, so I prayed daily for forgiveness as I remembered the teachings of our savior, 'Love all as yourself.' I no longer feel the way I once did about your soldier, in fact — I like him! What really did it for me, was that I watched (looking for a reason for my dislike-and found none) your soldier every Saturday afternoon when he came to pick you up, and I noticed, that the moment he laid those cold, hard eyes behind his eyeglasses on you coming out the convent door, down the stairs from the second floor or walking across the courtyard, they became soft and bright as his entire face would light up! By our standards your soldier is not much to look at (as they attempted to suppress their smiles at the truth of that statement) but you can see he's a real man who would never harm you." Raising from her chair, and Lee with her, the Sister Principal told her, "Now, come and give me the Kiss of Peace and go with my eternal blessing as you are to remember-we shall always be here for you." Lee did as she was bid, walking out of the office, and the convent, to the bus stop on the corner with tears in her eyes, knowing that a part of her past, safe, and clois-tered life was ending, but held no doubts about the life she was about to undertake with Jones as the reason for her very existence.

The Sunday in July of 1962, at the end of the first week of Lee returning home every day after school, Jones came out by bus as he promised, arriving at 7:00 A.M., to spend the day. From the beginning of Jones' first Sunday visit and thereafter, Lee would always, rain or shine, meet him at the corner bus stop. When she saw him (searching for him on the bus, even before it had stopped) it was as if her world was complete. Nothing mattered at that moment, except that Jones was there! After kissing Lee and being kissed in return, Lee, her eyes bright, and face softly aglow with pleasure, while being held in Jones arms she would tell him, "You came!" And receiving the same reply from Jones, "Of course. I love you and will always be here for you!" After being released, Lee would take hold of one of Jones' arms, hold it as tightly to the side of her body as she could, as they slowly walked to her home. They would normally go in the back door because Lee's father was often still asleep that early in the morn-ing. Jones would sit at the kitchen table as Lee prepared his breakfast of eggs, bacon, toast, jam, rice and plenty of coffee. Neither Lee or her father drank coffee, only tea. So Lee had to purchase a coffee pot, and coffee before Jones first Sunday visit — in order to make coffee for him. After that first visit to her home, and thereafter, before Jones left that night to return to Flamenco Island, Lee would always be sure to ask him what he wanted for breakfast that coming Sunday morning. Once informed, Lee would be sure to purchase, and prepared it for Jones when he arrived, which became the breakfast routine. After the meal, Lee had only tea, some type of fresh fruit, and toast for her breakfast. Jones offered to help in the clearing off the table and helping washing the dishes, and was told by Lee, "No thanks, continue to sit at the table and drink your coffee as you talk to me. It's my duty as the women of the house to clean up after meals. "Shyly, blushing, looking at Jones from the kitchen sink before turning away, "and take care of you." Jones made no reply to Lee's comments, as he continued to slowly drink his coffee while continuing to converse with Lee, about her job, his job, the health of her father, was she happy, etc. He watched her body move beneath her clothing as she moved about the kitchen-pleased with all he was observing and hearing.

By the time Lee had finished straightening up the kitchen, her father came in for his breakfast-they had heard him moving about at the other end of the house as they were eating their meal. Lee's father cheerfully greeted Jones as Lee gave him a kiss on the cheek and a "good morning," as he sat down at the kitchen table across from Jones as Lee went about preparing his breakfast, which was the same as Jones. They made small talk before, during and after Lee's father's breakfast. Years afterwards, Jones said that Lee's father appeared to be on his best behavior that first visit and those afterwards. Lee mentioned to me once that she had read the riot act to her father-telling him that if he messed it up between Jones and herself, through some malfeasance or ill-advised spoken word, she was going to put him out into the street (it was her savings from her teaching salary that had purchased their home). Adding that she had found her happiness and was not going to be deprived of it because of some misdeed by him! Jones often told me that he had found Lee's father a very interesting man to be around. At that time in his life — 1962 — he did not drink or smoke, he was well read, physically active at sixty-five years of age-even though he had only one leg and one eye, fluent in two languages (French and English) other than his own, and an active correspondent with friends in five different countries. When Lee and Jones would reminisce about her late father, Jones would always comment how he no only looked forward to his Sunday visits with Lee, but also the varied and interesting conversations he had with her father. Lee apparently approved of this for when they were going at it over some point of decision, she would smile, at last, her father was accepting Jones as part of their lives-because for her he was!

While her father was eating his breakfast, Lee sat down in a chair beside Jones while laying one of her hands on top of his laying on the table. She informed her father that once he had finished eating and she had cleaned up the kitchen eating area, she and Jones were going into the city to the Big Market to shop for their dinner and the rations to prepare a weeks lot of meals for him. After they returned from the Big Market with their purchases, she would fix their dinner, clean up, and then she and Jones were going out for the evening, and not to wait up for them. Her father replied, "Fine," and continued to eat his breakfast.

Lee, like most women of Panama City of that time, shopped daily for their food, even though they had the same access as Americans who lived in the Canal Zone to pre-prepared foods.

They also had the option of going to the Big Market, corner store or pushcart vendors that came through every neighborhood, selling every conceivable item. After that first trip to the Big Market with Jones in July of 1962, and seeing how happy and excited he was to see all the people selling and buying — that was where Lee took him every Sunday to shop for their meal and her fathers weekly rations. Even today, you can say, "Big Market" and Jones' eyes will light up and will readily tell you of what the Big Market was all about and the varied things he saw each time he went there. According to Lee, the Big Market was a government of the Republic de Panama run indoor-market of enormous space containing stalls, counters, scales, etc. that could be rented for a minimal fee by farmers and other vendors desiring to sell their goods to the population of the city from a centralized location.

The government built the Big Market, according to Lee, to assure that all edible products met the countries health standards — Health Inspectors, inspected everything, before being allowed to be sold. Lee said that the Big Market contained varied types of in-country, grown and imported vegetables and fruits. There were Yucca, Plantain, Yams, Breadfruit, and etc. Farmers from the interior, including San Blas Indians from San Blas Island would have for sale in cages live chickens, ducks, and other edible fowl, along with pigs. What was surprising for Jones was that they also sold turkeys in the Big Market. He thought for some reason that it was only an American custom to eat turkeys. In buckets, plastic, and tiled lined tanks were live fish of every known variety to include eels and turtles — all for sale. Jones often mentioned that going to the Big Market with Lee every Sunday taught him never to pay the first price quoted. The vendors never expected it to be paid — it was just the staring point of negotiations. While in Panama, Lee said, and Jones confirmed, she never paid the posted price for anything she purchased. After two to three hours shopping at the Big Market, loaded down with their purchases in hand-held straw woven shopping bags, they carried to the Big Market, Lee and Jones took the bus home — with their dinner for Sunday and a weeks rations for Lee's father. Lee, also, purchased whatever Jones wanted.

Arriving home, Lee would immediately begin to prepare their Sunday dinner, while also preparing her father's week of prepared food. Jones watched this process from behind his cup of coffee at the kitchen table. Finishing his coffee, Jones would go into the living room to keep Lee's father company if he was not in his bedroom; or to read the English Sunday newspaper that Lee purchased for him before he arrived: then a book from their small library or that he had left there during a previous visit: or holding forth with Lee's father on some topic that was of interest to them both. Around 2 P.M., they would be called to their Sunday dinner of chicken, beef, pork, fried frsh fish, a variety of rice dishes, fried plantin, soup — containing yucca. A green salad, fresh fruit, and after Jones third visit — freash baked bread (the only bread eater in the family). Once Lee discovered that Jones had a sweet tooth, from watching him buy sweets from the many street vendors as they went around the city, she stared baking him fresh fruit pies and his favorite desert — three-layer coconut cake. Lee always sent Jones back to Flamenco Island Sunday nights with a large portion of the desert in a plastic container for later.

Lee, when reflecting on the Sunday visits with Jones, she would often mention, that she quickly learned that no one had ever done anything for him. He was always so appreciative for the smallest kindness. This knowledge, Lee said, at times angered and saddened her when she thought of all the things he must have missed out on in life, and how that must have made him feel. Lee told me, in 1962, Jones didn't know it — but he had her! Lee was determined that she was going to love, care and give Jones a life in the areas she controlled that would make him forget all he had missed out on growing up. Feed him. Keep him clean. Give him as many children as he wanted. Keep his house. Protect him — no one better, never, hurt him. He could do anything that made him happy, and she would be happy.

I am getting ahead of my story, but that is exactly what Lee did. She did not realize that she was operating from were most women do — human compassion for her man. Because women's moral judgments place great weight on emotional ideas like caring.

That first Sunday in July of 1962, when Jones went to Lee's home for the first of many Sunday dinners, Lee laughing, describes their first dinner together by telling this story:

After she had prepared the table in the dining room, after they all had been seated, Jones and her father at each end of the table and Lee in the middle. Grace said by Jones — being the guest, and after everyone had served their plates, Lee and her father for ten minutes just watched Jones, eat with gusto the food on his plate. Jones happened to look up from his plate and noticed that they were not eating, but watching him. Becoming embarrassed, he asked, "Have I unknowingly broken some rule of etiquette?" In unison, Lee and her father quickly smiled and replied, "No, nothing is wrong," with Lee's father proceeding to explain the reason they were watching him eat his meal. They and most Panamanians had been led to believe that Americans would not eat Panamanian food. Yet, here he was, eating it with gusto. Jones laughed as he leaned back in his chair saying, "Of course, your daughter is a great cook! The food is delicious. And I am always hungry," there was more laughter.

After their laughter had subsided, Jones continued to tell Lee and her father, "I still have the curiosity to experience new food that I have taken to every country I have ever visited." Thereafter, when he noticed Lee or her father watching him eat, he knew that it was more than their delight in seeing him enjoying some of the national dishes of Panama.

After Sunday dinner, they had left Lee's home, Lee said that their routine, generally, never varied during the two pulse years of their serenade. After arriving in the city and leaving the bus at the main station that boarded the Canal Zone, they would walk hand in hand sight-seeing in the Zone and Panama City. After they had completed their walk around, they would find a motion picture at one of the city's many theaters that Lee wanted to view.

After leaving the movie Theater, they would take the bus out to Auntie's home, where they would always be welcomed. Auntie told Lee in Spanish as she smiled at Jones (which she now knew he understood). "Your soldier is good for you. You never looked so beautiful! Your eyes sparkle now. Your hair is radiant. Your face glows with what can only be called happiness. There is a spring in your walk that I have never seen before." Jones would pretend that he did not hear or understand what was being said. Lee, in mock anger, would tell Auntie, "Stop it, or I will not come out to see you anymore!" Auntie would look at Lee knowingly as she smiling, took Lee in her ample arms as she gently rocked Lee while telling her, "Yes you will Baby, because you know I love you more than life itself!" Still standing, lightly laying in Auntie's arms, Lee would barely audibly reply, "I know."

It was to Auntie, Lee told me that she confessed her fears relating to being in love with Jones. She would do anything to make sure Jones did not ever leave her. Auntie told her, "Baby, you don't have to worry your head — you don't need to do anymore than what you are doing, feeding him, making him welcome amongst your family and friends, going out with him and enjoying yourself. He's no fool — every time you look or speak to your soldier, the love you feel for him shows in the way that you go to him when he calls. The way you speak to him (in a different voice then you speak to everyone else), the way you are content just to be near and have him in your sight. He may be a Gringo, but you got yourself a man, Baby! I like him a lot and know that he loves you just as much as you do him. How do I know? Your soldier has the coldest and meanest pair of eyes behind those eyeglasses of his that I have ever seen in a human's face! But when those same eyes look at you, Baby, they sparkle, become soft and warm, as if he never tires of beholding you. Now, don't ask me how I know what I am about to tell you, other than I have lived a good many more years than you and have met more people than I care to remember, but you represent your soldier's ideal woman. You can also see that he's had a very difficult life up until now. He never ask for anything, not even a glass of water — somewhere in his past life he has learned (maybe painfully) not to ask for anything — do without. But no matter the difficulties of his past life, they have not defeated him!" Lee continued with her concerns, "he hasn't said anything to me about marriage — not even in a round about way." "Don't worry, Baby, he will." I assure you that it will happen! When he's sure that you will not refuse him, he will ask you to marry him. Trust your Auntie who loves you!"

At other visits to Auntie's in the privacy of her bedroom, Lee often told her, "You can not imagine how empty my world becomes when Jones returns to Flamenco Island Sunday night. I see him off at the bus stop with a kiss, smile and a wave. As soon as the bus is out of sight I can't control my tears, knowing that it will be six days before I see him again! Living through those six days of separation with the constant fear in the back of my mind as I go about my normal routine — What if he doesn't come back? What would I do? I would die!" "Baby," Auntie replied as she took Lee in her arms, "I do understand your heartache of being separated from the one you love, for this — being in love —was something that you never planned or expected to be a part of your life. Now that it is, it's natural that you would have fears of losing you new found happiness — which will not happen! Jones will marry you! You and he will have some hard times in your life together, but the love you have for each other will never waver; it will pull you both through any and all adversities you may confront. Try not to worry Honey, it can make you sick. Believe what I tell you, Baby."

Once the word got out by word of mouth that Lee had a Gringo American soldier, friends of her families and from the University of Panama began to drop by Auntie's Sunday afternoon in hopes of running into Lee and Jones to get a look at the him. Auntie would feed all comers, as they made small talk in Spanish (although, they could all speak English — Lee told Jones) with Lee and Jones, while they were silently inspecting and evaluating this American for his worthiness to be keeping a Panamanian woman company. They all made sure they spoke to Lee in private before leaving. When I asked Lee what did her friends have to say about Jones, she replied with a frown on her face, "It didn't matter, because he was hers, and not theirs, and she was satisfied!" I assumed, from the lack of positive response to my question, Lee must have heard some negative comments from her family and friends about Jones.

Lee was an exceptional dancer and her face would come alive when she talked about how after leaving Auntie's, she and Jones would go to one of the many covered rooftop dance halls along the water front. These places opened their doors after the sun had set in order to catch the cool breeze coming off the Golfo de Panama as they danced the night away. I have had the pleasure to see Lee and Jones dance together and have danced with her myself at weddings and parties that we have attended in this country. When it was a Spanish party, Lee danced the Tamborito and was graceful liquid in motion. According to Lee, each of the dance halls had their own local five to ten member band. There were no hard drinks — only tonic, and you paid twenty five cents per person to enter and you could dance all night until they closed at 1:00 A.M. What Lee said she and Jones did, along with many other couples, was to go from hall to hall — as many as four a night, in order to dance to music of the various bands. Lee said that her father and mother had taught her to dance while she was attending St. Carmen's school when she went home on the weekends, they told her, "All young girls should know how to dance and don't tell the Sisters." All the parents with girls in Saint Carmens were doing the same thing because when they returned to school Monday mornings, they used to compare the steps they had learned over the weekend, with a cautious eye out for the Sisters.

Around midnight, Lee and Jones would leave the dance hall they were in and catch the bus to her home. Upon arriving, they would find her father already in bed fast asleep. Lee prepared coffee and food from Sunday's dinner for Jones to eat before he returned to Flamenco Island. Out of eyesight of her father, Lee would sit in Jones' lap at the kitchen table after she had served him his coffee and food. With his arms around Lee's waist, she would cut up his food with his knife and fork, as she smiling, and very, very slowly fed him. With each fork full of food, Lee would softly kiss Jones on the lips as she

112

mouthed the words, "I love you Honey." Whenever Lee recounted the story of their return to her home after dancing, she would always add, "The best of times!"

After Lee had fed Jones, they would both, very quietly, wash the dishes as they stood side by side. She would give him his sweets in a plastic container with a fork and put it into a brown, paper bag to take back with him. They would go out the back door, leave the porch light on and walk slowly and silently with Lee holding tightly to one of his forearms as she lightly leaned against his body as they walked to the corner. They went to the bus stop for the 2:00 A.M. bus. With Jones' arm across Lee's back, he would hold her tightly to his side with both of her arms around his waist — they waited in silence for their moment of parting. The bus would arrive on time; they would kiss each other while declaring their eternal love. Jones would enter the lighted bus, find a seat near a window, and wave good-bye to Lee looking so sad and forlorn standing at the curb until she no longer could be seen by him as the bus sped towards Panama City. Lee said that she would not move from her attention position at curbside until she could no longer see the two red rear lights of the bus that Jones was on. Then the uncontrollable tears would begin to flow, as Lee half ran, half walked to her back door. Once inside, she would turn the porch light off, locked the door, took a quick shower, put on her nightclothes, then kneeled beside her bed to say her prayers. She asked the Lord to protect and look after Jones until he returned to her — then she would do that. Getting into bed, Lee said was when all of her self-doubts washed over her like a stormy ocean wave as she cried herself to sleep. Jones will learn for the first time, when he reads this, how traumatic their partings were for Lee in Panama during their Serenade period.

In October of 1961, there was a month long map mock war game called by the Commanding General, United State Southern Command (CGSC). It was held in the War Room of Southern Command Headquarters, to repel a mock invasion of the Republic de Panama and the Canal Zone. Bilingual representatives (for there would be military observers from the Organization of American States — OAS), were called up from throughout Southern Command to staff the mock war game "J" Headquarters. Jones was sent from Flamenco Island to fill the Senior Sergeants slot in the "J-1" (Intelligence) Department because he spoke Spanish and Portuguese. The mock war game would be conducted Monday through Saturday, with Sundays free for all participants to include the OAS guest to pursue their individual active. Once the five hundred member staff of officers, senior non-commissioned officers, enlisted personnel, civilian defense personnel from Republic de Panama and the Canal Zone, and the civilian clerical staff (all Canal Zone female senior high school students) assembled at Southern Command Headquarters on a Monday morning, a week before the mock war game was to commence, for a speech by the CGSC.

This narrative about the mock war game and its aftermath was told to me individually by Lee and Jones and often together. At the meeting the CGSC, briefly outlined the contents of the individual handout that Jones and the other members of the staff of "J" Headquarters had been given. In it was the mission of the map mock war game, the rules by which it was to be played, time allotted for each situation, etc. The CGSC then moved on to what the dress code would be at "J" Headquarters during the duration of the mock war game — a freshly laundered Class "A" Khaki uniform with all earned decorations, service medals and qualifi-action badges displayed — everyday! For those in attendance with only six uniforms, they had better purchase six more before the mock war game started. God help the man he saw out of uniform. For the male civilian staff: suit, jacket, shirt, and tie. For the female staff: no trousers, dress, skirt, sleeved blouse, silk stockings and appropriate foot wear (no opened toe shoes). Any civilian that felt that he or she could not meet this dress code for any reason may be excused the CGSC called from his position on the auditorium stage. None left.

Those in attendance were dismissed by the CGSC, with Jones following the map in his hand-out of "J" Headquarters, to his "J-1" Department, meeting his boss — a full "Bird" Colonel (that he did not know), and the other thirty enlisted men who would be working for and reporting to him. Along with these men, there was one civilian clerical staff member — Sissel. She was a nineteen-year-old female American Balboa Senior High school student who lived in the Canal Zone, and would also be working and reporting directly to him. From that first meeting, Jones could see that Sissel did not appreciate reporting to him — she would not look him in the eye when he spoke to her and gave him curt answers to all of his questions. After organizing his staff as to their duties through the handout they had all received, Jones told them to remember what the General has said about the dress code. An incentive to having sharply dressed members on his "J" Staff, the OAS members assigned to each Department ("J-1" would have seven), Section, Group, will vote amongst themselves, as to which American member (to include civilians) was the most sharply dressed for the week. He or she, would receive a $100 U.S. Saving Bond. The CGSC announcement was well received by those in attendance, as Jones thought, "Count me out, for I have never won anything in my life." He would see them all back there in a week, and they would show the world how a "J-1" Department should really work during hostilities — real or mock, operated by personnel that know their stuff!

Having the rest of the day and week free, Jones telephoned Lee at San Jose School, asking if she could take a long lunch hour. He said he would come into Panama City to see her and they could have lunch together. Lee immediately accepted the invitation with, "Oh yes! I will have a Sister take my class until I return. Oh Honey, I am so happy to know that I am going to see you! Love you," and hung up. They had a glorious two-hour lunch, with Jones telling Lee as much as he was allowed, of what he would be doing for the next month. Lee asked Jones, "Do you have twelve Khaki uniforms?" Jones answering in the affirmative. Lee continued, "Bring them all out to my home tonight including your low quarters (dress shoes) you are planning to wear. I will rewash and iron all of your uniforms and shine your low quarters. So, you to Honey, also may become a contender for the weekly award for the sharpest dressed member of your department. I have some vacation time due to me, so I will take the rest of the week off to put your clothing and shoes in order." Jones looked at Lee accross the restaurant table in total amazement while commenting, "No one has ever done anything for me before! I don't care anything about being sharp — my uniforms are clean and I do not shine shoes!" Lee reached across the table and took on of Jones' hands in both of hers, brought it to her lips as she kissed and squeezed his hand in hers and told him, "But I care for you! I never want you to be left out of anything." Jones leaned across the table with Lee still holding his hand in hers next to her body and kissed her softly while mouthing the words close to her lips, "I love you Honey! You are so good to me. I will never make you sorry for your goodness!"

Jones had his Khaki uniforms and other washable civilian

clothing done by the Canal Zone Government run laundry. The few times Lee saw Jones in his uniforms, every crease in his shirts and trousers where they had been folded, were very noticeable! His low quarters and his civilian shoes looked as if they had never seen shoe polish or a shoe brush since they were purchased! Lee often mentioned that she never cared what Jones looked like in his clothing — military or civilian — for as he said, "They were clean." For Lee, the most important matter was not Jones' clothing, but the fact that he loved her. Jones did take his uniforms and low quarters to Lee's home, and came out to see her every night that week before the mock war game began. He took back to his quarters on Flamenco Island the washed and ironed uniforms that Lee had done for the day. Jones said that his uniforms were so beautifully ironed (not a folded crease to been seen on them), that he hated to put them on because it would mess them up. When he took his beautiful, shined low quarters back to his quarters before leaving Lee's home, Jones hugged Lee as they kissed while saying, "I never knew they could look so good," with them both laughing at the underlining message in that statement: nothing can look the way it is suppose to, if you do not care and clean it. All of Lee's washing was done in a tin tube with a scrub board. Ironing, an eclectic iron.

During the month long mock war game, Jones won the award for the sharpest dressed three times. He commented to Lee," The first time I have ever won anything!" Lee said how happy she was to see the delight in Jones' face when he came out Sundays after winning the first and subsequent awards — making the OK sign to her just as soon as he saw her at the bus stop. As soon as he got off the bus, he picked Lee up in his arms while hugging her tightly around the waist as he kissed her and shouted, "We won!" Jones told me when Lee was telling the story of the mock war game that he would never attempt to insult Lee by offering her money for washing his uniforms and shining his low quarters for a month, but each time they won, they did the town. Eating at an expensive restaurant, travelling by taxi, and dancing in the ball room. The best of times! After the mock war games were over, Lee told Jones that she wanted to continue to do his Khaki uniforms and civilian clothes because she did not like the way they were being done at the Canal Zone Government laundry, along with shining his low quarters and combat boots. And so it came to past, that Jones gradually began to like his uniforms and civilian clothing to look good on him. For thirty-two years Lee continued to shine Jones' shoes.

In many of Lee's conversations with me over the years, only once did I ever see her express any anger, and that was when she remembered Sissel. What Lee first learned about Sissel was told to her by Jones after the mock war game started when he came out to her on Sundays. This is what Jones told Lee and she repeated it to me.

During the first Monday of the mock war game, Jones noticed that every time he gave Sissel, his only Balbo Canal Zone, high school senior student, clerical help, something to do, she would always ask him, "Did the Colonel say so?" After the fourth time of this type of response to his orders, Jones got up from his desk and told Sissel to follow him. Taking her into their conference room, closing the door, he proceeded to tell Sissel in a firm, no nonsense voice, "Let me tell you something young lady, you work for me, and not the Colonel! Now is you have a problem with that or can not accept that fact, then I suggest that you pick up your things from your desk and leave right now! If you ever question anything I tell you again, I will personally boot your ass out of my department! Do you understand?" Sissel looked at Sergeant Jones in shock with her eyes wide and mouth hanging open as she nodded her head up and down. "Fine! Now get back to your desk and lets get this show on the road!"

Jones came in early the next day, as he always did, to an empty department and saw Sissel with the Colonel in his office (assuming she was telling him about their conversation yesterday), with the door open. Neither of them saw or heard him when he entered. Hearing only the end of the Colonel's comments to Sissel standing before his desk, "Even I do what Sergeant Jones tells me, because he runs the department and knows what must be done if we are to fulfill our mission here in the "J-1" Department. If you have a problem with that, maybe you better leave as he suggested." Jones told Lee that he did not hear Sissel's reply because he quietly went back into the hallway, and reentered the department again and slammed the door. Sissel, startled, turned to look at Jones, with her face beginning to turn a bright red, as she silently left the Colonel's office and went to her desk after saying good morning to Jones.

Jones told Lee, from that second day, through the duration of the mock war game, he never had anymore problems with Sissel's attitude. "In fact," he told Lee, "I could not get rid of her!" Thereafter, Jones would find Sissel in the department when he arrived each morning to open up. Sissel worked very closely and efficiently with Jones. After her conversation with the Colonel, she was there early every morning when he arrived and would not leave until he did — which sometimes would be as late as 10:00 P.M. Sissel was only paid by the United States Army to 5:00 P.M and when 6:00 P.M arrived, Jones would tell her, "Go home!" She would refuse, telling him once, "That the time after 5:00 P.M is my own to do with as I please, and I please to be right here with you until you are finished. And don't ever tell me again to go home!"

119

Jones' main function as the N.C.O.I.C. of the "J-1" Department was to assure that the compiled intelligence data by his thirty man staff for the day was accurate and put into report format for his Colonel to personal present at the daily morning briefings with the Commanding General, Southern Command (CGSC). If the incoming data was late arriving at "J-1", it made for a long day. Jones loves flowers, and no matter the assignment, always had pictures of some under the glass on the top of his desk. Sissel noticed and went out and purchased a small vase and daily kept it full with fresh flowers that she brought to work with her. Jones' normal work habit was to never stop working on what was beneath his hands until it was completed, even through lunch and dinner. Again Sissel noticed. When lunch hour arrived, and Jones was engrossed in his work, Sissel would quietly leave the Department go to the twenty-four hour cafeteria (no charge), and bring lunch back for them both telling Jones, "Stop and eat!" As they ate, Sissel would watch Jones from her desk to assure that he did not place one fork full of food in his mouth then go back to work. Once Jones had finished eating, Sissel would clean off his desk, as she told him, "Now you can go back to work." As she returned their trays to the cafeteria. With Sissel performing the same service when they both stayed past 6:00 P.M. Jones had always had a sweet tooth (he says because when he was growing up his care givers could not afford to spend their meager wages on sweets), and Sissel purchased a covered crystal candy jar — placed it on his desk and kept it full with candy. She forbid the other members of the department staff from eating from it. By the second week of the mock war game, Sissel was anticipating Jones' every move to include his every need — all he had to do was to look up from his desk towards her and before he could complete his sentence — Sissel would put what he wanted in his hand or on his desk. Even Jones' boss, the Colonel, noticed the uninhibited support Sissel was giving his Senior Sergeant in the performance of his duties, commenting once, "You and your girl Friday are the team to beat. Keep up the good work!" "Thank you, Sir," Jones replied as he continued to work at what was beneath his hands.

When the mock war game was over, the CGSC threw a "Job Well Done" party at his spacious quarters in the Canal Zone the last day (a Saturday) of the game for the five hundred members of his "J" Headquarters and the military guest from the Organization of American States. During the entire two hours that Jones was at the CGSC party, (when invited to a CGSC party, you attended and stayed for at least two hours), Sissel tightly held onto his left forearm as they circulated through the throng. A number of the US Army officers knew Sissel and all the Zone civilians and spoke as they made their floating passage through the guests. When greeted, Sissel would respond, with pride in her voice, a toss of her flowing, light brown hair, and a smile on her lips, "This is my boss, Sergeant Jones, a smart man!"

When he made his exit from the CGSC party, Jones thanked Sissel again for her unwavering support during the mock war game, while wishing her well when she graduated form high school, knowing that whatever she set her mind and hand, she would successfully accomplish. Again Jones told Sissel, "Many thanks for a job well done." Sissel grabbed one of Jones hands, as he was about to walk away, and held his hand tightly in both of hers and she gazed tearfully into his eyes, while pleading, "Will I ever see you again? You can not begin to imagine how I feel about you and how you have affected my life since we met! Please tell me that I will see you again!" Gently removing his hand from hers, Jones replied, "Probably not, for we live and travel in two different worlds, military and the zone." Jones left the CGSC party and thought not more of Sissel.

All of the above working relationships and past difficulties with Sissel, Jones told Lee about over the duration of the mock war game when he came to see her every Sunday. Lee listened and never made any comment until he told her about the CGSC Job Well Done party and Sissel's parting question to Jones. Lee responded with some anger in her voice to what Jones had told her and said, "Why would she want to see you again? Who does she think she is? I don't like her!" "I don't know why Sissel would want to see me again, I have no desire to see her - she attempted to give me a hard time and make trouble for me with my Colonel. You have to remember she lives in the Zone, and the people there believe that they breathe different air than us. There is nothing to like or dislike about Sissel," Jones told Lee. Adding, "She was hired by the US Army to assist me doing the mock war game and that is what I forced her to do.

That's it! I, (we) in all probability, will never see her again, so don't get yourself all upset for no reason." Lee said, "Yes, I know what you say is true — for I trust you completely. But that woman has a thing for you." "No way," replied Jones. "Anyway, I don't like or want her! Forget about Sissel!"

It turned out Jones was wrong about never seeing her again, Lee told me. Sissel did put herself in Jones' path in 1962. There was a motion picture theater in Balboa, Canal Zone, that Lee and Jones attended. Meeting at the round house, when Lee and Jones knew that they were going to the afternoon movies in Balboa, Lee would bus in to the combination snack bar, restaurant, general meeting place and teen hangout in the center of Balboa, early in the morning from her home, and meet Jones at The Round House — have breakfast there, go sight seeing around the Zone until the theater opened at noon. Jones bused in from Flamenco Island this particular Sunday morning to meet Lee at the Round House, got off at the main bus station, crossed over into the Zone, and began to walk towards the center of Balboa. He had been walking for approximately fifteen minutes when he heard his name called, "Sergeant Jones!" He stopped to see who was calling him, when he heard the sound of screeching tires; he looked towards the street. There, running towards him with one hand holding her white pillbox hat on her head and in the other a small white handbag, was Sissel. When she reached Jones on the sidewalk, flushed of face and blue eyes sparkling with mischief and delight, she held tightly to his left forearm while lightly jumping up and down in place with glee, while telling Jones, "It's so good to see you again! I look for you every time that I go out! Come meet my parents!"

The car that Sissel had ran out in the middle of the street, had since pulled over to the curb with its engine still running. When they reached it, Sissel happily made the introductions, "Mom, Dad, my Sergeant Jones!" Which Jones said he immediately corrected, "I am not your daughter's Sergeant Jones," (he was only Lee's Sergeant Jones), "just her former boss." Extending his right hand, as he leaned towards the car window on the passage side where Sissel's mother was sitting. The father, leaning over his wife, looked at Jones dressed in civilian clothes and said, "So, we finally have the opportunity to meet the Sergeant Jones that my daughter never tires of talking about!" I have to tell you Sergeant, you have really impressed my daughter with your intelligence — saying that there is nothing you don't know or can't do and that she never knew there were men like you!" Jones told Sissel's father, "Thank you sir." With Sissel still holding tightly to his left forearm as she stood beside him, as she asked, "Where are you going?" "To the Round House to meet my fiancee," Jones replied. "Good, I will go with you and keep you company until she arrives." Turning to her parents, Sissel told them, "You go on to church, I will meet you there or back at home." Sissel's parents said, "Fine, nice to have met you Sergeant," and drove off waving to Sissel and Jones standing on the sidewalk, as she waved them good-bye. Once her parents were out of sight in traffic, Sissel, turned to Jones smiling, as she squeezed his arm and told him, "Now that I have found you, I am not going to let you go!"

Still holding onto Jones' arm, they reached the Round House, obtaining a table near a window so that Jones could see Lee when she came up the street from the main bus station. He gave the waitress their order for his coffee and tonic for Sissel. After their orders had been delivered, the first thing Sissel told Jones was, "I had a birthday since I saw you last. I am now twenty years old." "Congratulations," Jones replied, at the same time he saw Lee coming up the street. When she came abreast of his window, waved with Lee waving back. When Lee reached the table, Jones stood, made the introductions, with Sissel extending her hand — which Lee shook as she commented, "So, you are Sissel?" Lee said that what she saw that Sunday at the Round House, was a very beautiful young American woman (she would not dignify her with "lady") with light brown hair to her shoulders and bright blue eyes, straight nose, thin lipstick covered lips, lightly made up to include her eyebrows and eyelashes, and bright red fingernail polish on he nails. Wearing a white square neck dress, that accented the contours of her body in all the appropriate places, with matching pillbox hat and handbag. Smiling up at Lee, as they sized each other up — as only women can. Lee claimed that women see things in each other that men can not. Sitting down, after declining Jones' offer to order something to eat or drink for her. She sat just as close to him as the chairs would allow, as Lee and Sissel made small talk — excluding Jones in their conversation. In about twenty minutes, Sissel stood, excused herself with the statement that she had to meet her parents at the church while telling Lee it was nice meeting her. Then leaning across the table towards Jones — as he was about to stand, so that the front of her dress fell from her chest (which Lee said, that even she could see her breast captured by her bra) as she told him, "I will see you again, for I will never forget you! Don't get up," as she straightened and lightly touched him on the hand then left the Round House with Lee watching her leave with fire in her eyes — according to Jones. They watched Sissel, in silence, through the window of the Round House as she faded from view with her confident lascivious buttock-rolling walk towards the church in her high heel white shoes, swinging her handbag with a smile on her lips. After Sissel had faded form view, Lee asked Jones, "What was she doing here?" Jones told Lee the story of their chance meeting as he was on the way to their meeting, and all that had transpired before she arrived. Then Lee asked Jones, "Did you see the way she carried on with you — leaning across the table so you could see down her dress before she left? It was disgraceful! American women have no pride! I told you so, Sissel has eyes for you!" "It seems so, why I don't know, for I have not knowingly done or said anything to encourage her," Jones replied. Lee took his hand in both of hers and told Jones, "We will not do this again, meet at the Round House because I don't like that woman and don't want her in our lives." Jones kissed the hands that were holding his and told Lee, "Right," as he nodded his head in agreement.

They have never returned to the Round House Lee said, but went directly from the main bus station to the theater in Balboa.

Two months before they were to be married in 1963, one Sunday night, while leaving the balcony of the Balboa theater after viewing a motion picture, with Lee holding his right arm as they descended the very long flight of stairs to the lobby — Jones and Lee heard his name called, "Sergeant Jones!" Stopped, turned and looked up the stairs, it was Sissel. She was leaving the man she was with and came hurriedly towards them with a smile upon her face and in her eyes. Upon reaching them, she said, "Hi Lee" with Lee not responding to Sissel's greeting. I will walk down with you, tightly taking hold of Jones left arm as they slowly descended the stairs. Sissel made small talk about what she had been doing since the last time she had saw them at the Round House. She was twenty-two employed by the Canal Zone Government as a clerk, spending all of her money on clothing, had her own car. Her father gave it to her when she graduated from High School, her parents wanted to send her to college in the States, and she did not want to go. "I have not and will not ever forget you," as she smiled brightly at Jones and then at Lee. As much, and as often, Jones told me during the telling of meeting Sissel, at the theater, how he attempted to bring Lee into the conversation — Sissel would cut her short with a curt answer and continue to direct her comments to him. When they reached the lobby, Sissel offered Lee and Jones a lift in her car to anyplace they were going, to which they, in unison, declined. By that time, Sissel's date had reached them in the lobby with Sissel introducing Lee and Jones as her, "Sergeant Jones." To which Jones immediately corrected by saying, "I am only Lee's Sergeant Jones!" As they shook hands, Sissel's date commented, "I am glad to meet the man Sissel calls the best man in the world, and how she looks for him in the people walking the streets every time she goes out — no matter who her escort is." Jones replied that he heard the same comment from Sissel when they last met, as he and Lee bid them good night and left the theater to walk to the main bus station. During the bus rise to Lee's home, while holding hands, Lee said, "That's it!" With Jones immediately knowing what she meant. Thereafter, they would stay out of Balboa to keep from running into Sissel! Which they did, never returning to Balboa for any type of social activity during their remaining time in Republic de Panama.

Sissel is the only event in Lee's and Jones' life that I am aware of that they did not laugh together over. When after I heard the story of Sissel, I asked Lee, "Why?" With some annoyance, for asking about something that really "ticked her off," she replied, "Sissel wanted Jones for herself! As a lover, boyfriend, husband — I don't know what! You can believe me, I know she wanted him! The only reason Sissel did not succeed in her efforts to let Jones know he could have her, and how she really felt about him, was because Jones never reads any motives into what people say or do to him — he accepts everything at face value. Because of his face value concept, Jones did not notice or respond to the signals through words and body language I saw Sissel sending to him. I hate that woman for trying to come between us by offering Jones her body!" On another occasion, I asked Jones why was Lee so predisposed, adamantly negative towards Sissel, after so many years. Explaining, that my questions were based upon Lee's attitude concerning Sissel, was so out of character for her (she forgave)! He replied, "Lee has cause! Form our last meeting in the Balboa theater in 1963, Sissel demonstrated that she was just another Canal Zone snob! She attempted to ignore Lee by closing her out of the conversation, just because Lee was Panamanian. "I am better then you because I am an American, and live in the zone, and do not have to recognize or respect you because of these facts." This snobby attitude of Sissel's, according to Lee, was also held by many Americans living in the Canal Zone, which fed on her own Anti-American attitude that she carried throughout her life. Lee did not like Americans with very few exceptions. I considered myself privileged to have been included among her few exceptions, because to be loved, called friend, and cared for by Lee was to be blessed!

Lee often laughed (with her husband joining in), about how Jones proposed in November of 1961, after his detached duty during the war game at "J" Headquarters ended and Lee's disastrous reaction:

Unbeknownst to Lee, after their second date, Jones had been saving a portion of his monthly paycheck and all of his winnings from poker to purchase an engagement ring for her. It was then the custom in the Republic de Panama, that you went to a jeweler and he would design an original ring for you. Once you approved the design, the ring made, the design was burned in the customer present. It was felt by the citizens of Panama that each woman should have their own individual designed engagement ring.

It was Panama's Independence Day (November 3), a week day, schools were closed, and Lee was at home with her father when Jones telephoned. He told her that he would like to come out to see her after work because he had to ask her something. Lee told Jones, "Please come, just so I can see you, even if it's for only a few hours." Lee, in telling the story, said that she never thought that Jones was going to ask her to marry him (although from the time she admitted to herself that she loved him — she had been anxiously waiting for him to ask for her hand in marriage) even though he had only told her that he had something to ask her. For Lee, it was not what he was going to ask her — the meaning in the visit for her was that Jones was coming.

When Jones arrived, they met at the corner bus stop, hugged and kissed. When they arrived inside of Lee's home, they kissed again, and remained in a long, tight embrace as they savored the closeness and clean fresh smell of each other's bodies. When they broke their embrace, they quietly went down the hallway hand in hand, to the kitchen/eating area, for Lee's father had already taken to his bed. When they entered the kitchen, facing each other, standing under the ceiling light, Jones without any preamble, asked Lee, "Will you marry me?" While taking the ring from the box in his trouser pocket, he slipped it on the ring finger of Lee's left hand before she answered his question (Jones claimed, to make sure she did not say no). Lee held her left hand outstretched towards the light with the ring on it, while answering his question, "Yes, I will marry you, but just because you have given me this ring — does not mean you will marry me!" Jones was silent. When Lee looked at his face, she saw that he was perplexed (and for a second, Lee thought she had blown the moment) when for the first time ever, Jones spoke to her in a harsh voice, "What's the matter with you? Woman, what the devil do you think I would give you a ring for, if I did not intend to marry you?" Lee immediately replied, "I am sorry Honey! Thanks for the ring — I love you! I just was not thinking," while beginning to kiss Jones over and over about his face — as Lee stood in his tight embrace with their arms around each other bodes, as Jones accepted all of Lee's kisses with a bright and happy smile on his face.

The first time that I heard the story of how Jones proposed, I asked Lee what had prompted her to make the comment she did about the ring. Lee told me, "I had been anxiously praying, hoping, and waiting for Jones to ask for my hand so that I could quickly and happily say, Yes!" When the occasion arrived, her first comment after accepting was not in the way she had planned, it was a nervous reaction based upon her own insecurity. She wanted to be reassured by Jones that he really would marry her. Adding, that from the first time she laid eyes on Jones, she lived daily with the persistent fear that through some word or deed by her — she would lose him, or he would just decide on his own that he would leave her. Lee's fear was constantly being reinforced by others when they learned that she loved an American soldier, for they all knew some naive young girl just like her — in love, trusting and faithful — that had been left in the lurch by some soldier, as they often quoted to Lee:

> "Love is to submit oneself
> to the death of one's soul."

That first night they became engaged, Jones sat at the kitchen table with Lee in his lap and her arms around his neck as she periodically softly kissed him about his face while telling him, "I will be a good wife to you! I am so happy! I will always love you, for you brought into my life — something I never expected to ever have — love, and its' great! The ring (looking at it on her finger) is so beautiful," as Lee said they planned their future together as man and wife. First, they would wed in the Spring of 1963, in order that they both could have some money towards the cost of the wedding, for her father could not help. Jones stateside savings would be used to purchase their home after being transferred to Panama (Lee's savings had already been used to purchase the home she and her father were presently living in). Second, there would be three wedding ceremonies — the church,

Panama City Hall and in the Canal Zone, all performed on the same day. With Jones telling Lee that the reason he wanted the three wedding ceremonies, was to demonstrate to those doubters the she was really married, and not a scam, just to have his way with her, under the church, Panamanian and American laws. Third, he would always love her with or without children. But, if they did have children, then she would have to give up her teaching career and remain at home to love and nurture them — with his help. Jones continued by saying, "No matter what you may read, hear or believe, nothing is more important to a child than to come home from school and find his mother there. I know form which I speak, for I was raised by a sixty-some-year-old woman, and when I came home from school with my daily bad experiences, (fist fights) it was she who was immediately available to tell me if I had been fighting to uphold my dignity as a male, principle — what I new to be right, justice — for someone smaller and weaker then I. Had she not been there for me to bare my soul to, I might have grown up believing that fighting was my right, and what I had to do! I learned from that old woman there was another way, brain power, not fist power." Lee quickly replied to Jones comments about children, "Not a problem, for that is what I would want to do anyway." Fourth, that Jones planned to leave the United States Army when his enlistment was up in 1964. Once they wed, they would remain in the Republic de Panama, Jones told Lee, as he has repeatedly mentioned that he liked the country, lifestyle, and people. Commenting, that he had never lived so free (not even in America) before coming to her country. He could go anywhere throughout her country without fear of what might be said just because he was a soldier, or done to him unlawfully, by law enforcement personnel — just because of who he happened to be.

He was fluent in the Spanish language and had an open job offer as the Assistant Manager at the General Motors Parts Distributorship located in Panama City for the Central American area. The GM parts distributorship was managed by a former US Army captain from Texas who Jones knew from Fort Bliss, Texas. The former captain offered Jones employment as his assistant once he left the Army when Lee and Jones ran into him and his family at a restaurant in Panama City. Fifth, there are those that claim marriage is 50/50. Well, I dispute this, Jones told Lee marriage is 100/100. For if it is 50/50, then what are the partners doing with the other 50%? Sixth, he wanted no arguments about money. Whatever he earned, Lee would know from his pay stub (with Lee adding the same for her) and she and any children would always have first claim on how they spent the money. With him being the last claimer because his personal needs were almost nonexistent (did not smoke, drink, etc.). Jones promised Lee that she would always live in their own home. Lee asked, and received this promise from Jones, "Never to put her face in the dirt — embarrass her in public." According to Lee, she and Jones spent that first night of their engagement kissing and hugging each other until 3 in the morning, she in Jones lap, as they declared their eternal love for each other as they planned their future together. Then Lee became reflective in telling me the story of the first night of her engagement, commenting, "Jones and I never had any problems in our marriage, all our problems came from outside."

When Jones reminisces about that first Christmas of 1961, he spent with Lee and her father in their home, if Lee was present, she never made a comment or contributed anything to the story her husband was telling, except to add as they smiled at each other when he finished. "Yes, it's all true. I love Jones, and would do it again or anything else to make or see him happy — as he would do for me!" The story of that first Christmas.

Panamanians celebrated Christmas as we do, but without real Christmas tress, for they have to be imported from the United States and Canada, making them externally expensive for the average citizen of the Republic de Panama. Not knowing the cost of Christmas trees in Panama, two weeks before Christmas, during Sunday dinner, Jones asked Lee, "Are we going to have a Christmas tree?" Lee looked at her father, who made no reply, then smiled at Jones saying, "We will see Honey." When Jones came out Christmas day with his presents for Lee and her father, there, on a table in the center of the living room, was a twenty-four inch piece of a real Christmas tree branch in a milk bottle. The bottle was weighed down with small stones and sand, heavily decorated with multicolored balls, lights and beads, with a lighted small star on top all covered with silver strainers. Jones wished Lee and her father a Merry Christmas, laid his presents on the table containing the tree, as he took Lee into his arms and kissed her on the lips (Lee's father had been told that they were getting married), while saying to her as she remained in his embrace, and happily watched the delight and happiness on Jones face, and in his eyes, "Thanks Honey! We have our Christmas Tree and it's beautiful! You have made me so happy!" They all spent a happy and enjoyable first Christmas together in 1961.

It was not until late in 1962, that Jones learned how his Christmas Tree came to be. It was Lee's father that told him one Sunday the story of what he called, "Jones' tree." He said that his daughter, after school, walked the docks of Panama City, looking for ships that had sailed from America. When she found one, she stood on the deck and waited until she saw someone topside, then shouted at him, "Do you have a real Christmas Tree?" It was not until three days before Christmas that Lee found a ship that had originally sailed from New Orleans, Louisiana, which had a crew's real tree and Lee asked, "Would you sell me a piece of it? A branch?" The crew member she was talking to said, "Sure, for twenty dollars." Lee paid and came home with her prize. When Lee arrived home, she called to me, "I got it!" When I came into the hallway, in responce to her call, Lee's father told Jones "There she was. Still standing in front of the closed door, looking down so protectively at that piece of branch lovingly cradled in her arms — you would have thought it was made of gold." Saying to no one in particular, 'I would have died if I had not gotten it for him!'"

In their many years of marriage, Lee and Jones have had many beautifully decorated (by Jones, with Lee taking the ornaments off the tree, and packing them away) real Christmas Trees — some as tall as twelve feet high. It had been a ritual in the Jones household, that at least once, during the holiday season, Jones would not fail to tell his children the story of Lee's first Christmas gift to him — the Christmas tree in a milk bottle. And if Lee was not present when he was telling their children the story of his first tree, he would go through the house to find her, to give Lee his lovingly kiss of thanks, for all the happiness she had brought him him through her love.

> "I felt the while a pleasing kind of
> smart; the kiss went tingling to my
> panting heart. — When it was gone, the
> sense of it did stay; the sweetness
> cling'd upon my lips all day, like
> drops of honey, loth to fall away."
> *John Fairfield Dryden*

11.

WEDDING

Lee often happily reminisces about her wedding, and in the beginning of her story, she would be aglow with happiness revisiting the memories of that day once again. By the time she finished her recounting of that day her happiness had turned to sadness. "Sadness," because everything (wedding dress, presents, wedding album, etc.) connected to that happy event was lost when Lee's home was burned to the ground during the riot of 1964 by her longtime neighbors — just because she was married to an American. When Lee reflects on the destruction of her home, her eyes well up with tears as she relives that horrible day in January when her neighbors came at her like a pack of African wild dogs that sensed a kill.

The night that the riot started, Jones had been ordered to immediately report to his duty station and was not at home to prevent the attack on Lee, his father-in-law, and the killing of his dog. Jones was licensed by the military to carry a Caliber 45, automatic pistol. If he was home, a number of the attackers would have paid with their lives. "They were not satisfied in punching me about my face and body, knocking me to the ground, then kicking me, as I pleaded with them to stop; for I was recovering from an operation. My women attackers just laughed and jeered as they continued to kick me as I laid in a ball attempting to protect myself as they shouted their insults, 'Bitch! Whore! American Whore! Femenino Negra! Who do you think you are?' They clubbed Jones' dog, Sooner, to death when she came to my defense. After they pulled the crutches from under my father's arms, resulting in him falling to the ground as he still attempted to crawl to my aid, as I pleaded with my attackers, 'Leave my father alone! He's ill! He's just got out of the hospital! He's never done anything to you!' As I was repeatedly kicked laying on the ground in a ball while my father was stood over by two male attackers with wooden clubs to keep him form crawling to my aid, he cried and cursed them in every language he knew. My neighbors looted my home before they set it afire! If there is a God in Heaven, every one of my former neighbors in Panama City will have to pay for what they did to Jones' dog, my father, and me! I had never done anything to any of them, in fact, I thought we were all good neighbors. I know now that my neighbors always hated me." Then Lee would begin to cry, and if Jones was there, he would take her in his arms, attempting to kiss her tears away as he told her, "I know Honey. I am so sorry. Had I been there, some of those that attacked you would have paid with their lives! We still made it! As long as I live, it will never happen to you again Honey, I promise," as he held Lee tightly in his arms as he rubbed her hair and back with one of his hands. If Jones was not there, I would remain silent, after telling Lee that there was no rationalizing the evil that people do. As I waited for her to compose herself and continued the story of her wedding, which I never tired of hearing. After she had cried herself out, Lee would wipe her eyes with the back of her hands and say, "Enough! That was then, and this is now."

Continuing with the story of her wedding, Lee described how Jones and herself had agreed on the first of April as the date that the ceremonies in the church, with the Panamanian and

American governments, would be performed. As they went about making the arrangements, starting in January of 1963, for their wedding, Lee and Jones first went to see a priest at San Jose for the church ceremony. After being congratulated, and sat down, the priest was told that they wanted to be married on the first of April of that year. The priest exclaimed, "Oh no! You don't want to get married on April first!" Lee said that she and Jones looked at the priest and then at each other in bewilderment and asked, "What's wrong with the first of April?" The priest, smiling, told them, "April first is April Fool's Day!" They all laughed. That is how it came to pass that Lee and Jones came to be married on the second of April, enabling them both to always remember their anniversary because it follows April Fool's Day.

From San Jose Church, they went to Panama City, City Hall and filled out the necessary marriage application forms to include the date and time they would be there for the official of the Republic de Panama to perform the civil ceremony. Lee and Jones in their wedding clothes, seated in two very ornamented, red upholstered chairs, before the official of the Panamanian Government seated at the same type of ornamented table as the chairs. With a red, white, and blue sash over one shoulder of his Morning Coat, containing the Great Seal of the Republic de Panama. After the official married them, they would be required to sign their married names to the cities official marriage book.

After leaving Panama City, Lee and Jones went to Balbo, Canal Zone, to apply for their American marriage application and laughing recall, that there was a $3.00 fee, (there was no fee at Saint Jose Church nor at Panama City, City Hall) which Jones did not have with him. Not knowing that he would be required to pay for the clerk's time, he borrowed the three dollars form Lee. They were given a time when to appear in the Chambers of the Federal District Judge for the Canal Zone, on the second of April to get married. Thanking the clerk, Lee and Jones took the bus to her home, with Jones telling Lee during the trip, with his arm around her shoulder, and she leaning her body against his, "Well, we have accomplished what we started out to do in one day, and come the second of April, there will be no doubt in anyone's mind that I love you, and that we are legally married. I know that their are some who have advised you not to marry me — believing they know who and what I am about as a man and a soldier, but thank God, you have never wavered in your love for me. I love you, Honey and will never make you sorry for giving me your love in return!"

Concerning the $3.00 Jones had to borrow in 1963 from Lee in Balbo, Canal Zone (which he repeatedly claims he has repaid) to pay for their marriage application. Lee laughing, often, over the years, told the story to Jones and others, "How she had to pay for her own marriage application, and to tease Jones, claimed, "that he still owes me the three dollars!" Jones faked annoyance, denying her claim, while explaining that she knew he never carried more than their bus fair and one dollar in his pocket unless they had other plans. A trick that an Old Timer had taught Jones when he first entered the United States Army. There were civilians that preyed upon soldiers. Robbed them at gun or knife point, and if he only carried a dollar, that would be all they would get. Jones would reach into his pocket and give Lee three dollars commenting, "Now, I have repaid you that three dollars that I borrowed from you in 1963!" Lee , smiling, would pocket the money commenting, "You owe me interest." All present, to include Jones, would laugh loudly at Lee's perception of the long overdue amount owed her. Later, even the children would support their mothers position about the claimed three dollars owed her; sporadically asking their father, "Dad, when are you going to repay

Mom the three dollars you owe her?" That borrowed money was a on-going running joke in the Jones' household for years, but in the end, Jones had the last laugh. For their thirtieth wedding anniversary, Jones had made for Lee, a wide gold band ring, set with six diamonds (each diamond representing five years of marriage) with an inscription inside the band which read, "For the inter. due $3 from 1963." At the small gathering in their home on April 2, 1993, when Lee opened her anniversary gift and read out loud (after Jones told her, "look inside the band") the inscription for all to hear. For we had all heard the story of the "borrowed three dollars," and once read, to include Lee and Jones — laughed loudly, saying, "He got you Lee!" Slipping the ring on Lee's finger, Jones took her in his arms, kissing her on the lips wishing her a happy anniversary concluding with, "Now, what do you have to say?" Still in her husband's arms, leaning back in them, smiling, kissed Jones back, as Lee told him, "You still owe me." To which Jones replied as he pulled her close, "Whatever the price is, tell me and I will gladly repay you," as he showered he with kisses.

When Lee returned to San Jose school the next day after she and Jones had become engaged, she told the sisters about her wedding plans to her soldier. She told them that they would all be invited to her wedding. Overjoyed with the news, they told her, "We just knew it was meant to be!" The following morning, when Lee reported to her classroom, she found the Sister Principal waiting for her. After exchanging greetings, the Sister Principal told her, "Last night, all of the sisters in the convent had agreed, that if Lee would give them the pattern and materials, they would hand sew her wedding dress. "We understand form what you told us yesterday, that we have eighteen months to finish the dress." With delight in her voice, Lee said that she replied to the offer with and oh yes! As she hugged and kissed the Sister Principal on the cheek, with repeated, "Thank you! Thank you all!"

Lee said that she provided the pattern and materials for her wedding dress and walked down the aisle of San Jose church, in a formal wedding gown of white satin, with a high collar, conservative neckline, closed back, long sleeves, and a veil of lace covering her face. Because Lee had chosen to wear a long-sleeved gown, she did not have to wear gloves. Lee said her shoes were made of white silk. There was a strand of pearls around her neck, on her left wrist — a tiny, borrowed diamond-studded gold watch, and a gold bracelet that her father gave her, and Auntie's pearl earrings (something old). A white satin covered prayer book with a flower attached to the top of it (something new) and a blue prayer book marker (something blue). Lee wore her engagement ring to the alter on her right hand, because traditionally, once the wedding band was placed upon the finger, it was never to be removed.

Lee always smiled to herself as she told how beautiful she felt as she slowly walked towards Jones waiting at the alter with his best man with the unusual name of — "Jones Jones." She knew that it would always be right between them for life! Lee also laughing, told of how the night before the wedding, in her living room, her maid of honor was helping her one last time to try on her wedding gown. Lee stood on a footstool, completely dressed in her gown, with her lace veil covering her face and her prayer book in her hands, saying to no one in particular, "I wonder if I am doing the right thing?" Her father, who had been in the living room the entire time, watching in silence his daughter preparing to give herself to Jones, with a degree of sadness. He once told her, "The world has turned over many times since that day I brought you from Panama to San Andres Island and you have truly grown into a very beautiful young lady. Your mother would have been proud! Jones is all right. He loves you and I know that you feel the same about him and that is enough."

From his easy chair, he replied to her question, "You damn better know if it is the right thing, because it is too late now to be asking that question." Her maid of honor smiled, gave Lee a hug and told her, "Of course you are doing the right thing. Jones really loves you and you him. You are just having pre-wedding jitters. It will pass." And the doubt did pass when through her veil she saw Jones waiting for her at the alter in his immaculate be-medaled Khaki uniform, with a glow of happiness radiating from his face as he watched her coming to him. In that moment, as she slowly walked down the white runner on her father's arm (he had attached his wodden leg), she said that she smiled behind her veil, knowing the reason for her existence, to love and keep Jones happy.

In their long courtship and serenade, Jones had confided to Lee some of the difficulties he confronted growing up: days without food , war experiences, the number of people he killed, the prisoner of war camps where he was repeatedly tortured, and the twenty-nine Americans that had betrayed him in the POW camps and after their release — men whose lives he saved after a duration of two years, seven months and seven days of captivity. Lee has often told me of the many times during her and Jones' courtship, and marriage, after Jones had shared a piece of his life's history with her, she often cried! Because no on had ever bothered to see the person her husband really was, and not what society and experience had made him through their neglect. If an individual has a duty to society, then society also has a duty to the individual — to assure thet he has enough to eat. Lee included the US Army in the mistreatment of her husband, by taking his youth, then demeaning his faithful and honorable service when it was time for him to retire. After surviving two wars, POW camps, and wounded three times, they tried to send him back to the Vietnam War after three months in the States for a second time! Just once, Lee said after one nights pillow-talk, she asked Jones, "How do you mange with those war memories?" He replied, "I don't know." Lee said she snuggled close to her husbands warn body, kissed him on the lips placing her arms around that portion of his body she could reach laying on their sides, face to face, as she pulled Jones closer, as she told him, "It's all right Honey. I am here for you and will never leave you alone with your memories. I love you, Honey!" As Lee said she kissed and rocked Jones in her arms, she felt his hot, silent body wrenching tears on her cheek, as she tried to convey by the closeness of her body that he was no longer alone when his demons came back to visit.

The big day arrived, and according to Lee, beginning at 8 A.M., everything went as planned. The two off-duty National Policemen that were hired for the occasion, enabled Lee and Jones to arrive at all of their wedding ceremonies on time. Without them, it would have been impossible, because of the heavy traffic in Panama City. San Jose Church, 8 A.M., full with the Priest, Sisters of the school, and the students from all three schools, friends and family of Lee and Jones. The ceremony at the Church took one hour. Then on to Panama City, City Hall — 10 A.M., accompanied by those with automobiles filled with other invited guests. The ceremony at City Hall took a half of an hour. The chambers of the Federal District Judge, Canal Zone, Balbo, Canal Zone — 11:30 A.M., whose chambers would not hold all of the wedding party, so they waited outside. Lee and Jones were married and congratulated by the Judge by noon, then the entire wedding party left the Zone for Panama City, and the roof-top dance hall that Lee and Jones had hired for their wedding breakfast reception. On the way to the reception hall was when the National Police in their patrol cars turned on its siren and all the cars in the wedding convoy began to also honk their horns, with people on the sidewalks shouting well wishes while clapping their hands and waving. From 1:30 P.M., until 9 P.M., Lee and Jones danced, ate and received the well wishes of their guest, until they slipped out unnoticed — still in their wedding clothing, to be driven by the best man, Jones Jones, to Lee's home. The reception was to continue until one in the morning.

Lee said they were exhausted when they arrived home. Her father had proceeded them, and was fast asleep in his bedroom, as they quietly closed the front door and made their way down the hallway to Lee's bedroom. Once they entered the bedroom, turned on the light, Lee threw herself across the bed, fully clothed in her wedding dress, on her back, with her arms outstretched, eyes open — staring at the ceiling, exclaiming, "I am so tired, that I feel I am about to die!" Jones, still in his uniform, slid down to the floor beside the bed replied, "Me too!" Lee said that she had no idea how long they both had stayed in their position with the ceiling light on, making no sound, as they attempted to catch their breath and balance after their whirlwind day. Lee asked Jones, "How much money do we have?" Jones put his left hand in his trouser pocket and replied, "I have a nickel. How much do you have?" Lee sat up in bed, took her handbag off the bed post where it was hanging, fumbled around inside of it an held her right hand out for Jones to see, "I have four napps (a napp was valued at half a cent)." They looked at each other, smiled, then in unison, burst out in uncontrollable laughter — they were starting their life together with all of seven cents!

Jones had purchased a used car from a American soldier who was returning to the United States of America two months before the wedding, which had been driven out to Lee's home on the outskirts of Panama City by a friend stationed on Flamenco Island. This happened on the day of the wedding and parked (Jones had moved half of his clothing from his quarters on

143

Flamenco Island to Lee's, one month before the wedding), in the carport. The next morning after the wedding, after getting up, shaving, bathing, dressing in fatigues, and eating his first breakfast prepared for him by his wife. He kissed Lee good-bye and returned to his Battery for their field readiness test. Lee was on leave from Saint Jose School, saying that Jones was gone for a week, causing no difficulty except that she missed his daily telephone calls. "No difficulty," because she knew about the field readiness test before their wedding. The only way they could have prevented their forced separation during the second day of their marriage for a week, was to change their wedding date. They both agreed, Lee said, that their wedding plans were too far advanced to change them. The positive side to their immediate separation upon their marriage, Lee said was, which she kept reminding herself during Jones' week absence, that when her husband returned, he would be on a thirty day leave and they could then begin their honeymoon sight seeing in the interior of the Republic de Panama — seeing the real country and its people. Which is what they did for a stress free thirty days together — "the best of times," Lee happily recounted.

> "Love is the most terrible, and also
> the most generous of passions; it is
> the only one that includes in its dreams
> the happiness of someone else."
>
> *Alphonse Jean Karr*

12.

MARRIAGE

The views expressed here, about Lee and Jones' marriage, and how they made it work for them are my own. For neither of them ever spoke about what made it real for them when I was around. They only replied to any questions, "That we love each other and want the same things in life." From my years of observing, participation, and befriending them both, as I loved their children as my own, my general opinion is that Lee and Jones, possibly, unknowingly, daily, followed Abrham Flexner's maxim, "One has no business to be married unless, walking and sleeping, one is conscious of the responsibility." Responsible to each other Lee and Jones were, always conscious of the other's opinion and feelings.

I also noticed that when Lee and Jones became angry with each other — often Lee at Jones for not thinking before he acted — it was easily resolved. If Jones did not like something, mostly his bosses at his 16 places of employment, he was in their faces about it. Lee repeatedly told her husband, "You never let people know what your inner most thoughts are, for with that knowledge, they know how to control you!" They also never left the area where the argument started until both had vented their anger. When Lee became angry with Jones, she would become excited and revert to rapid Spanish as she was chewing out Jones,

145

with him reverting, in kind, as he told her, "Go slow! You are talking to fast!" Lee would stop talking, look at Jones with eyes that would change from anger to love, smile (attempting to hold in her laughter — not succeding) and told him in mock anger, "You are lucky that I love you!" Jones would sheepishly look at Lee, smile, and say, "I know, Honey!" as he joined her in laughter.

Responsible to their children, to the degree that many of their friends often told Lee and Jones (not I), "You do too much for your children!" They never commented to that type of advice. They also never stopped their loving and caring of the children for both Lee and Jones believed that no child asked to be born into this world, and if you decide to have children, (and it is a choice today) then it was your *duty* and *responsibility* to provide them with a nurturing, loving, supportive, and safe environment that helped them grow and develop. Your individual life style comes to an end, in order to always be there for your children until they can care for themselves. As Audrey Hepburn was once quoted, "If you want a career, which I did, why bring a child into the world who won't get the benefit of your total attention? You can't concentrate on more than one thing at a time." For example, at an early age, Lee asked each child what they would like for dinner. What was asked for had to be eaten and it was not uncommon for Lee to cook a fish for one child, beef for another, and chicken for the remaining members of the family. I observed that Lee was operating from two important philosophies she held dear with regards to her children. First, that mealtime in her home would not become the hellish experience it was for her when she attended Saint Carmens School, San Andres Island, Colombia. She was forced to eat what she didn't want while also being forced to swallow spoiled food. Second, that children were little people with likes and dislikes, and wherever possible, their desires should be considered, along with being consulted when it affected their well being.

In observing Lee and Jones' marriage after they returned to the US in 1964, the majority of my revelations will be about the interaction between Lee and Jones, the children, friends, and situations she confronted loving and caring for her family. For Jones, because of his difficult life growing up, (a living mother that abounded him to a state institution), he knew that he had a blind spot. That blind spot, a tendency to see most things as black and white even though he knew there were gray areas in life, he was for some reason unable to allow for them. So he readily deferred to Lee most matters relating to their children except one — their education! He had been the benefactor of a quality public school education, and knew how helpful it had been for him because it does lift all boats, if it's of quality. By the time Lee and Jones' children became of school age, public school education in this country had deteriorated — no longer providing its students with the necessary knowledge and skills for them to be able to call themselves educated citizens! Why we are not turning out educated citizens through our public schools is because of the deteriorating society we live in. The school systems of this nation are being used to attempt to solve the country's many social problems because the taxpayers, courts, and politicians are to gutless to solve them at the local level, where they can only be solved was Jones' opinion. "Schools are for developing minds and not for attempting to solve the social ills of the society," Jones often proclaimed.

Jones said he had to send his children to private schools (k thru high school), to assure that they receive the quality education that they had often heard him talk about while they were growing up. "You see your father, everything built upon what I was originally taught in school! Quality." The staffs of those institutions that called themselves private that their children attended, Lee and Jones said were only interested in turning out students who were educated citizens. I have often heard Jones tell his children in a private school setting, "You do not have to learn, but you have no right to disrupt those who wanted to." Jones was not a grade pusher parent (no F's) whatever passing grade his children received were fine with him while commenting as he was reading their report card, "You received a 'C', which means that you do not unlearn that level by going to a 'D'."

Another benefit Lee and Jones said they obtained from a private school environment, was a continuation of the values being taught at home: respect for themselves and others, practice tolerance, address adults properly, be courteous and mannerly, don't lie, take responsibility for their actions — good or bad, acquire as much formal education as they could, stand up for and defend what they believed in, and be charitable to others with their money and time. Each child, while attending school had a daily assignment book, and after they completed their homework, they had to take it to the dining room — lay it neatly with their assignment book on the table for their father to check when he arrived home. Jones would check all of his children's homework every day to insure that his children had done all of their assigned work. If it was not complete, no matter hour, when he worked nights, and arrived home at 1:00 A.M. in the morning, he would take them out of bed, bring them to the dining room table and have them complete the unfinished work! All of their children learned at a very early age that their father stood for no nonsense when it came to their schoolwork — other things, maybe.

The most direct influence Jones brought (with Lee's approval and support) to his sons was his periodically reminders, "That men are born male, but learn to be men and accept responsibility for their actions. No babies out of wedlock!

No living with a woman you are not married to. No drugs! Adding, that if he ever caught or suspected any of them using drugs, he would personally take them by the back of their neck to the police station and have them locked up! Because not only was drug use against the law, it's dangerous to their health. The brain is the only part of our body that can not heal itself — if you use drugs you damage your brain. Never lie to me or your mother, for the only way they can help them when they have a problem, was to know that it was the truth being told." For his daughter, that Jones adored just because she was a girl (he had wanted five daughters), "no babies out of wedlock! If a man wanted to lay with her — tell him to marry you! The same message concerning drugs and truth as for her brothers. Just because she was female she had the same rights as her brothers or any other male. She could choose in today's society to be a liberated women (career, no husband or children), but she was to learn under her mother's instruction how to cook, bake, take care of a house and family, in order that she would be able to take care of herself — no matter what path she chose, liberated or traditional women. For her brothers, some woman would do the things she was learning from her mother. He and her mother both hoped that she would not have sex outside of marriage, but if she could not control her sexual urges or she allowed some guy to get next to her then she could come back to him or her mother — and they would put her on the pill. She never requested to be placed on the pill. Adding, always remember, even in these so-called Liberated times, in a sexual adventure it's only the woman that the stigma of loose is attached —the man leaves the relationship with nothing attached to his name. Jones continued by telling his daughter, "by being the only daughter, it was the custom in your mother's country that when your mother dies, her body is prepared for burial by her daughter. In this country, before leaving the home or hospital bed were she died. You are required to wash your mother's body, place clean underclothing and nightgown on her, comb and brush her hair, close her eyes and cross her hands across her lap. All of this is to be done before your mother's body is transported to the hospital morgue or undertakers. Until you were born, this was a constant worry of your mothers — "Who would take care of me when I die?" I promised your mother that if we had no daughters, I would do what was required, but our prayers were answered — God sent you to us," Jones told the sunlight of his life.

Lee's philosophy, along with Jones, regarding how their children were to conduct themselves toward each other and their parents was very simple and easy for all to understand. No hitting and the ability to understand yes and no would result in certain behavior when these two words were spoken to them by their parents. Concerning the no hitting rule, and the children's relationship to each other — there were no exceptions to the non-hitting rule!. They could shout, yell, become mad, pout, remain silent or any other expression that would demonstrate displeasure toward each other, but they could not, no matter the provocation, hit! As all of the children could understand 'yes' when 'no' was given by either parent (with the reason) to a request, it would be accepted for the reasons given. If the children readily accepted the positive results of a "yes" answer, then they equally had to accept the negative results of a "no" answer — without a public demonstration of their displeasure.

It was Lee who exercised the most influence in the Jones household, for it was to her Jones and the children and I all came to with our problems. As I now look back, I realize that we often brought things to Lee just because she was there. Lee never complained, no matter how often we came to her. We brought to Lee questions about morality. I could easily claim that it was Lee's past active religious background that made us all turn to her and readily accept her edicts as morally correct without question, but I doubt it. Having a mother who came from a long line of pious Catholics and the religious indoctrination at Saint Carmens School, San Andres Island, Colombia, staffed by priests and nuns, then repeating the same influence when she became a lay teacher at San Jose School, Panama City, Republic de Panama, and having already arrived at the decision to become a nun upon the death of her father, laid one to believe that Lee knew from which she spoke. I believe, the reason Jones, the children, her friends and I listened to Lee when she spoke to us about our problems and morality was because we trusted her. Trust — we all know that Lee loved us with an all encompassing love, and would never tell us to do or say anything that would harm us. I remember Lee and Jones' youngest son telling me once, when he was a teenager, "If Mom tells me not to do something, I don't do it because I am afraid that something bad would happen to me if I did not do as she says!"

During their long marriage, Jones, by his own admission, had done many stupid, careless, and not completely thought-through projects because of his impatience. Never once, in her loving wisdom have I ever heard Lee make a derogatory comment about her husband's many not-so-wise actions. As I watched Lee, many times, console Jones with kisses, (It's alright Honey, let me kiss it away"). Hugs, ("You are safe in my arms Honey"). Along with words of encouragement ("That didn't work, try something else, Honey"), after he messed up. I marveled at Lee's wisdom as I remembered the words of Richard Whately, "He is only exempt from failures who make no effort." When Jones came to Lee after he had messed up, he would be dejected and angry with himself because he could not get his project to work. After Lee's kisses, hugs, and words of encouragement, the dejection would lift, the anger would disappear and his eyes would brighten as he would tell her, "I know I will get it right this time!" as he would leave to give it one more try. With Lee always giving him one more kiss as she told him, "I know you will Honey." Every time I witnessed what I came to call putting Jones back on track, I was always amazed at Lee's caring and loving ability to make everything right for Jones. I asked Lee once, after witnessing another right tracking, "How do you do it?" Lee gave me one of her Mona Lisa smiles, and told me, "I love that man! No one seems to be able to really understand me when I say 'love' — he's my life!"

When it came to Jones, anything that made him happy was just fine with Lee and no one was allowed to interfere — not even their children. For example, their eldest son had returned home from college for a visit during his freshman year, and as he came into the sitting room, in the middle of the day after a rainstorm, saying, "Hi" to me, asked his mother, "Where's Dad?" Lee told him, "He's outside weeding the patio." With indignation, their eldest son replied, "What's he doing that for? He can use weed killer on the weeds and don't have to manually pull them up. And I am going to tell him to stop and come inside!" Lee, very sternly replied, "No you are not! Leave him alone! Your father is very happy weeding." Another, their daughter at the age of thirteen, once asked her mother, "Why does Dad only drive ten to fifteen year old rust buckets? I get so embarrassed sometimes when he comes to back me up at school. His is always the worst looking car in the parking lot!" Lee took their daughter in her arms as she told her, "First, it's very expensive to provide each of you children with a quality education, and it is your father who pays for it. Secondly, we can not afford a new car. Thirdly, I makes your father happy to buy his rust buckets for $50-$100 and repair them. It gives him a great deal of pleasure and a sense of accomplishment to be able to make them operational again. Fourthly, you must learn to accept your father for who he is, and not for who you would like him to be. He's not rich, as are the parents of *all* your classmates. You also know, that your father cares nothing about appearance — as long as it's functional. Fifthly, I hope that when you marry, your husband will be able to find happiness as easily as your father," as Lee gave her daughter a kiss on the forehead and released her.

Jones likes eggs and has eaten them all of his life — asking Lee when he first started to see her on Sundays, Panama City, Republic de Panama, to please include them (fried) with all of his breakfasts. Lee couldn't stand to prepare any style of eggs, but did it because that was what would make Jones happy. Lee had an American friend from New York City as a house guest one weekend, and when she came downstairs Sunday morning from the guest room (Jones was outside with the dog) and saw Lee standing in front of the stove with a pot lid, looking over and around it at two eggs frying in a skillet. With surprised, perplexed indignation, Lee's friend asked, "What in God's name are you doing?" Lee explained her disdain for eggs. When she finished her explanation, while still keeping her eyes on the eggs frying in the skillet, her friend told her, sternly, "Don't do it! Tell Jones he has to eat something else because you won't prepare anymore eggs for him!" Lee looked at her friend, standing beside her in the kitchen at the stove as if she was out of her mind and said, "Are you crazy? Do you think I am a fool to tell Jones that I won't cook his eggs? Let me tell you something — when Jones found me, he was eating his eggs and asked me to fix them for him, and I told him that I would (He didn't know, and I didn't tell him, of the problems I have with eggs). Now, how could I tell him I won't fry his eggs? He pays the food bills; I should make unnecessary problems in my marriage over eggs — no way! I am not going to tell Jones anything! Also, I will never tell Jones what I won't do for him as his wife — as he would never tell me what he would not for me as my husband!" Lee's American friend told her, "Sorry."

A incident occurred one summer afternoon while Jones was cutting the grass of his very large backyard of their fourth home, and came unknowingly close to a ground level beehive and they swarmed on to Jones' right hand before he could reach the safety of the house. By the time he located Lee in the kitchen, his hand had swollen to twice it's size. Lee screamed (I was in the kitchen drinking coffee) when she saw Jones' condition shouting, "What happened?" He explained, as Lee treated his hand with meat tenderizer paste, becoming angrier by the minute as she treated her husband while repeating, "They stung you! Just you wait! I will fix them all!" Very calmly, Jones told Lee, "Leave the hive. I will take care of it when it's dark and the bees are less active." Lee shouted in reply, "I will not! I will fix them all, and don't tell me again not to!" That was the end of the conversation on who would destroy the bee hive. When Lee had finished treating Jones, she placed her very large canning pot on the stove, filled it with water, let it come to a boil, then told me to carry the pot to the backyard (having gotten the location of the beehive from Jones) and proceeded to pour boiling water into the hive via a smaller pot she carried — not relenting until her canning pot was empty. As Lee poured the water, I stood a safe distance form the location of the beehive. The bees swarmed all around Lee's head and body, and I was sure that it would not be long before she also would have to seek the safety of the house — but not one of the bees stung her as she killed them with hot water while angrily shouting, "You stung him!" When she had finished, carrying one in each hand, the empty pots back to the house, I asked her, "Why did you do that? Don't you know you could have been seriously injured? Jones told you that he would take care of it!" Lee looked at me annoyingly, "Didn't you see

Jones' hand? It is so swollen that he can not bend the fingers. You know that he has a high tolerance for pain and would never complain, but I know he's hurting and I made those responsible pay! You hurt him, and I will hurt you! I don't care who or what it is that does the hurting — I assure you, they will pay!" And Jones was hurting. Even with three days of Lee's intents treatment, using every home remedy she knew to stop the swelling, Jones was finally hospitalized for two weeks before regaining complete use of his right hand.

There was only one, what I took to be a major instant in Lee and Jones' long marriage that I witnessed, and still do not fully understand what actually happened. It was doing the manufactured oil storage of the seventies, and Lee and Jones owned a completely electrified home. The electricity in their state was generated by oil, and they saw their electric bill go from $42.00 a month in stages, to $289.00! At first, Jones took a second night job — 11:00 P.M. through 5:00 A.M, even with the additional income it still was not sufficient to meet their monthly electric bill. Selling the house was out of the question, no one wanted the staggering electric bills — later they did. He sat down with Lee, who at that time did not work, explained the problem of their monthly electric bill while asking her to help out by taking a day part-time job — which she immediately agreed to do.

After Lee obtained her part-time job in a small local optical manufacture company in the town they lived in, their new schedule was: Jones went to his main job in the city from 6:00 A.M. through 2:00 P.M., (picking up the car from Lee's place of employment) from three onward, he picked up the children form school and took them home, at 4:00 P.M., he would pick Lee up at her part-time job and they would both return home for dinner. Then at 11:00 P.M., Jones would go to his second job until 5:00 A.M. In the morning, Lee would take the car, drive the children to school beginning at 8:00 A.M., with Jones already having taken the train to the city and work. After leaving the children at school, Lee would return home to make beds, and clean up the house, arriving at her place of employment by 10:00 A.M., work until 4:00 P.M., when Jones would arrive to take her home. During the oil shortage, they had only one automobile and there was no public transportation serving their community.

This particular afternoon, Jones arrived at Lee's place of employment at 4:00 P.M., and she was not there waiting for him in the lobby behind the full-length glass door! Jones said that he did not panic because it was a nice day and Lee might have decided to start to walk home following a predetermined route she had told him about. She said she might walk home someday if it was nice, and he could pick her up along the way. Jones very slowly drove the route Lee would have taken if she was walking home and didn't see her. Jones said that he then drove the route a second time with the same results as the first — no Lee! Then he panicked, believing that some misfortune had befallen her. He returned home (an hour had elapsed) and telephoned me telling me that Lee was not at her place of employment when he went to pick her up. Would I come over and stay with the children while he went to the three local hospitals to continue to search for her? After Jones hung up, he said that he telephoned Lee's job and without identifying himself (embarrassed to have to admit that he was looking for his wife), asked to speak to Lee, maybe still in the plant, working overtime, and was informed by the switchboard operator that she had left work an hour early and could she take a message?

When I arrived at Lee and Jones' home, he filled me in, including the information he obtained from the companies switchboard operator, adding that the children were in their rooms doing their homework, and if they should happen to come downstairs asking for their mother to tell them that he was picking her up. I was to stay near the telephone in the sitting room in the event that a call came in from the police or hospital. I nodded in agreement to all that Jones had told me to do, while telling him, "I will take care of this end, you just be careful driving and when you find Lee." As I walked to the door with Jones, as he was about to start his search again for Lee and even when he was bringing me up to date, for the first time in our long friendship, I was afraid of him! It was not in Jones' demeanor, for he appeared to be in control of himself. It was his eyes that caused my fear. They were not the eyes of another human being I was looking into, but slits for eyes, in the face of a human being. He did not want me to see in his eyes what he was thinking. I was never afraid for Lee once Jones found her, and I was confident that he would — even after hearing that she had left work an hour early. There had to be a good reason for her action which I knew she would be able to explain to Jones once they both returned home together.

The sitting room of Lee and Jones' home is in the center of their house on the first floor (there home has three floors), facing the eating area where the family took their meals, with the kitchen off from it. Behind the sitting room, toward the front of the house, was a formal dining room, living room, vestibule, and railed stone front steps. I never heard Lee when she arrived home nor when she entered the house. It had been three and a half hours since Jones had gone to pick her up from work, and not found her there. Now, there was Lee standing in front of me as I began to rise from the sofa where I had been sitting beside the telephone. I saw a flushed face Lee standing in front of me and very noticeably nervous, with a worried expression on he face. She, also, appeared to be unharmed, and was breathing very fast. As she was about to speak, I quickly angrily interrupted her,

"Where have you been? Jones and I have been out of our minds with worry!" Clasping one hand over the other, Lee replied, "I have been very stupid and naive! I don't want to talk about it! Where's Jones?" "Out looking for you at the hospitals," I replied. "The children?" "Upstairs in their bedrooms doing their home-work, and thank God, none of them came downstairs while you were gone." At that moment they all came running down the stairs (as I sat back down) shouting, "Mom's home!" Saying hi to me as they hugged and kissed her and in unison, clamored, "When do we eat? Where's Dad?" Lee told them, "Dinner is ready," as she walked into the kitchen, while telling them, "Go up and wash for dinner, your father will be coming home soon." When the children returned form washing up, they sat around the table and ate their dinner as they all tried at the same time to tell their mother what kind of day they had with Lee following each of their conversations. Lee had offered to feed me when she fed the children, which I declined — telling her that I would wait and eat with her and Jones.

It had been one hour since Lee came home. As the children were eating their dinner, I watched her in the kitchen at the sink washing the same pot over and over with a far away look in her eyes. At the same time, we all heard Jones coming up the street, driving his self repaired rust-bucket. Lee wiped her hands on a dish towel, with the flush gone from her face, and only the wor-ried expression still remaining, along with her noticeable ner-vousness. She told the children, "Continue eating," as we both hurried to the front door to greet Jones. With Lee standing on the top step, one hand holding the other at her waist and I behind her — not as protection, but support. For I knew that whatever Lee had done, she now realized — and had admitted, was stupid and naive. After the fact, she would have to explain to Jones and live with that knowledge for the rest of her life! We both watched

Jones nosey car come up the street and parked in front of the garage. As Jones got out of his car, it was as if his every movement was in slow motion, as he looked at Lee and I waiting for him to come to us. Half way out of his car, Jones stopped for what seemed to be an eternity. Then it was as if he had reached some decision, and came all the way out of his car, closed the door very quietly, and came unhurriedly to Lee and I standing on the top step. The first thing that I noticed was that Jones still had slits for eyes, and for the first time ever, he did not kiss Lee in greeting, and asked her so quietly, that it sounded as if he was shouting, "How did you get home?" I got a left," she replied. Jones looked at Lee a few seconds in her heightened nervousness and told her, "Don't ever do that again!" "I won't Honey! Come eat."

The children noisily greeted their father as he took his place a t the head of the table. I sat down while they asked him, "Where have you been? Why are you so late? What words did you bring us today?" (Jones brought new words home each night for his children to spell, and for each correctly spelled word, that child receive $.25) Smiling, Jones replied, "I was late. I have been busy! And yes, I have some new words for you." Adding, "This is time for eating — I am hungry, and not a time for talking," with all of the children laughing loudly at their father sitting at the head of the table with a knife and fork held upright in each hand as their mother served his plate. I also noticed as Lee finished with Jones, and served me, that from the moment of his children's greeting — Jones eyes were no longer slits.

After dinner, the children left first, giving their father a hug and kiss on his cheek, and being hugged and kissed in turn while being told, "I love you! You, along with your mother — are my reasons for living," receiving the reply from each child, "We know Dad." They loudly raced each other up the stairs to return to their homework. When Jones had finished eating, he also left the table after thanking me for coming while commenting, "I am going upstairs to my den to pay some bills." All during the exchange between Jones and their children, Lee made no comment, just silently watched her husband eat his food. I returned to the sofa in the sitting room after I had finished my meal. Lee remained at the table as she spoke to no one in particular with relief in her voice that was also reflected in her face, "It's going to be all right." I watched Jones while he was eating, and he ate good! Lee had often maintained that she could tell how Jones was really feeling by the way he ate his meals, with gusto — he was happy; picking at his food — something on his mind; not eating at all — ill; that meal-cutting up his food into bite size pieces — he had come to some decision that he could live with. I told her that I believed she was right in her observation, for I also noticed a change in Jones when he greeted their children — without elaborating. I stayed with Lee downstairs until she had finished cleaning up, which took he longer then usual. After another 'thank you', I left for my home as Lee went upstairs to the second floor to join Jones in his den.

And it was alright. For the three and a half hour absence of Lee was never spoken of again in front of me. What ever reconciliation that had to be made, was done when Lee went to join Jones. After the oil shortage was over, Lee and Jones sold their completely electrified home, Lee quit her day part-time job and never obtained another until 1988. Now and then when Jones could not leave his main job in the city (he also quite his night part-time job) because of some problem that had to be solved that day, Jones would phone me, asking that I pick up the children form school and Lee from her job. I was, by then, a 100% disabled veteran and would willingly do as requested. After leaving the children at home, I would pick Lee and would always find her standing out in the hot sun, rain or snow, which made me very annoyed with her. I told her, "Wait inside! There is no need for you to wait outside in the weather because I can see you through the glass door." Lee never made any comment to my suggestion, and each time I picked her up, I would always find her standing outside. When I first discovered her waiting outside in the rain without an umbrella, I asked her, "Why?" She told me, "So that Jones could immediately see me as he turned into the parking lot and would know that I am here! Never again will I cause him to worry and suffer the way he did that one time because of my stupidity and naivety." As I drove Lee home that day after she had answered my question, I made no comment, but even today I wonder was her standing outside a penance for that time she was missing?

After that missing instant I watched for changes in Lee and Jones' marriage. Their relationship towards each other — kissing, hugging, touching, laughing, and joking with each other. I found none that I could relate to Lee's disappearance. Jones continued his attentive, caring, supportive, loving, and touching self to Lee. Concerning touching — whenever they were together, Jones always sat just as close to Lee as he could to the degree that their bodies touched. When he came into her presence he would always hug and kissed Lee. If he was cutting the grass or working on one of his projects, periodically he would stop, seeking Lee out in the house or another part of their backyard to tell her as he kissed, touched her face and hair, "I love you Honey!" I asked Jones once, "Why the seeking, kissing, and touching of Lee?" He smiled, and replied, "It makes me feel good just to be near Lee and feel her hair, flesh and lips." As to Lee, I noticed what might have been normal behavior, that I just became aware of when no one was watching, Lee would caress Jones from afar with her eyes. Her eyes would become soft and misty, as a glow would relax her face and body, as she watched Jones with what I interpreted as a smile on her lips. Once noticed, she would immediately, embarrassed, revert back to her normal demeanor of private women.

After a six year interval, I asked Jones as we were both sitting in lawn chairs smoking cigars, in his backyard watching Lee sitting on the ground, some distance form us, working in her flower garden, what he was thinking as drove around looking for Lee. This is what he told me:

Ever since they married, he had always told Lee that all of his eggs of happiness were in her basket, and if she ever dropped that basket, there was no way that he would ever be able to put the eggs back together again. As he was searching for Lee, he realized that he also had the power to make her drop her basket — depending on the first words that came out of his mouth when he found her. This was why it took him so long to come out of the car — he was thinking of what to say to Lee that would not cause her to drop her basket. He knew that he loved her, and that she loved him, and that, he never doubted. As he drove, he could make no sense out of why she was missing. The thought would not leave his mind — what if Lee had found someone else and left him? Although he knew of no reason for Lee to leave him for they had a loving, strong and healthy relationship (she never had headaches and he was always ready), but he always lived with the fear that it could happen. "For I was under no illusion about myself — I am no prize! Unashamed — Jones would readily tell all that would listen, "You see me! You see my wife, Lee. She civilized me." I also thought as I drove, that if Lee had been attacked, I would kill all involved! No matter how long or difficult, as sure as the sun rises and sits — that the attackers of my wife would die by my hands — if that was the reason Lee was missing!"

"The more we know, the better we
    forgive —
Who'er feels deeply, feels for all that
    live."

Mad. de Stael

13.

LESTER

Although Lee held a life-long disdain for writing because of her unpleasant experience while attending Saint Carmen's School, San Andres, Colombia, over her penmanship, unknown to anyone, throughout her life, beginning in 1963, Lee made undated notes on her children. She wrote about her hopes for them, her fears, problems she perceived they may have that she may need to comfort them about, their relationships with their siblings and their father, and most of all, her undying love for them.

I acquired Lee's notes in a locked metal document box, and the accompanying key, from Jones. He said to me, "Lee always kept this in her walk-in closet and told me that it was for you. I have no idea what's in it."

When I opened the box and saw that it was filled to the lid with Lee's handwritten notes on lined notebook paper, I asked Jones if he wanted to read them first. He declined and said, "No. They are for you. I knew and approved of how very important your friendship was to Lee, and you may not have known it, but it was important to me too. I also knew that you loved Lee. That knowledge of your love for her gave me peace of mind in the event that if something ever happened to me, I knew that you would have taken care of Lee and the children.

Although we had never spoken about what I expected of you, it was as if we both knew that was the way it was destined to be."

I replied, "You are right, and it would have happened exactly as you described." I locked Lee's box and put the key in my pocket, setting it aside until it was time for me to go home.

When I arrived home, I placed Lee's box on the top of my roll top desk where I would be forced to look at it and remember her every time I entered my den or sat at my desk. It remained there—unopened—for two years. During the third year, in the silence of the night, I opened the box and read the contents at my desk. No matter how I attempted, unsuccessfully, to ignore my grief as I read sheet after sheet bearing her distinctive scrip, it overwhelmed me as I forced myself to continue to read. When I reached the bottom of the document box I found this:

"Hi. If you are reading this then I am gone. Jones gave me a life that I never imagined existed through his love and our children. What prompted me to write these comments about our children was that when neither Jones or you were around to talk to when I thought of something, I took to writing these notes to myself. (And you know how I hated to write!) After I had placed my thought on paper, I sometimes discussed with you or Jones, what I had written, but not often. You may do with them what you please.

"Now, as to why I left my notes to you and not Jones. There have only been two men (not counting my sons) in my entire life that I have ever loved (not even my father — I was his caregiver) and that is Jones and you — in that order. I wanted you to have something personal from me after I was gone, and nothing, I believe, is more personal than my uncensored words on paper about my children.

"You know how very much Jones enjoys reading poetry aloud, and at no time in their development (although we tried) did any of the children ever want to hear any of it! So I used to sit with Jones as he read aloud from some book of poetry, and truthfully, there was much that I did not understand or like. But these lines have always remained with me from one of his first readings together after we had come to this country in 1964. From the works of Letitia Elizabeth Landon:

'I have no parting sign to give,
so take my parting smile.'
"Good-bye, Lee."

When I had finished reading, the sun was making its appearance on the horizon and I returned all of the notes to Lee's box after separating and paper clipping them together by child. I placed the locked box back on top of my desk, where it remained until I started to write this book. All comments about Jones and Lee's children taken from selective notes contained in Lee's box will be quoted and marked with an asterisk (*). The only liberties I have taken with the material that has been entrusted to me has been to change some Spanish words into English, utilizing an English/Spanish dictionary. Upon completion of this work, I shall burn the entire contents of Lee's box in my backyard, for it was a part of herself that she left to me, and no one else. I cringe to think that after I die someone else would be handling Lee's actual notes that she meant only for me.

During Lee and Jones's thirty-day camping honeymoon in the interior of the Republic de Panama, leisurely traveling from hamlet to hamlet via automobile, they were, for the first and only time in their marriage, totally at peace. During their travels, they took pictures of the breathtaking scenery, the inhabitants of the hamlets, and for some, Jones was the first American they had met. Once the people discovered that they were newlyweds, they readily made them feel welcome, according to Lee. They fed them while extending them lodging for the night, and vehemently refused all offers of payment.

It was during their honeymoon that Lee said she became pregnant with Lester, and as she knew he would be, Jones was very gentle and patient with her as they consummated their love. Years later, in a moment of reflection upon her honeymoon, Lee shyly and coyly mentioned, "With the right man—and I have my right man in Jones—married life is great!"

I asked her in what way and she turned away blushing, and replied, "Nothing. I was just thinking about a night of my honeymoon." I knew not to pursue my line of questioning any further as I sat at Lee's kitchen table drinking my morning coffee (I could see she was embarrassed). As with Jones, when I arrived, the coffee pot, which was always on the stove — was turned on with Lee serving me coffee along with feeding me.

After missing her second monthly menstruation, Lee told Jones in bed that night as she snuggled close to his warm body, that she was sure that she was pregnant with their child and that it had happened during their honeymoon. Lee said that Jones was elated with the news as he pulled her body closer to his under the bed covers while repeatedly kissing her on the lips. He told her, "You bet it happened during our honeymoon—I would think so!" They both laughed softly, fondly remembering their honeymoon, and their first time alone together as man and wife.

"Have you told your father?" Jones asked.

"No." replied Lee. "We will tell him tomorrow during dinner."

Jones and Lee were living in her home as they went about house hunting on the weekends, beginning when they returned from their honeymoon. Their new routine as man and wife was that Jones would drive Lee to her teaching position at San Jose School in Panama City and would continue on to his Battery on Flamenco Island. He would pick her up at the end of the day, and they would return home together.

Still in bed the night that Lee announced that she was pregnant,

Jones told Lee, who was still laying in his arms, "We now have to think about where you are going to receive your pediatric care once you reach three months. You have a choice, Panama City or the Canal Zone via the United States Army."

Lee snuggled close to Jones' body as she told him, "I have heard of a very good women Pediatrician in Panama City that I could go to."

Jones replied, "I have no problem with that, but there is something else I believe we must consider in determining where to have our child born — citizenship. You and I have already determined that we will live out our years in the Republic de Panama, but what if any of our children, having an American father, decides that they would like to live in the States? By them being born in Panama (a citizen), our children would find it very difficult to obtain the necessary documentation to live and work in America as a citizen of another country. But, if they were born in the Canal Zone they would become American citizens and thereby be free to travel between the two countries with ease. If they decided to remain in Panama as American citizens, there is still no problem for their mother is a citizen. What do you think of my reasoning? Does it make sense?"

Lee replied, "Yes. We will have our child at the hospital in the Canal Zone." They happily drifted off to sleep in each other's arms.

According to Lee, she had an easy time carrying Lester. She had no morning sickness, and so swelling of any part of her body—excepts her breasts. Her belly just became noticeably round, as if she was carrying around a basketball under her clothing that she could not keep from unconsciously, happily, rubbing throughout the day. Sometimes as she was rubbing her enlarged belly, she would say aloud, "Jones put you there, and I enjoyed every moment while he did, but you belong to us both. I love you baby."

She had no problem performing any of her household or teaching responsibilities, and in her fifth month, she resigned her teaching position. Receiving a clean bill of health from her Army Major obstetrician at each of her monthly check-ups, she was just ecstatic that she was having Jones' baby. Lee has told me that when she and Jones were courting and going through their serenade period, she had never given any thought to what it would feel or be like to carry the life of your husband inside of your body, only that she loved Jones and by having their child she knew that they were now really one. When Lee became with child, she said it was "heaven on earth."

When they became engaged, sitting in Jones' lap in the eating area of Lee's home, Jones had told her that he would like to have five children—all daughters. Lee told him, "as many as you like. I am ready." Being from a Spanish culture where all the men she knew wanted sons, she asked Jones, "How come you want only daughters?" This is the story that he told Lee:

"When a son marries, he must care for his wife and children first. If his mother and father fall in need he must go to his wife, explain the need and ask, 'Can we help?' If she says no then that's it.

"When a daughter married, she also must care for her husband and children first, but in the caring she never forgets her father and mother. When they fall in need, she can over cook the pot to take them food, visit regularly to see how they are doing, assist them in the things that have become arduous that they cannot do themselves, and generally include them as part of her family to be cared for.

"If God blesses us with only daughter, we will experience a loving caring existence that neither of us ever imagined.

"Now as to my selfish motive why I only want daughters," Jones said smiling. "Most daughters take the bulk of their genes from their fathers and I have a desire to have five other 'me's' around in my twilight years."

After Jones finished his story on daughters and sons, Lee said that she laughed at his reasoning as she kissed and hugged him around his neck as she continued to sit in Jones' lap in the kitchen/eating area of her home the night they became engaged, thinking about what he had said about daughters and their father and recognizing her present relationship with her own father. Lee readily admitted to herself that she did not love her father (and had told Jones why, early in their relationship), because of the horrific things that her father had done to her mother while Lee was growing up. Yet, there she was, caring for her father in style — he wanted for nothing. At first, Lee said that she cared for her father because she told herself that it was her duty. After hearing Jones' theory, even though she laughed at it, she now had another word to add to duty to explain and understand the care of her father: genes.

The beginning of the fourth week of October 1963, when Lee was entering her seventh month of pregnancy, was when her father was admitted to Gorgas Hospital in the Canal Zone for high blood pressure and a mild stroke. (Jones made Lee's father his dependent for medical care only immediately after returning from his honeymoon.) Lee recounted that both she and Jones were shocked by her father's sudden illness and hospitalization because he appeared so healthy. That was when Lee said that she realized that her father could die, although the doctor's at Gorgas had told them that he was in no danger and that they had only hospitalized him to bring his blood pressure under control. Although she attempted not to, Lee could not help herself — she was frantic! The reason Lee gave as to why she attempted not to worry about her father dying, was because she knew that any type of stress was not good for her or the baby she was carrying.

No matter how hard she tried not to, Lee said, "That she did worry." About her father dying. Her baby, and what would they do if something happened to it. Her worries, compounded the normal stress of being pregnant, Lee said. During that period, Jones was doing all he could through word of encouragement Lee said, to assure her that his father-in-law would recover.

"Didn't the doctors at Gorgas say that your father was a strong man?" Jones asked. "The baby will be fine, are we not two healthy people? You have me and I will always love and take care of you no matter what happens." Lee had repeatedly told Jones before they married that she could never be overworked, but she could not take mind problems. With her fathers hospitalization and that resulting stress, how would it affect the baby she was carrying and her own health were all perceived by Lee as "mind problems." Jones knew from his combat experience that if he was unsuccessful in removing Lee's mind problems, over time something had to give.

The first week of November 1963, the second week of Lee's father's hospitalization, Jones returned from Flamenco Island at 6:00 P.M. for dinner before returning to Panama City and the Canal Zone, to visit with Lee, her father in the hospital—their routine ever since he had been admitted. While sitting at the table in the kitchen/eating area, eating their dinner, Jones said that he noticed a strange expression come over Lee's face as she stopped eating and screamed, "My God! No! My water has broken! It's too soon! What's happening? God, don't let anything happen to our baby!"

As Lee sat upright in her chair with tears running down her face, she held the edge of the table with both hands as if she was afraid to move from her chair. Immediately when Lee screamed while hearing the water hit the tiled floor, Jones said that he jumped up from the table, knocking over his chair, and ran into the bathroom and came out with an armful of bath towels. He placed some between Lee's legs, and as he gently lifted her from the chair, with the bloody water still running out of her body, as she held the bath towels in place with one hand. As Jones told her, "It will be alright, honey. Don't worry. We are going to the hospital. I will take care of you."

From the time Jones came out of the bathroom, helped Lee from the chair and into the car, and during the mad ride to the hospital picking up an Republic de Panama National Police escort, once they reached the outskirts of the city. As Lee sobbed during the raid to the hospital, she screamed through her sobs, "No God. Not the baby! Not the baby!" While she was sobbing in the seat beside him, Jones repeated to Lee, as he dogged in and out of the evening traffic in his mad rush to the hospital, "I love you, honey! Don't worry! It will be alright!"

Many years later, while they both were recounting the birth of Lester, while holding Lee around her shoulders, sitting very close on the sofa in their sitting room, Jones mentioned, "Even as I was mouthing sincere words of encouragement back in 1963, I knew our baby was in trouble for during that entire ride to the hospital, I could not help but to notice that bloody water was still running out of Lee. My armful of towels were soaked on the car floor in front of Lee's legs. When we reached the outskirts of Panama City, a two man, manned National Police cruiser pulled me over for speeding, and before I could explain the situation, one of the officers looked in the passenger side where Lee was and saw the pile of blood soaked towels and said only one thing: 'Follow us!'"

Upon arriving at Gorgas hospital (Americans living in Panama City, had special plates on their automobiles), which was how the Police knew to take us to Gorgas. The Emergency Room (ER) personnel gently took Lee from the car and placed her, still sobbing, on a dolly, as they hurried her into the ER with Jones right behind her. As they worked around Lee on the dolly, as the

LEE

ER Doctor asked Jones, "How long has she been discharging water and who is her obstetrician?" The information was provided, and Jones was asked to leave the ER for the waiting room across the hall—someone would be out to see him in a few minutes. It was a half hour before Lee's Major Obstetrician came out of the ER. Jones mentioned that he had never seen him either, even though his eyes had been rivited to the ER door. He joined Jones in the waiting room and attempted to console Jones by telling him that Lee was alright. He told him that these things sometimes happen and the most important thing they had to do was deliver the baby. They had immediately taken her into a delivery room and told Jones that he was not to worry.

Jones asked, "Could I see Lee before she leaves the ER?"

The doctor replied, "Sorry, she has already been prepared for delivery. It's very important that we waste no time in delivering this baby. Once that is done, you may see her first thing."

Jones asked, "Will the baby be alright?"

The doctor replied, "In Lee's last check up, everything was normal and appeared to be progressing as it should. Now tonight, the condition of the baby depends upon how well it has done without its fluid home. I have to go. I will back to see you just as soon as I finish with the delivery." He then hurriedly left the waiting room.

Jones said that he sat alone in that quiet hospital waiting room enveloped in more fear than he had ever known in his entire life. He added that his past fears dealt with circumstances and situations that he always felt that he could successfully manage to overcome—but the questions of their child's life overwhelmed him. All he could think about sitting in that quite and semi-darken room was, "Lee! Lee! My God, Lee!" The longer he waited, the more he thought about what fears Lee must be experiencing, all alone, without him being near her to love, reassure

174

and comfort over the ever present question of "why?" Try as he might, Jones said that he could not take his eyes off the clock on the wall as its minute hand moved at a snail's pace from minute to minute. Even with is back to the clock on the wall, he kept turning around to look at it.

An hour and a half had passed when Lee's doctor came into the waiting room in his green gown, cap, and shoe covers, and sat across from Jones on the other sofa and told him, "You have a son, 3 1/2 pounds. Lee withstood the delivery operation well. We had to operate to get the baby out of her. It now seems that during her fifth month of pregnancy, the baby did not turn as it should have. During Lee's check-ups, I listened for the baby's heart beat and it was always where it should have been. I never ordered x-rays to confirm the exact location of the baby's position because it was dangerous for the fetus and I had no reason to believe that anything was amiss with Lee's pregnancy.

"By your son not turning in his fifth month, his insides did not fall into place," (coming to sit beside Jones) he said as he began to draw on a piece of paper from a notebook he took from amongst other papers in a folder, that he carried into the waiting room. This can be corrected with surgery, and we can place his insides where they belong. If we do nothing, your son will not last twenty-four hours. If we operate there is some chance, not much, but some chance that he is strong enough to withstand the seven to fourteen hour procedure. Any questions?"

The entire time that the doctor was talking, Jones sat beside him (and was thankful that he did not have to stand for he believed that he would have been unable to) stunned. Not surprised, just stunned, as he attempted to regain his composure to ask the doctor, "When may I see Lee?"

The doctor answered, "As soon as we finish here, a nurse will come with some forms for you to complete and sign, to include those for you to name your son. Afterwards, she will take you to Lee's room."

Jones then told the doctor. " I have no questions. Some chance is better than no chance at all. Give me the consent forms for our son's operation, and I will sign them."

The doctor then said, "After you see Lee, you can return to your home and I will telephone you when the operation is finished."

Jones told him, "No way! I will remain right her until you finish."

"Okay," said the doctor. "I will send in the nurse." He then hurried away to try to save Lee and Jones' son's life.

The nurse arrived with the necessary admitting, consent, and birth certificate forms to be completed. Afterwards, Jones was escorted to Lee's room on the same floor, then left them alone with his wife and mother of their son. Jones noticed immediately that Lee was still under the effects of the anesthetic and never knew that he was sitting beside her bed laying across her motionless body, crying. Between sobs, pleadingly, repeatedly, he asked, "Why, God? Why, God?" Receiving no answer in their moment of anguish and despair, he remained until first light.

Before leaving, in the meantime, with Lee still not completely conscious, he kissed her on the face, holding her tightly and told her that they had a son and that he had named him Lester (and nothing else). When telling the story of their first son's birth, Jones said that he could see that Lee had been through hell. She had been cut open, was exhausted and in pain, and just plain worried!

Lee asked, "Is the baby alright? I don't remember a thing after they rolled me into the Emergency Room."

Still with Lee in his arms, Jones replied, "As far as I know (a half truth), you have to rest. I have to go see your father to explain why we did not visit last night and to let him know that he has a grandson! I'll be back later. I love you, honey." He kissed her gently as he laid her gently down in her bed.

As he road the elevator five floors above to his father-in-law's ward, he was thankful that Lee never asked him how Lester looked, because he had not even seen him. Lee's father looked well, and Jones explained why they had not come to visit the previous night. He also told him that he had a grandson named Lester, and gave him the full and complete details regarding the birth, and the fact that he was undergoing an operation at that moment to save his life. Lee's father remained sitting on his bed and began to cry as he lamented, "God, no! How could you do this to her? She has never had it easy in life, and she has never hurt anyone. I am to blame for much of her unhappiness and now you add her first born? Have you no mercy?"

Jones made no response to his father-in-law's anguished cries as he stood in front of him because he was feeling the very same way—and possibly worse. Jones gave him Lee's room number, and reminded his father-in-law not to repeat anything of what he had told him to Lee because what she needed right then more than information was rest and peace of mind. Then, Lee's father, while wiping the tears from his eyes with the back of his hands, asked, "How are you doing? I am sorry."

Jones told him, "I am doing because I have to. It's all I know."

Jones said that he returned to the Emergency Room waiting room and telephoned his friend, the First Sergeant of Flamenco Island, giving him all of the particulars surrounding the birth of Lester, and requested an extended leave, returning to duty when he was ready. The First Sergeant immediately granted the leave over the phone, asking Jones to keep in touch—which he said he would do. Jones said that he then went to the hospital cafeteria, purchased a tray of food, and returned to Lee's room. She was still sedated, but knew that he was there. He sat in a corner of

Lee's room and ate the food on his tray as he watched Lee sleep while the doctor's and nurses went back and forth as they checked the instruments Lee was attached to, changed her dressing, and so forth. After finishing eating, and leaving Lee's room, Jones said, "that he left word at the ward desk for her doctor, that he would be in her room — and if for some reason, he left the hospital, he would inform the personnel at the desk of his whereabouts — to include a phone number." Jones stayed with Lee until 11:00 A.M., and with each passing hour, Lee became more coherent—with still no call from her doctor. Each time Jones asked at the ward desk, he was informed, "They are still in the operating room."

At eleven, Jones told Lee, as he gave her a hug and a kiss that he was on an extended leave and was going home to clean up the house, shave, shower, and change his clothes, and that he would be right back. Before leaving the hospital he gave the same information to his father-in-law and the ward nurse. He arrived home and accomplished all that he had intended.

Returning to Gorgas Hospital at 2:00 P.M., Jones checked in with his father-in-law (who told him that he had went down to see Lee), then at Lee's ward desk. Jones said that he then returned to Lee's bedside and that she looked much better than when he left for home, but very anxious as he told her of Lester's problems and what her doctor's were attempting to correct with the operation. When Jones had finished the story of the condition of their son, with Lee laying in his arms with her head on his chest and tears running down her face, she softly sobbed while repeating over and over, "Why, God? Why?" They softly (Lee mentioned during the telling of Lester's birth that they didn't know why they were speaking in whispers — but they were), attempted to reassure each other that their son would be okay when, in unison, Lee and Jones and admitted that they could hear the fear in each other voices. At 10:00 P.M. visiting hours were over so Jones left Lee's bedside and room as he kissed and hugged her and told her that he would remain in the Emergency Room waiting room until the operation was over.

At 11:00 P.M., Lee's haggard looking doctor came into the waiting room and sat across from Jones on the sofa and told him, "I never called to locate you. I knew you would be here. The operation is over and your son is still with us. He has turned one major corner—the operation—now all he has to do is make the next three days. He has been under the anesthetic for a long time and as he comes out of it, we have to watch how his very small lungs react. Three and a half pounds is a very small area to work in, and he appears to have a will to live—and that counts for something in the scheme of things."

Jones thanked the doctor for making the attempt to save his son's life, and asked, "Can I see him now? Can Lee also? She remembers nothing about Lester's birth."

"Yes. You may see your son," the doctor answered. "We have in the pediatric intensive care unit. I will take you there. I am afraid that Lee will have to wait until she is able to sit up in a wheelchair, for she has had a major operation contacted with the birth of her son, and it appears that she will be bedridden for two weeks. I will be seeing Lee first thing in the morning to explain her medical condition, and why we have to be very careful about her activities until she is completely healed."

Again Jones thanked the doctor as they hurriedly left the waiting room on their way to the intensive care unit for the first meeting with his son, Lester. Jones was gowned up by an intensive care nurse, then she laid Jones to a mobile incubator as the nurse said, "Here's your son. He's had a rough time of it so far, but he's hanging in there!"

A chair was brought for Jones as he was told by the nurse that he could place his hands (they were scrubbed as he was gowned-up) through a hand hole in the side of the incubator to touch his son is he liked. Jones sat beside the incubator as he placed one hand through the hand hole and began to rub Lester's forehead with one of his fingers, while talking to him. He said, "Now that you are here early, we are happy to see you. You are a Jones, and Joneses are fighters. You will make it! I will always be here for you. We love you boy!"

Throughout the night of the second day of Lester's life and into the morning of the third day, his father sat beside his incubator, only moving when requested by the nurse in attendance, as he talked to his son, watched his labored breathing, rubbed parts of his small arms, legs, face, and forehead with his finger, all in an attempt to make Lester aware that he was there! As Jones kept his vigil, he later said when telling the story of Lester's birth, he was amazed how very small three and a half pounds of life was, and that for approximately fifteen hours a team of doctors had worked in that very small space, attempting to put his son's organs in their proper place. During this vigil, Jones said how he observed that Lester had a full head of straight reddish/black hair, pinkish skin, tightly closed eyes, Lee's nose, and his wide forehead and chin. Lester appeared to be in no pain, with a "T" shape closed incision starting at the top of his chest running to the bottom of his belly, with just a light removable bandage covering it, which the nurse changed every fifteen minutes, along with being hooked up to monitoring and medication machines. Thus was spent the second day of Lester's life with his father.

At 8:00 A.M. on the third day, Jones said that he left Lester's side and went to Lee's room, as he did every day since their son's birth, to give her information on how he was doing, how he looked, how he was breathing, and how attentive he was being taken care of by the staff of the intensive care unit. Each time

Jones came to report to Lee, neither of them asked the burning questions that was crying out to be asked: Would Lester live? Years later, when they were telling me this story, they also gave me the reason for not asking the question that they longed to be answered: fear. Fear as to what the answer of their unasked question might be.

Lee was still bedridden and would remain so for another week, saying that her doctor had been in at 6:00 A.M. to see her with a group of other doctors that had assisted in Lester's operation, along with the supporting nurses. He explained her condition. Lester's chances — needed to make the next three days. Why they had to operate on her to deliver the baby. What was involved in her recovery. They answered all her questions and assured her that she would be able to have more children. Jones remained with Lee half of the morning. He sat on the side of her bed with her in his arms. She was still very weak, and he kept her head on his chest as he kissed the top of her head and rubbed her back with his hand. At mid-morning, Jones left Lee and went to his father-in-law's room, bringing him up to date as to Lee and Lester's conditions while informing him that he was going home for a bath and change of clothing. Lee's father said that he would go down and stay with Lee until Jones returned, and inform her that he had only run home and would be right back.

Before leaving the hospital, Jones called his First Sergeant again, telling him that Lester had survived his operation and would keep in touch. Jones and his First Sergeant, Joseph P. Sliva, were long-time friends and Catholic, going back many years in the army, when they were not Senior Sergeants. Unbeknownst to Jones, Sliva had sent the Army Catholic Chaplain serving the Battery on Flamenco Island to the hospital to have Lester baptized. He told Jones, "After hearing of Lester's operation, I thought it was the safe thing to do."

Jones thanked his friend and hung up the phone. As Jones drove home, he thought about what his friend had done and realized that Sliva's decision was a wise one. If Lester died, he would be able to be buried as a Catholic.

Jones returned to the hospital at 1:00 P.M. of the third day, and checked in with Lee and her father, who was sitting beside her bed, holding her hand as he gently stroked it with his other hand. He softly repeated, "I am so sorry! I am so sorry!" Jones could see that they had both been crying and made no comment about his observation. After inquiring about how they both were feeling, as he hugged and kissed Lee, telling her that he was going to divide his time between her and Lester for the remainder of the day.

It was late in the evening of the third day of Lester's life and the second day after his operation, that Lester, as Jones was rubbing his forehead with his finger, he just stopped his labored breathing and the tension lines around his eyes just disappeared. The lines on all the monitoring machines he was attached to went flat as the clock displayed 10:06 P.M. Before Jones could remove his hand from the hand hole of the incubator and call for help, the incubator was surrounded by doctors and nurses. A nurse helped Jones from his chair as the doctors and nurses busied themselves around the now opened incubator and Lester's motionless body. One of the nurse told Jones that she was very sorry. He thanked her and said, "I have to go see my wife."

He removed his gown, cap, and face mask as he left the room, and walked in a slow, trance-like state through the quiet hallways of the hospital to Lee's room. Without stopping at the ward desk, he entered Lee's room and closed the door. He stood in front of the closed door in the semi-darken room whose only light came from a lamp over Lee's bed, as he watched her sleep: the sleep of the undisturbed. He took a chair, placed it beside her bed, and calmly waited for her to wake up so that he could tell her that their son had died!. After a few moments, a nurse entered very quietly and whispered softly in his ear, "We have just been notified of your son's death, and are very sorry for you both. As you also know, your wife has been through a very trying ordeal and this leaves us with no idea how that news of the death of your child might affect her. If it's alright with you, I would like to sit with you until she awakens—just in case. We will also move a bed in here for you when she wakes so you may stay the night."

Jones thanked the nurse and told her that she could stay and that he appreciated the offer to spend the night. The nurse took another chair and went to a darken corner of the room to sit. They both waited in silence for Lee to awaken from wherever her restful sleep had taken her. Once Lee returned to the conscious world, she would be confronted with the news that the life she had lovingly nourished for seven months was no more.

Lee eventually awoke, saw Jones in the dim light, and immediately, anxiously asked, "What's the matter?" With her eyes wide with fear, Lee waited to be told, what she said years later she already knew when she awoke, and saw Jones sitting beside her bed — that their baby was dead. Leaving his chair as Lee was asking her questions, sitting on the side of her bed, Jones took Lee in his arms while kissing and holding her tightly against his body, "Lester didn't make it. He's dead."

Lee screamed, "God, no!" and fainted in Jones' arms. In an instant the nurse was beside the bed and she pressed the button for assistance as Jones laid Lee gently back on the bed and took himself to a corner of the now fully illuminated hospital room as the doctor and nurses proceeded to revive her. After the doctor and nurses had left the room, an attendant rolled in a completely prepared additional bed and then left.

While Lee was laying on her side in her bed, crying softly, as if her very soul was being squeezed out of her body with each tear, Jones took off his outer clothing and shoes, and putting on a hospital gown, got into Lee's bed and took her in his arms, as the only words of solace he could offer were, "I know, honey! I know, honey!" As Jones' hot tears also ran down his cheeks, he heard Lee softly repeatedly asking, "Why, God? Why?"

Thus was the birth and death of Lee and Jones' first son, Lester. In all of three days began the unraveling of Lee and Jones' planned world, never to be put back together again!

* "I never even saw you baby! You died without ever knowing your mother's love and kisses. When I think of you—which is all the time—my heart aches with the thought of what you must have been feeling during your short life. Pain and loneliness during your to short life, even though your father was with you right up to the end. I wonder if you knew he was there?

* "God, you are mean to have taken my first born!

* "After you died, I was moved out of the pediatric ward to the recover ward, two floors up and three below the ward my father, your grandfather, was on. The day you were buried, two days after you died, I asked the nurse to roll my bed (I was still bedridden and not allowed out) to the window of my room so I could bid you good-bye, with your grandfather standing at his window three floors above doing the same thing. You death has brought us closer together. Your father had hired a funeral director from Balbo, Canal Zone, and as the black hearse and the only family car, with your father as its loan passenger came down the street and stopped in front of the hospital morgue, I began to cry: for you, for myself, for your grandfather, and above all for your father.

"When the craven stopped at the morgue's door, the funeral director went to the back of the hearse and opened the door, then went into the morgue to retrieve the casket with your body that he had already prepared for burial.

"Your father got out of the family car, dressed in a black suit (the first time that I had ever seen him in a suit — since he got married in his Khaki uniform—I later learned he borrowed it), white shirt, black tie, and black shoes, and stood at attention at the open back door of the hearse—waiting for the funeral director to return with your casket. I could not see your father's face— his back was to the window—but when he came to see me after your funeral, still in his black suit, he never said a word. He was so overcome with grief. He just laid his head in my lap and cried uncontrollably as I attempted to comfort him by gently rubbing his hair and face.

"As I saw your father standing behind that open hearse back door waiting to receive your casket, every fiber of my heart and soul went out to him. I cried uncontrollably as I thought, 'There he is, once again, alone with all his pain!' The funeral director came out of the morgue with your very small, white casket laying across his outstretched arms, placed it in the back of the hearse, closed the door, entered the hearse on the passenger side, with your father entering the back of the family car at the same time. Then your funeral craven, very slowly left the hospital area for the cemetery and the grave side service. That is when I knew that you were really dead.

* "The first anniversary of your birth and death has just passed and your father and I have tearfully relived your to short life and burial all over again. There is no forgetting.

* Your father wants to have your remains exhumed and returned to the United States of America and reburied with your grandfather because having you buried in the Canal Zone where he can not even visit your grave, he says, is like having a part of him out there that he could not reach. I told your father that in my culture we do not disturb the dead. And when I saw the tears of pain and sorrow in his eyes, I relented and told him to go

ahead and attempt to bring you to this land of sorrow and heartache.

* "We have children! I willingly and happily leave the naming of all our children to your father, and he has given one your first name as his middle name, only spelled, 'Less.' He has also given our only daughter you name, again spelled Less and the name your father always called me by from our first date — Lee. Her name is Less — Lee. Your father has never forgotten you, son. Nor have I, and I know with the naming of our children, it's his way of giving you life. He often quotes this Chinese saying, 'You are alive as long as you are remembered.'

* "Twenty-seven years after your death, your father has finally been able to bring your remains to America for reburial. Again, there was a black hearse and one black family car containing only your father and I. We never told your siblings, nor our friends, of your return to this country and reburial. The anguish of your death was so intensely personal between your father and I, even today, that we did not want to share it with anyone, not even our children.

"We had a graveside service, conducted by a priest from Saint Peter's Church, our first church when we came to this country in 1964. As I listened to the priests words, with tears running down my cheeks and your father's arm around my shoulder, about 'resurrection and life with God,' again I was made aware that I was not to see you until I joined you in heaven.

"Oh, my first born, the results of my first act of love, my son, sorrow of my life; all I have of you is only a wooden box with your remains that was placed in the grave atop your grandfather! I silently cry for you everyday, for the life and love you were denied by a mean God.

* "After your return to this country, and reburial, your father has withstood (before, unable to function during the period of your birth and death), the anniversary of your birth and death much

better, as he hugs and kissed me when he thinks of you, as he comments, 'I have brought our son home.' I hug him back and tell him, 'Now you are both at peace.' He smiles into my face, as his arms remain around my waist and tells me, 'Yes, honey, you are right. I love you so much for understanding and putting up with my desire these many years to bring him to this country.' I kiss your father as I tell him, "It's okay Honey, I love you." Your father still doesn't understand that I only exist to make and see him happy.

* "I have never thought much about what you might have looked like as a man or done with your life—only that God did not allow you to live, for which I shall never forgive him.

* I am saddened, when the only thing that I am able to tell your siblings is that they had a brother who died three days after his birth, and I can not describe you to them or show them a picture.

* "Life is cruel, and it does not help me in my pain over your death to know that there are others in the world who have also lost their first born. The pain is too personal. It was not someone else's first born, but my was my first born! The difference between me and others is that you were something that I never expected to experience in my life. Most other women I know expect during their child bearing years, to experience child birth, but not me until I met your father. I never wanted to love in my life, and when it happened, God should have allowed for my past feeling about love and allowed you to live. He's mean!

* "Your father is right! As I remember you, son, you are always alive for me."

> "How do you live out the
> rest of your life when an
> incalculable absence hunts
> its every day."
> *Oscar Hijuelos*

14.

RIOT

It was always with profound sadness that Lee discussed and remembered the riot in Republic de Panama in January 1964, not only because of the physical harm that was afflicted upon her and her father, nor just the material loss — their home looted then burned to the ground along with it's remaining contents, but the fact that it was done by her countrymen. When she told the story, Lee would sadly ask and answer her own question of : "Why? Because I had happened to fall in love with and married an American! It didn't matter that my American was a soldier, because anyone even slightly connected to America came under attack during the riot. They were physically assaulted, their cars were burned, their homes were broken into—looted and burned, and often by long-time Panamanian friends and neighbors."

The hardest burden Lee said she had to bear as a result of the riot was the lost of her handmade wedding dress made by the Sisters of Saint Jose Convent as their wedding present to her after she announced the forthcoming wedding to what they called, "her soldier."

The second heaviest burden was that the riot facilitated her departure from Republic de Panama—her country! She nor Jones ever had any desire to live in the United States. She disliked the peoples because of the degrading way they have always treated

Panamanians. Yet, because of the riot, that was what they were forced to do. Lee reflected sadly how all within eleven months she married, spent an enjoyable honeymoon, became pregnant, saw her father unexpectedly hospitalized, and surgically gave birth to a three and a half pound son—and never being able to hold him. She was not even able to attend his funeral and only able to mark his passing by watching from a hospital window. Attacked by her longtime neighbors during the riot. Their home was looted and burned to the ground and she had to leave her own country. This was a heavy load to bear within such a short time frame.

The only way Lee said that she managed to get through what she came to call her "unexpected period of adversity" was with Jones. Lee recalled that as often as they experienced disappointments, tragedies, illness and setbacks, Jones never became discouraged or complained. He would always find someway through or around the difficulty, taking her and her father with him. In a very short time, because so much was happening in their lives so fast, Lee said that she stopped becoming upset (asking why) and worried (what would they do) because she was secure in the knowledge that Jones loved only her, and in his love he would take care of her. He would somehow make it right, no matter what the problem was. And, according to Lee, he always did.

It was during Lee's "unexpected period of adversity" that she said that she realized why Jones had come into her life with his love when he did. She said that he was the half of her soul that was needed to make her world a normal place to live, thereby allowing her peace of mind.

I once asked Lee what the cause of the Panama riot was and she answered, "The treaty giving the United States of America the right to build their canal through our country was drafted and signed by French Engineer, Philippe Bunau-Varilla. He was appointed by the new government of the Republic de Panama in

Panama City to act as their ambassador to Washington, DC. It granted concessions even more outrageous than those the Americans had sought in earlier, unsuccessful negotiations with the Colombian government. The terms of the Panama Canal Zone treaty has caused resentment by me, and most other Panamanians, for that Frenchman and the 1903 treaty ever since, because at no point were the citizens of the newly proclaimed republic ever consulted. We were never asked is we wanted a canal built through our country.

"There have also been other aggravations. Such things as insularity, even arrogance, of Americans living in the Canal Zone in relations with the Panamanians. This included segregation, which we have no history of, with labels of "gold" for white, "silver" for Panamanians and Negroes. These labels were on drinking fountains, toilets, etc. and stemmed from the canal construction days. Skilled workers, mostly white, were paid in gold coin and unskilled laborers, usually Panamanians and Negroes were paid in silver.

"Although this type of discrimination was stopped in the sixties, we Panamanians still remember it, and those long old standing factions exploded in January of 1964. A flag raising incident in the Zone, between Americans and Panamanian high school students touched off three days if rioting and gunfire. Twenty-one Panamanians and four Americans were killed.

"Ask any American about how many Americans were killed during the Panamanian riot of January 1964 and I will wager you that they will not know. Ask any Panamanian that same questions and they will all know—some will know even the names of the people killed."

I admitted to Lee when she finished her story that I knew of that riot but not how many had been killed on either side. Yes, resentment to a given situation may seethe beneath the surface for years before coming to the fore. History is filled with such examples.

After their home was looted and was burned with some of the looters standing around smiling and watching, Lee told how she and her father were taken to the hospital in the Canal Zone after she told a fireman who was fighting the fire that her husband was an American soldier. Gorgas Hospital was built half in Panama City and half in the Canal Zone and the fireman informed her that they would bury Sooner (Jones' dog) behind the house. After being admitted, Lee said that she and her father were hospitalized for a week. Jones was notified of what happened, but could not leave his position as the NCOIC (Non-Commissioned Officer in Charge) of something called a Mobile Task Force, made up of men from his Battery, that was part of the military forces maintained along the boundary of Panama City and the Canal Zone to keep the rioters at bay. He was able to telephone.

Lee said that then Jones called her (telling her that he would also phone her father) that evening of her first day in the hospital, all she could do was to cry and repeatedly ask, "Why? Why, honey? We never bother anyone."

Jones attempted to comfort Lee by telling her, "Please don't cry. I don't know why, Honey, people do all the evil they do. What was done to you and your father was pure evil. Please don't worry. I love you and we have each other. No matter what they do to us, I promise you that we will make it. I am so sorry for what happened to you and your father, (She was glad that he forgot to ask about his dog, Sooner. Lee did not tell Jones until later how his dog died attempting to defend her from being attacked by her long time neighbors.) But listen. I can not leave my post here, so I am sending my friend, Sliva, tonight, my First Sergeant, to the hospital to see you and your father. He will take of everything until I can get to you both, but I will phone you every day."

Lee recounted how just by hearing Jones' voice she stopped crying and her pain lessened. As he was talking to her she knew just how Jones would make everything right, through their contact with each other by telephone.

Jones' friend, First Sergeant Joseph P. Sliva, did come to the hospital that first night as Jones had told her he would and did take care of everything. Upon their release from the hospital, Sliva moved them into his quarters at Fort Amdor, Canal Zone with his family, his wife, his seventeen-year-old daughter, and his fourteen-year-old son, who immediately made Lee and her father welcome. Although the firing had stopped, the military personnel — to include Jones, still manned the "riot line."

It was two weeks into the riot before Lee actually saw Jones in person (he telephoned twice a day), when he came out for dinner with Sliva, which was to be the routine thereafter. The battery was still on alert, and Jones still the NCOIC of the Mobil Task Force, requiring him to be quartered (remain) on Flamenco Island. Even if that was not the situation, they had no place to go! For privacy after dinner, Lee said that she and Jones retired to his automobile parked in Sliva's driveway to discuss their future, which looked very bleak. They had no home, no chance of obtaining quarters in the Canal Zone, and could not return to Panama City because the government of The Republic de Panama had broken off diplomatic relations with the United States of America and they could not stay in Sliva's quarters for more than thirty days. That first visit from Jones Lee said all they did sitting in their car was to render reassuring hugs and kisses to each other as they held each other in a vise-like embrace for four hours. Then Jones had to return to duty on the riot line.

Time and again Lee said that she would smell his clean body

through his fatigues as she squeezed him just as tightly as she could, while softly confirming her love and sense of well-being by telling Jones, "You are here! I love you, honey!"

Since Jones experienced the same feeling with regard to well-being, he would softly reply as he held her tightly to his body, "I know, honey. Don't worry, I will take care of you. All I care about is you, and that you are safely in my arms." In recounting the story of the riot, Lee would never fail to mention that when she and Jones reunited she never cared or worried about anything other than the fact that he was near.

It was during Jones' second visit for dinner, while sitting in their car, that Lee told of how she totally broke down into uncontrollable crying, laying in Jones' arms as she relived all that had happened to his dog, Sooner, during the attack upon her and her father. Her words gushed out of her mouth like a water spout that has been turned on full force. As Lee relived the horrific experience, Jones gently rocked Lee in his arms as he silently listened in anger. Lee said that she could feel his body tense up as she described how her female neighbors beat and kicked her to the ground. He attempted to console Lee by holding her tightly in his embrace as he thought of George Eliot's words about hate; "There are glances of haters that stab and raise no cry of murder."

It was during the third visit that Jones told Lee, and later his father-in-law that the United States Army had issued orders for all of them to return to the States in February. There were no quarters available for the large number of military personnel with their families who had been brought (or came on their own) into the Canal Zone for safety at the start, and during the riot, whom had formerly been living in the Panama City area. The Army, through Sliva's efforts, had arranged for Lee and her father to remain as his "guest" until their departure. Lee and Jones dressed as Panamanians, with Jones carrying nothing that would identify him as American, would be allowed to crossover into Panama city via Gorgas Hospital to obtain Lee and her father's passports, valuables, and other papers from their safe deposit boxes. During this time they would be allowed to visit the necessary Panamanian governments offices and agencies in order to acquire the necessary documentation for them to leave the country. They were forbidden to return to their burned out home during their excursions into the city because of the fear on the part of both governments that if they did return, someone might recognize them and do them bodily harm. Jones also told Lee that he believed that although there were no diplomatic relations between the two countries, they had reached an understanding to turn a blind eye to the crossings in order to allow for a smooth departure of those and their families that had been displaced, and could not return to Panama City because of the broken relations or remain in the Canal Zone.

Lee often mentioned when reflecting upon her period as a guest of the Sliva family, how very quickly a very amiable relationship developed between she and her father, and all members of the family. Particularly between her and First Sergeant Sliva, mentioning that he was the second American, after Jones, that she came to like. Lee also mentioned that during her stay as a guest in the Sliva household, she did what Mrs. Sliva would allow her to do, as her contribution toward maintaining the house and its members. They both washed and ironed together the household linens and all its member's clothing. They alternated cooking the dinner meals and cleaning the house. Lee said that she insisted that she be the care giver for her father, to include the cleaning of both of their bedrooms, and volunteered to help the children with their homework when asked—which was every day once they discovered that

195

Lee had been an elementary school teacher before she married Jones. One night at dinner, Sliva's son told all at the table, "We have a secret weapon in Lee. Now all of our homework will received A's because she knows all the answers!" There was much loud laughter.

Lee and Sliva's seventeen-year old daughter hit it off from the moment her father brought Lee home from the hospital. Lee said that she became the sister to each other that neither of them never had but always wanted. In the short time Lee and Sliva's daughter were together, Lee taught her to knit, and advised her about things of particular interests to women that she did not choose to ask her mother.

One day Sliva's daughter asked Lee, "How do you know when you're in love?"

Lee answered, "When you look at your love and know that you can never be parted from him."

"What should I be looking for in a man to love?" Sliva's daughter questioned.

"Nothing!" Lee retorted. "Ask yourself: What can I bring to him that will make him the type of man that I can spend the rest of my life with?"

Sliva's daughter then asked, "What if he's not Catholic?"

"If you are absolutely sure that you are in love, talk to your parents about him not being of your faith. But remember, love is blind—it just happens. Look at me and Jones!"

They both laughed at Lee's comparisons for she had already told Sliva's daughter how she never expected to fall in love and marry, "Then along came Jones."

Lee admits that she imagined that the reason she was immediately drawn to Sliva's daughter in a caring, protective, and sisterly way was because she remembers how much abuse and the accompanying suffering she experienced growing up because she was taller than most Colombians and Panamanians. Joanie was six feet tall and still growing! During that time, the sixties, Lee reminded me that tall women of any culture had a difficult time developing relationships with the opposite sex, and often with their own sex, because few men wanted to be seen with a woman taller than they were. Joanie and Lee remained friends to the very end. They kept in touch with letters and telephone calls even when Sliva's family returned to the States, her father's retirement from the army, her marriage to a member of her father's Battery and their settlement in Ohio, and the progress of their children as they grew into adults, went to college, fell in love, married, and made them grandparents. Whenever Lee talked about Joanie, it was always with a softness in her voice and she would end her remembrances with, "I liked Joanie, and often wondered: If I had parents like Sergeant and Mrs. Sliva, what type of woman would I have become?"

I would always reply to Lee's unanswerable question with, "We have no say in who our parents are, it's all a roll of the dice. We do the best we can with what we have."

After Jones started to take his dinner meal with Lee, her father, and the Sliva family, two weeks into the riot, he and Sliva used to arrive at the house at the same time each evening in their own cars. During dinner, Sliva would always tease Lee concerning the merits of the Republic de Panama as compared to the United States. Everyone in the Sliva family spoke Spanish, which was what they spoke at dinner, except Joanie. Her father used to say that for some reason she refused to learn the language. Lee said when she, with Sliva — sitting at the head of the dinner table. Jones at the other end, she to Sliva's right, and Mrs. Sliva to his left: with the rest of the family to include Lee's father; continuing the seating arrangement down both sides of the table; were going at it tooth and nail, there would be Joanie from her place at the table waving her arms and shouting, "English! English I say! English so I can understand, too!"

When Joanie performed what all members of the family began to call "her English act," everyone laughed. They didn't laugh at Joanie for not speaking Spanish, but the seriousness in which she was attempting to follow what was being said.

Lee remembered that Sliva would come at her during dinner with comments like, "America is the best country in the world! You're tickled pink to be going to the land of the big P.X., but you're attempting not to show it. Women the world over think that American men are great, which is why so many of them marry real men. Panama would not even be a country if it was not for the United States."

After Silva's above pronouncements, Mrs. Sliva would give her husband a hard slap on his ample forearm as she told him, "Stop it! Lee is our guest! You go too far!"

Jones pleading would tell Mrs. Sliva, "Leave them be! Lee can give as good as she gets. Joe has picked the wrong Panamanian." This would make everyone laugh, including Lee's father. Lee would look down the table at her husband, thank him, then with a smile she would proceed to answer Sliva.

"If America is the best country in the world," she replied, "then why does The Republic De Panama have more retired Americans living in it then any other country in the world? You don't leave the best, especially when you retire.

"And to call me tickled pink. I would give you tickled pink if the children were not present! Laughter. What I am attempting not to show is my disgust, because I have to go to your God-for-saken land of the big P.X. More Laughter.

"You have it all wrong. Not great, although Jones is, (laughter) but love. Love is truly blind. For I never thought in my wildest dreams that I could and would ever fall in love with and marry a gringo American soldier. (Looking at the other end of the table at Jones) Love you Honey. More Laughter. And Panama not a country without America? Who asked you?" There was much loud laughter.

Lee often mentioned that she had a soft spot in her heart for Sliva. If he ever called upon her for assistance, she would gladly and willingly respond. It was not until they had returned to America and started to put their lives back together again that Lee told how she then realized what Sliva was doing via his outlandish remarks during dinner — he was forcing her to deal with something other than the tragic experiences relating to the riot. And it worked! Lee said that she healed in mind and body before she and her father left Sliva's home, which she credits to Jones being there for her, even it was only in the evenings. Lee also told me that she did not minimize the part that Sliva played in her healing process because it was something that Jones could not have done effectively. Jones always blamed himself for the beatings she took, along with the destruction of their home, no matter how often she told him the contrary.

February 1964 arrived and with a tearful farewell from all the members of First Sergeant Sliva's family with accompanied hugs and kisses. There was an extra kiss and hugs for Sliva around his ample chest. With Sliva getting in the last word as he waited with his family, Lee, her father, and Jones for their flight number to be called, he attempted to lighten up the mood by telling Lee, "You enjoy yourself in the land of the big P.X., you hear?"

Lee said that she gave Sliva another kiss and hug as she attempted to smile through her tears as she told him aduie. Lee recounted how she sadly waited to depart the country of her birth that she had only recently returned to and loved and did not want to leave.

They boarded their flight from Howard Air Force Base in the

Canal Zone with other military personnel and their families who had formerly lived in Panama City via an Air Force Air Transport Command aircraft for Charleston Air Force Base, Charleston, South Carolina. No matter how Jones attempted to comfort and reassure Lee, he said that she could not stop crying for the entire flight.

> "How easy is it for one benevolent
> being to diffuse pleasure around him,
> and how truly is a kind heart a
> fountain of gladness, making everything
> in its vicinity to freshen into smiles."
>
> *Washington Irving*

15.

ROBERT

After a three day layover at Charleston Air Force Base, South Carolina, where they were treated with compassion by the Air Force personnel and the citizens of Charleston, Lee said that she, Jones and her father took a Pullman train to a city fifty miles from Jones' new duty station. After their arrival, all in one day they rented a two bedroom unfurnished house, they bought a new 1963 Ford (nothing down — their funds still tied up in the Panama City banks) and began their new lives in America, or as Sliva would have called it "the land of the big P.X.!" After several months in the United States, the government of America and Panama (each paying half) made a generous monetary reimbursement for the house in Panama City and, all of the items that were either looted, burned, destroyed, or lost during the riot of January 1964. Sadly, Lee said that even though the monetary reimbursement was more than generous she could never forget what her own people had done to her. It was as if both governments were embarrassed, and wanted to put the riot behind them — by willingly paying what was asked by the claimants. The sentimental loss was bad enough, but coupled with the knowledge that it appeared that her home was looted, burned, and that she and her disabled father were attacked by their long-time neighbors for no other reason then she had met, fallen in love with and married an American, it hurt. After the settlement with the two governments, they purchased the house that Lee and Jones had been renting. Lee told me, "One of Jones' promises to me has been kept — I am in my own home!"

Robert was born in January of 1966, a healthy baby boy, Lee happily told me when she and Jones brought him home from the hospital.

* I carried you to term, Robert. During the entire time of my pregnancy, as much as I attempted not to, I kept thinking about Lester and what if I lost you also (I will tell you about your late brother as you grow). My first loving child. Now I am a complete woman and wife to your father. My joy knows no bounds!

* I remember your birth, Robert, with great pleasure. I was conscious the entire time, and my Army Obstetrician told me afterwards, that you were a textbook delivery. When they laid you on my belly and I saw you for the first time, I felt that my happiness would take my breath away. Truthfully, you were not much to look at — all wrinkled, pink, wet and slimy, but definitely alive! I hope you never have to experience the dreadful loss of a child — it's something that haunts you for the rest of your life! You can never put the thought out of your mind, 'What might I have unknowingly done that might have caused my baby's death'. With your birth, I am not haunted by that thought any longer! I still believe that God was mean to take my first born, but I also thank Him everyday for you. You are the very life-breath of my body!

* After I had been cleaned up and taken to the Pediatric Ward, your father immediately came to my bedside giving me many, many kisses and 'Thank You's'. All during that first visit after your birth, your father kept repeating, 'We have our son! We have our son!' Then a cloud came over his face, and he became silent, and I knew instantly that he was thinking about your late brother, Lester. I pulled the hand that I was holding, and told him, 'Hey, this is our pay-back. What did you name our son?' He told me, 'Robert,' and I replied, 'I can live with that!' He slowly reverted

back to his excited, happy self and kissed and thanked me as we continued kissing and hugging each other. We were so happy and relieved over the safe birth of you, Robert — our living son!

* It was four days after your birth, Robert, before your father brought a box of cigars and told his friends and associates on Post that I have given birth, and that he had a son! When I learned of his delay in announcing the good news, I asked him, 'Why?' He replied, 'No reason.'

After thinking about what I initially thought was your father's strange behavior concerning announcing your safe and joyful birth, I realized I knew why. After Lester's operation, his doctor told your father that he had to make the next three days. So now I realize, what he was told concerning Lester has become a mind set of your father that he would wait three days to be sure that his newborn babies lives, before saying anything — just in case! Your poor father! He has been marked forever by the fear of the inability of his children to live, once they are born.

* You will never know, son, how your birth righted our world. We were not to be cursed not to have children. Much love, son, for the light and joy you have brought back into your mother's life. My soul lives in your love, Robert!

* As I care for you — hold, kiss, cuddle, and watch you make funny movements in your sleep, I am always amazed, Robert, at how much you look like your father! You have his high forehead, dark brown eyes, and the rest of his facial features. I am pleased to know that you will grow with your father's appearance, and pray everyday that you will become the caring and responsible man he is. I am happy to have you to love and care for! You are a good baby, and complete my life. With you, I live and love!

* I never learned Robert, how you knew when your father was returning from the Post, but not that you are walking, when that time draws near, you and his new dog (Sooner II) go to the storm door standing side by side, waiting for his Ford automobile

to turn into our street. The moment you see his light yellow car, you began to shout, 'Dad, Dad!' jumping up and down, laughing, waving with both of your hands as the dog barks her greetings. As I stand behind you both, my heart swells with joy as I share in your happiness that your father is coming home.

* I am so sorry that my father never lived to see you born, Robert. He was not a nice man, but I knew he would have loved you, his first grandchild. Your father has no family that he knows anything about and it saddens me to know that you will grow up without any grandparents, but we will give you quadruple the love!

* I watch you, Robert, and your father together as he teaches you his rudiments of being a man, and your responsibilities as the oldest son when he dies. You nod, and with a seriousness that belies your young age, tell your father, 'Don't worry Dad, I will take care of them. Anyway, you are going to live for a long time!'

As I watch, listen while remaining silent, I sometimes wonder if he is not talking too much to you about death, duty, responsibilities, but I don't say anything to your father or you. Nor, do I attempt to interfere because I tell myself that I know where your father is coming from. Your father loves you, Robert, with a love that you will never be able to understand, even if you live to be a hundred. He wants to pass on to you all he knows about what it takes and means to be a man, while he can. It's so easy for me to love you, son, when I watch you and your father together.

* You will never know how proud you make me feel Robert, when you are asked your name and you automatically include your middle name (your father's first name). It tells me that you love and are proud of your father as we are of you. No one will ever love you like I do!

* I am pleased to see that you are doing very well in school, Robert. After reading your report card today, I see that you are no genius, but that is all right because most of us are not. However,

you are in the top 20% of your class and if you maintain that position throughout your education experience, you will reap the rewards of an educated person.

All that I have written here, I have also told you while we were reading your report card, but I am so happy for you that I just had to place my happiness on paper! My love for you will always be unquenchable!

* The Sister Principal told me of your fist fight in the school yard with a high school student who was twice your size Robert. All because he took your basketball while you were shooting hoops and would not give it back. She also said that you gave as good as you got, requiring two Sisters to keep you off your opponent because of your anger — once they had separated you two. The high school student was going to be suspended for one week for taking your basketball and fighting. At the same time, asking me to tell you that everyone knows that you are tough and not afraid, but the next time, go to one of the Sisters or lay teachers in the school yard and you will have your basketball returned. She did not like fighting in her school.

I have told you all of the above when we arrived home because I too, am concerned about your 'toughness'. In many ways you are exactly like your father, quickly reverting to the use of your fist — but there are other ways to solve a dispute without fighting, which I have also talked to you about. Consider what you are about to fight over and about. Consider the source that has made you angry enough to fight him — in many cases they are stupid, and just walk away. You are not less a person for walking away from a fist fight, but more of a man. Son, if you don't learn to utilize the other ways during a quarrel, your very toughness could lead to serious injury, trouble with those that are suppose to uphold the law — and do not, and God forbid, possibly cause your death! All of this I have told you before. Please listen and understand what I am telling you!

Love of my life, we have waited for you all of our lives, and for something tragic to happen to you now, because you reacted, rather than thought first, would kill us! Think before you react! All situations you will confront during your life will not require toughness, which I have also told you. Often, only love and patience. Remember your father's heart is tender although he is tough!

* You said that you wanted to take music lessons in the Spanish guitar. We purchased your guitar and case, enrolled you in a class for the instrument, and after only three lessons, your instructor told us that there was nothing more he could teach you because it appeared that you were born to play the guitar. I often listened to you playing in your room as I passed your closed door and my cup of happiness runneth over, Robert!

* You have never been seriously sick a day of your life Robert. When you caught a cold, without any type of treatment whatsoever, you'd throw it! You have had all of your shots, to include an annual physical that your father paid for, because our health plan would not, always receiving a clean bill of health after each examination. Two months into your thirtieth year, you began to lose weight and complained of always being tired, while experiencing shortness of breath. We immediately had you brought to the Medical Center in Boston, for you to you to be seen by their specialist. After two months of tests, we were told that you had a hole in the back of your heart, and that there was nothing they could do.

* My God! Not again! My child is going to die! It has been five years since you died, Robert, and I have grieved for you every moment of every day. Your father came close to losing his mind after you died. It took all of my will power, strength, and love to keep him from going around the bend by constantly and forcefully reminding him that your siblings and I loved and needed him — here and now!

I cried out of your sight, during your wasting away, when

we brought you home from the hospital, at your request to die. After your funeral, I have cried everyday since for what might have been. But not your father! After your funeral, he shed no more tears in my present, just drew within himself. But I also know that he grieves for you the same as I do, as I wish he would cry because I know it would help him to release what's inside of him, 'Anger as to the unfairness of it all.'

All during your illness you were never afraid, and I found that so amazing in one so young the thought of dying appeared not to alarm you. We were all in your bedroom, standing around your bed, the night you died, as you told us, 'I am going now,' closed your eyes and left us forever with our memories and grief. I have attempted, unsuccessfully, to understand your death, because God has twice put his hands upon my young children. Has He no mercy?

I take comfort in my thirteen years of loving memories and most of the time they help. But sometimes, the realization of your death so overwhelms me that I have to take to my bed!

Good bye my son. If there is a heaven, you will once again feel your mothers loving arms around you, and her kisses upon your lips and face when my time here is done.

When Robert died, that was the beginning of a very difficult period in Lee's life. She had to keep Jones on track (he almost lost it), consoled the other siblings and their father, who became very angry at the world over the death of another of his sons and dealing with her own grief while holding her family together. As I attempted to be supportive to Lee and the other family members (in their home everyday) as I watched her keep what I felt were too many balls in the air at the same time, I became afraid for Lee's mental and physical health. But when it came to Lee's family, I worried needlessly, for she was stronger than I thought. I asked Lee why she did not seek for the family, religious or professional help to assist them in dealing with their grief? Lee told me with some annoyance, "All they are going to tell us in the final analyzes is to accept the situation. Well, I do accept that Robert is dead for we put his lifeless body in the ground. But that is not the question. The question is, 'Why?' And no one has the answer to that!"

During that period, I watched Lee scold, love, console, hug, kiss, and generally do all the things that for some reason, we men expect all women in love, with a husband, children, dog, home to do during a crisis. Robert's death was a crisis for the Jones household, which Lee managed through her love, wisdom, and strength to bring them all through spirituality and physically intact.

> "Women have more good sense, than men. They have fewer pretensions, are less implicated in theories, and judge of objects more from their immediate and involuntary impressions on the mind, and therefore more truly and naturally."
>
> *William Hazlitt*

16.

SEPARATION

When Lee remembered the Vietnam War that separated Jones from her for over a year, it still brought a frightful expression to her face. Since I lived through that period with Lee, I know how traumatic that duration of forced separation was for her. Lee was always thin, but she became thinner each day that Jones was in Vietnam. She would not, could not, eat — I had to constantly remind her that she had to eat in order to be able to take care of the baby. She could not sleep more than a few hours because she followed the war on television until the last station signed off for the night. She went on crying binges — she would be talking about Jones and some past or planned event and then start to cry uncontrollably. She lost her desire to cook — buying canned foods that needed no preparation and ate it right from the can. She withdrew into her own mental world — excluding all of us who loved and were concerned for her well-being. When I and others wrote to Jones, none of us ever mentioned how traumatically their separation was effecting Lee. Within four months of Jones being sent to the war in Vietnam, Lee demonstrated how very strong and resourceful she really was — pulling herself out of the doldrums. As I watched Lee rearrange her life alone, she told me once after becoming, once again, the Lee that I had known before Jones went off to war. "I love Jones more than my own life, and I have to be here for him when he returns, because

I knew that no matter how badly I may be feeling, it is a thousand times worse for him. Everyday he has to live with the constant fact that he could be killed!"

While reading the local newspaper, Time magazine, and watching the nightly news 1964-1965, Lee became ever increasingly concerned about the war in Vietnam, and the possibility that Jones might have to go and participate in it. She asked him once, "Honey, will you have to go and fight in Vietnam?" He responded with a resounding, "No! I was a former Prisoner of War (POW) of the Chinese Peoples Army, and the US Army had a policy of not sending ex-POW's into a war zone where their former captors were — the Chinese were supporting the North Vietnamese Army. Still, with what Jones had told her, Lee's fears of the war in Vietnam touching Jones would not abate through 1965 during her pregnancy with Robert.

What constantly worried and depressed Lee every waking moment, was the fact that had it not been for the riot of 1964, in the Republic de Panama, Jones would have been discharged from the army. They would be living the good life in their newly built home on the outskirts of Panama City as man and wife with no question of him being sent to the war in Vietnam and possibly placed in harm's way. When Jones' enlistment was up in 1964, they still had not been able to obtain their funds on deposit in the banks in Panama City. This was because of the still broken diplomatic relations between the two countries was still in effect and their claims for lost property during the riot had not been settled. Believing himself to be immune form being sent to the Vietnam War, Lee said that Jones reenlisted under something called the Retirement Reenlistment Program, two years, five months and twenty six days, in order to make his twenty years and a day. That type of enlistment, according to Lee, notified the Department of the Army that when Jones' enlistment was up, he indeed, intended to retire!

In December of 1965, eight months into her pregnancy with Robert — the other shoe dropped! Jones received orders to be shipped out with a unit from his Post in January 1966 to Vietnam. As they were in the process of selling their first house and purchasing a larger one to accommodate the forthcoming addition to their family in another city. Lee panicked! With Jones quickly reassuring her, "Don't worry, I will be here when our child is born — I will not leave you alone to face the birth by yourself! I love you, Honey! Also, we will proceed with the selling of this house, and the purchasing of our new home. I shall delay! I will use the system that the army has in place. Through its regulations, to attest that I am physically fit and mentally sound to withstand the rigors of serving in a combat theater of operations were the possibility exist that I could once again, become a POW of the Chinese People's Army." As Jones held Lee gently in his arms as she cried softly, sitting on the sofa in the living room, I watched as he attempted to reassure her of his love and protection. I remained silent in my easy chair as I watched them in their grief and bewilderment at life's apparent unfair and unexpected knocks, as I wondered, "How much of what is happening to them has less to do with knocks, then actions causing reactions?"

All during the time Jones was delaying his development to the war in Vietnam, Lee said that she daily lived with the abiding fear that her husband would not be able to survive another war or becoming a POW again. The last war he fought in Korea almost killed him. I watched and listened in silence — for I had no counter argument for what Lee was saying — and even if I had, I would not have made it. For I knew all of Lee's venting was because of her fear that Jones could be killed in Vietnam. Lee denounced President Johnson, the many that had never done their share in any war and eternal disdain for the wealthy of America, who were sending their sons out of the country to help them avoid the draft and service in Vietnam! At the same time that Lee was denouncing the unfairness of it all, she was also loudly proclaiming that Jones had already done his share. Why send him and others half way around the world to die for those that would not defend themselves. He had a wife! She was pregnant with their child. She had always hated the military, all military! They were moving to a new city in the same state where they knew no one. The US Army only wanted to send Jones to the war in Vietnam to get him killed, so they would not have to pay the retirement if he lived to make his twenty years and a day!" When Lee finished her angry outburst, I was still left with the thought, "How much truth was there in what her heart, mind, and soul was telling her was true?"

In January of 1966, the unit Jones was assigned to, left the Post for the Vietnam war without him, because he was still being evaluated by the medical board at the Post Hospital, Lee told me. Also that month, Lee gave birth to their first child born in the United States, and the day the baby was delivered, Jones was passing papers on their second home in another city that we both were then presently residing. When Lee reflected upon that period in her life she called 'half-life', because she felt that the United States Army was about to take the other half of her life away form her, sending him halfway around the world possibly to be killed. That fact alone, hung over her constantly like a cloud, which robbed Lee of the ability to completely immerse herself in the joyful birth of their healthy, normal son. Also mentioning that when Jones came that night to the hospital during a snow storm, to see her and their son, after thanking her with hugs and kisses, while mentioning that he had named their son, "Robert." Lee told me, "Then, as always, now that Jones was with her, all was right in her world. Smiling, she recalled that some of her female friends have often told her that they believe that she depends too much on Jones and allow him to sway in their marriage. Laughing, Lee said that whenever that subject came up, she told her friends, "That's not the way it is at all! There is nothing that Jones does, that he will not talk to me about first. Seldom, do I tell him no, but when I do — he does not do it! Jones accepts my decision without rancor because he values my opinion. The reason I can always say yes to Jones in everything he seeks my approval on, is because everything he does is for me — the children, the dog, or to maintain or increase the value of our home! He will not even buy with his pocket money, a hard cover book for $25 or $30 without first telling me in passing — to which I always reply to the good news that he is going to buy another book for his library — 'Good, Honey.' The reason Jones gives for informing me before he spent his pocket money, was to assure that I might not possibly need some additional money before he spent his. What he never knew, even when I needed some extra money, and he told me that he was buying himself a book, I never told him. He enjoys his books. As to dependency, I tell my female friends — You bet your life I depend on Jones, he's a problem solver. If he tells you, "I will take care of it," you can take it to the bank!" Continuing when I came to visit Lee the next day in the hospital after the birth of Robert, she passed on to me a thought that had been nagging her ever since Jones received his orders in December of 1965, assigning him to the Vietnam War. "I know! Something just tells me that no matter what Jones does — they are going to send him to that war! I now have to stop thinking about myself and what I am feeling even before it happens — being separated from Jones, and what would I do, and concentrate, on once he goes, to bring him back safely? By safely, God forbid, I mean with one leg, no legs, one arm, no arms, etc. I don't care! As long as I can hold and kiss him. And that he can talk — so I lightly and passionately kiss him on his lips every chance I get, he can tell me, "Love you, Honey!" I have to find a way and I will!"

Lee was right. Jones' delaying tactics worked, until the end of

April 1966, when his evaluation was completed, and the Medical Board, at the Post Hospital, render its decision — "He was fit for duty in Vietnam, and would be deployed there in May of that year. The Board did not consider the Chinese Peoples Army as relevant, because the conflict was with the North Vietnamese. He would not be assigned within twenty miles of a combat zone, which was meaningless — for the entire country was a combat zone, with daily attacks constantly taking place." When Jones arrived in-country, he was immediately given a infantry platoon and sent into the bush to hunt down and kill V.C.! I was visiting when Jones told Lee that he would be going to war next month and would use the time before then to put their house in order. They would put in place the necessary structures to enable Lee to care for herself and their son physically and financially until he returned. When Lee heard the news of the results of the Medical Boards findings, she did not panic, but cried softly in his arms with the baby in her free arm. Jones hugged and attempted to comfort her standing in the center of the kitchen as he held her tightly to his chest, as she told him, "I love you, Honey. I shall find a way to protect you while you are away, and to bring you back safely to me and our baby."

From the time Lee and Jones had passed papers on their new home, through Jones' announcement that he would be going to the war in Vietnam, they, with my assistance, had been making their new house livable. During that time, Jones and I relocated Lee's and Robert's living quarters all to the first floor of their two story home, with Jones giving as the reason, "Everything will be contained downstairs, and there will be no chance of Lee falling down the stairs while I am away — one less thing for me to worry about." Jones wrote in Spanish for Lee in a three-ring loose-leaf notebook, by month and date, for the year he was suppose to be in Vietnam, everything that she needed to know and do with regards to managing and maintaining their house, her finances, herself, Robert, etc. In the notebook that Lee was never without (she carried it from room to room) was information on what to do about medical care for herself and their newborn baby. Along with where to go for assistance in the event that a situation arose that was not covered in her notebook or I could not solve for her. Lee was very fortunate, or Jones was very competent, for she did not have to call on anyone (me once to show her the drain in the basement that her notebook told her to pour a can of Drain-O during October) for assistance while Jones was fighting the war in Vietnam.

In her remembrance of their separation during the war in Vietnam, Lee said that she often relived that day repeatedly in her mind that Jones had to report to the Deployment Center, a United States Air Force Base a few miles from the post were he was stationed, for airlifting to South Vietnam (he disliked flying). Even after receiving orders in December of 1965, through May of 1966, Lee said that Jones had been going out to his duty station on Post. Just as before he received his orders — some times earlier — later than normal when he had to meet with the Medical Board convening at the Post Hospital. On the surface, Lee remembered their lives appeared to all that came in contact with them to be normal, but Lee said that she was consistently reminding herself as she cooked Jones' breakfast each morning, as she made and packed his lunch for him to carry to work, washed and ironed his uniforms, shined his boots and low quarters, kissed him good-bye (trying to keep her lips from trembling with fear), and waved as she watched his car turn out of their street on the way to his duty station on Post. That there was a day coming when she would wave him leaving their street — and it would be a very long time before he returned to the safety of her arms and love. Lee said, that she also did not attempt to fool herself, that the day Jones shipped out, she could be weaving him good-bye forever! He might never return to her alive, but only in one of those shining aluminum boxes she saw on the nightly news that the military returned the dead bodies from the war in Vietnam.

The night before the day Jones shipped out neither of them slept, Lee remembered. Tightly laying in each other's arms as Jones continued to verbally, from memory, again go over the contents of her loose-leaf notebook as she would periodically add, "Okay, Honey I understand. I will. Please don't worry. I love you Honey!" Jones gently talked to her throughout the night, about what all lovers talk about when they are forced to separate. She would now and then kiss him on his lips and bear hairless chest, pat him on the back, run her hand along the contours of his body, and listen to the sound of his voice as she sniffed the smell of his clean body — all to remember him during their forced separation. And thus, Lee said, was how she and Jones spent their last night together before he went off to the war in Vietnam.

Dawn arrived and the day of separation. Lee said that she left their warm bed first to prepare Jones' last breakfast at home. She went into the bathroom off their bedroom to wash, brush her teeth, and changed into a pink, beltless every day dress, kept her slippers on, combed and brushed her hair out — the way Jones liked it, and went into the kitchen. Lee remembered that once Jones got out of bed to shave, shower and change into his Class "A" Green Dress uniform, how all during the time she was fixing his breakfast in the kitchen two rooms away, how acute her hearing was, commenting, "I could hear every move he made — including when he tied the shoelaces in his low quarters!" When he had finished dressing and appeared in the kitchen door in his uniform with all his earned decorations, service medals and qualification badges on his coat over the left pocket, greeting with Lee with a 'Hi! Good Morning! I am ready.' Lee said that to her as she smiled at him standing framed in the kitchen doorway, Jones never looked so beautiful and that frightened her!" She told him, "Sit down. Eat your breakfast," which he did after hanging his coat over the back of a empty chair at the table, as she began to serve his plate with his over easy fried eggs, fried potatoes, lightly cooked bacon, half of a grapefruit, toast, butter, glass of orange juice, and homemade strawberry preserves that she canned Lee canned for him already at his place — as she filled his mug with very strong black coffee. She quickly noticed, after placing a piece of egg on his fork, that Jones could not lift it to his mouth. He began to cry, sitting at attention in his chair, with tears running down his face. With the fork still in his left hand he told her, "I don't want to go! I am so afraid! Not of dying, but for you and our baby! After all of my years of loneliness and never being loved, used yes, but never loved until you loved me with a love that I only believed existed in books and the movies. And now I have to leave you all alone in a strange country and city without knowing if I will ever return to take care of you and our son!" Lee recounted that she knew immediately that she could not allow Jones to leave upset, as she forcefully controlled her own parting emotions and told him, "We will be alright Honey! I promise you! You have provided for our every need while you are away. Come, let me feed you — you have to eat or you will become ill! Remember the night we became engaged? With Jones smiling through his tears, as he nodded yes. Well, I will feed you like that again, Honey." As Lee removed his napkin, she then sat in his lap, with him placing both of his arms around her waist, she cut up all the food on his plate and very slowly fed him. As she placed each fork full of food into his mouth, she very gently kissed him on the lips, while mouthing the words, "I love you Honey! Please try and not to worry. We will be alright! Take care of yourself. Come back to us, we will be waiting!" As he ate, Lee said that Jones regained his composure, stopped crying, as she fed him all the food on his plate. In the telling of Jones' last breakfast before going off to war, tears would be running down Lee's cheeks as she would softly say, "He has suffered so much."

They got up from the table together, Jones went into the bathroom to brush his teeth and to wash his face, while Lee said she cleaned off the table, washed the breakfast dishes and gave a cursory cleaning to the eating area and the kitchen. When Jones came out of the bathroom, he telephoned for a taxi to take him the one hour drive to the United States Air Base Deployment Area. Retrieving his uniform coat from the back of the chair in the eating area, he laid it along with his Garrison Cap on top of his hand held, carry-on bag that he brought form the bedroom which he placed aside the front door.. Then he went into the living room to wait. Lee tells how she went into the baby's room, took him out of his crib — still sleeping and joined Jones on the sofa in the living room. She gave him their son before she sat down just as close to his body as she could and tightly held, dried eyed, onto his arm. Jones also dried eyed, cradled their baby in his left arm as he smiled at their sleeping son, while periodically gently kissing his soft, sleeping face. Lee recounts that they sat in silence for forty-five minutes waiting for the next taxi to arrive. "Silence," for each of them knew that there was nothing else to be said, because the moment they both dreaded had arrived — parting.

The taxi honked. Jones kissed his son on the forehead one last time as he gave the son back to Lee. They both got up from the sofa together, walked slowly to the front door with Jones' arm around Lee's waist, opened the door, with Jones telling the driver, "I will be right there." The driver, seeing Jones' in his uniform, seemed to know where he was going and replied, "Take your time soldier!" Turning to Lee, she said that Jones very gently took her face in both of his large hands, as he kissed her ever so softly on the lips, as he told her — while still holding her face in his hands, "From the first time that I saw you coming down the stairs at San Jose, I have loved you, and that will never change! And that you could ever love me in return, has been the miracle in my life! You take care of yourself and our baby. I will be back! Love you, Honey," as he released her face. With tears beginning to fill her eyes, Lee said that she gave Jones one quick last kiss, telling him, "You take care or yourself as you always remember that you are my life!" Jones put his coat on — buttoned it up, placed his Garrison cap squarely on his head, picked up his bag, went through the open front door, and briskly walked the length of their driveway to the taxi at the curb — turned, smiled, as he waved at Lee standing with the baby in the doorway. He entered the back of the cab, closed the door and the taxi immediately pulled away from the curb into the traffic.

Lee mentioned that she remained motionless in the doorway with the baby still asleep in her arms as hot tears of grief and despair ran down her face as she watched the taxi that was taking Jones on to his first leg of his journey to the war in Vietnam, until it turned left out of their street and passed from view. She then closed and locked the front door, returned the baby to his crib, went into the eating area, and sat down in Jones' chair, placing her head with her hair falling around her face, on her folded arms on the table and cried uncontrollably for hours until the baby woke up crying to be fed.

Although Lee never had a situation that required her to ask for assistance, she was assisted by me and the unsolicited assistance of her next door neighbor — Mrs. Jackson, and the mailman — Mr. Brown. Mrs. Jackson was an elderly widower without any children who made Lee and Jones welcome to the neighborhood when they moved next door in January 1966. When Jones left for the war in Vietnam, Mrs. Jackson would be there for Lee when she needed someone to talk to after days of watching the war in Vietnam on television form the time the station came on the air, until they signed off in the wee hours of the morning.

Mrs. Jackson, unsolicited, confessed to me that she looked upon Lee as the long-desired daughter that she and her late husband never had. Lee had brought a spark of light back into her twilight years, by having someone to be here for and she lived next door.

Mr. Brown, the mailman, after his deliveries were over, when it snowed, he would enlarge the path from the sidewalk to Lee's front and side doors, and stayed with the baby if Lee had to make a quick trip to the neighborhood corner store for milk or baby food, and took Jones' monthly care package to the post office to mail for Lee, along with her daily letter — after delivering Jones' letter each day (Jones and Lee faithfully wrote each other every day while he was in Vietnam). On Sundays, Mr. Brown would go to the post office, knowing there would be a letter there from Jones for Lee, locate it, and took it to Lee, telling me, "So she would have something to comfort her, by knowing that her husband was still okay through his letter."

After seeing me at Lee's home, at least once a week, and learning that I was a long time friend of the family, Mr. Brown and I would chat if I was there when he delivered Lee's mail, and volunteered to tell me this story:

He had married his wife during World War II (WWII), one week before shipping out to the war in Europe as an infantryman. His wife was just eighteen when they married, and his neighbors in their three-decker apartment building took care of her during her pregnancy and after the birth of their first child — a daughter, until he returned from the war. He was always eternally grateful for what those total strangers did for his wife and newborn baby! He also had been waiting to repay, in kind, what was done for his family during WW II.

Now that opportunity presented itself in Mrs. Jones, with her husband fighting in another war, Vietnam, the time had arrived. He gladly, and willingly, (with his wife's approval) did what he could for Mrs. Jones and her baby, because he still remembers how traumatic it was for his wife when he was away fighting in World War II.

I have never forgotten these lines:

"Gratitude is not only memory but the homage of the heart."

— Nathaniel Parker Willis

Lee's former mailman, Mr. Brown, died in his home, sitting in his easy chair on 11 November 1967, the new mailman informed her.

My observations of Lee while Jones did his tour of duty in Vietnam, was that she was fully functionally when it came to the care of the baby — fed on time, washed, changed as soon as it became apparent, played with when awake, took out daily when the weather permitted, taken to all it's check-ups, talked to constantly about his father — who would soon be coming home. Also, when it came to the house, she kept it immaculate (Lee enjoyed being a wife, mother, housewife, lover with her husband, and making every home they owned — beautiful). Lee and Jones new house was a Cape, containing eight rooms — four on each floor, along with a bathroom on each floor, which she cleaned every day, along with cleaning one room each day until she had worked her way through the entire house — including the rooms on the second floor that were not being used! Her only other activities, Lee had beside caring for the baby and the house, she watched television from the time the stations signed on, until they signed off in the early hours of the morning. I was still living in my original hometown — an hour drive away, still working at the bank, and made it a part of my life to check on Lee and the baby at least once a week and spending meaningful time with them both. Holidays, I had to force Lee, to spend them with me and my family, telling her, "It was no time for her to be alone, and that we all loved and thought of her and the baby as family, and she had to come with me!" When she often adamantly proclaimed, "I am not going! And you can't make me!" I would look at her sheepishly, and very softly reply, "If you don't come with me, I will write and tell Jones." Lee would look at me angrily for a moment, then smile as she would tell me, "You are bad!" My response would always be, "I know," and we would both laugh as to what ends I was prepared to go — to assure that I was able to get her and the baby out among those that loved and cared for them.

Jones had placed Lee on a food plan, that only required her once a month to telephone her order in to the plans office to include dog food for their new dog — Sooner II. Lee's order would be delivered shortly thereafter, thereby not requiring her to shop weekly or to worry about having enough food for her, the baby and the dog. Lee had a brand-new seventeen cubic foot upright freezer that she stored her monthly ordered perishable items. But now and then, there would be some food item that Lee needed that was not on the food plans list, and would walk the four blocks to the supermarket (Sometimes with the baby in his carriage — depending upon the weather) to purchase the item. Very annoyed with herself, Lee would recount how she would walk in the door of the supermarket and go completely blank! She didn't know why she was there or what she wanted!" Lee mentioned how she would attempt to remember what she wanted unsuccessfully, turn around, leave the supermarket and return home empty handed. Lee would repeat the supermarket exercise two more times — with the same results. She even wrote on paper what she wanted and once she reached the market, she forgot that she had a list in her handbag. Each time, there was the same results, before telephoning me, giving me the names of what she wanted, asking me to buy it, and bring it to her — which I would do. Lee remained in that mental state with regards to shopping, the duration of Jones' absence.

Jones has always been very lucky in the mongrel bitch's he has been able to obtain over the years — all very intelligent. They all knew what was expected of them as members of the Jones family without any type of special or professional training. Sooner II continued in that mode. During the winter of 1966, I went by Lee's to check on her and the baby after a very heavy storm, in order to shovel her out so that there would be a means of access to the house in the event of an emergency, and found a path already shoveled (the snow storm occurred late at night, so I knew that it had not been Mr. Brown that had done the shoveling), from the sidewalk to the house. I hurried towards the open side door. I found Lee unconscious, laying half in — half out of the side door of her home, dressed in heavy winter clothing, wool lined hat tied to her head, fur lined gloves on her hands, and wool lined rubber boots on her feet — lightly covered with drifting snow! Sitting at her head, inside the door, also covered with drifting snow, was Sooner II guarding Lee! I pulled Lee by her shoulders into the house, closed the door as I told Sooner II, "Good girl! Good girl! Then, I ran quickly to the baby's room to check on him, and found him asleep. I returned to Lee, still laying on the floor and started to revive her. Once Lee regained her consciousness, I helped her to the sofa and after removing her coat and boots, (I had already removed her hat and gloves), I had her lay down as I covered her with blankets that I had taken from her bedroom. As I waited for the water to boil on the stove to make her tea. I asked Lee as I attempted to make her comfortable by placing a pillow that I had taken off of her bed under her head, "What happened?" The first thing she said was, "Don't tell Jones! Thanks!" Then began to tell me that she had went to shovel a path to the sidewalk because the snow was so high. It was for an emergency so she would be able to get out quickly. So I started to shovel, and once I reached the sidewalk it must have exhausted me, for once I started back to the house, I felt faint by the time that it took me to reach side door (thank God I left it opened) before I could get inside the house — that's the last thing

LEE

I can remember." I told her very firmly, "Don't you ever shovel again! You know better! You also know, that I always come by to shovel you out when it snows, and if, for some reason, I can't come, you know that I will send one of my brothers or sisters' husbands to shovel for you! Okay? With Lee nodding her head, Yes. You could have frozen to death out there! I will not tell Jones." I then told Lee how I had found Sooner II, sitting at her head, also covered with snow, guarding her. Lee smiled, calling to the dog to come to her. When Sooner II arrived from her mat in the kitchen, she laid her head on Lee's chest, as Lee rubbed her back and sides, and scratched her between the ears (with her tail going a mile a minute), as she told her, "You truly are a good girl! You protect your Mama, even without having to be told! You love me as I love you! Good girl! Good dog!" I left them together as I went into the kitchen to make Lee's tea.

Sooner II truly was a good dog and lived a loving, happy, healthy, active seventeen of our years. Then she unexplainable took sick for the first time, problems with her lungs that the Veterinarian could not treat. After two days, Jones had to put her to sleep. We all cried and mourned the passing of Sooner II. Good girl! Good dog!

Jones received Combat Pay, once he went to the war in Vietnam, and when Lee saw the increase by that amount in her first monthly allotment check, from the United States Army after Jones arrived in Vietnam (the check arrived before Jones letter, telling Lee that it included the combat pay), she thought it was a mistake and asked me, "What's it for?" I explained it to her. Lee became very agitated, as she angrily protested, "I will never spend Jones' Combat Pay! It's blood money! I will save it until he returns, and he can do with it as he pleases. If I spent it, it would be as if I am profiting from his misery, and all of those who are suffering with him and being killed in that war!" I will not do that. How can a supposedly civilized and Christian nation pay its military something called "Combat Pay," for it cheapens their sacrifice and death — whatever happens to you, we paid you extra!" I made no comment to Lee's outburst about the morality of Combat Pay, but it made me think about it, arriving at no definitive answer — one way or the other. Lee did place Jones' Combat Pay in a savings account at their bank — never spending a penny of it, where it remained the entire time he was in Vietnam.

> "In every parting there is an image of death."
>
> *George Eliot*

17.

WAR

Lee, even with her often vocal anger at God, and her public pronouncements about the same subject — that she thought Him mean, she always, in my opinion, had remained a firm believer in Catholicism. Believer meaning you followed the rules laid down by the church as they pertained to your daily personal behavior and towards others. And always that God would protect you against the evils of the world and those that would attempt to harm you. When that often did not happen in Lee's life when she was growing up on San Andres Island, Republic de Colombia, Republic de Panama, then in the United States, Lee became very frustrated and angry with her God for not keeping his promises as she had been taught all of her life.

In line with being a believer, Lee's Patron Saint was Saint Jude Thaddeus. And in all of their homes, from the very first one that they rented, then purchased, the first thing you saw upon entering their vestibule (all their homes had them), was an alter covered with a white tablecloth containing St. Jude's statue, and two small vases containing flowers. Today, St. Jude's alter is an antiques cedar 1890 hope chest. It is covered with a red cloth to the floor, with a white crotcheted alter cloth made by Lee, covering it. The twelve inch statue stands in the center of the altar with the two flower vases on either side — containing fresh flowers that Lee grew in her garden during the summer, artificial flowers during the winter months. There are also several very artful perpetual memberships in a number of spiritual alliances for deceased members of the family and friends that surround the statue and vases in semicircle. What is noteworthy about Lee's altar to St. Jude is the three electric candles on display which remain lit 24 hours a day. Two of the candles are normal size which Lee said were there for favors that she had asked of St. Jude, and he had granted, for the two children — without identifying them. The remaining candle is marble based and brass, with a multicolored stain globe standing sixteen inches high! This was the first one that St. Jude received from Lee, saying when she placed it upon his alter that it was for fulfilling a favor she asked for.

It was natural, when Lee would talk about her concerns to bring Jones back safely from the Vietnam War, she would turn to her Patron Saint. Lee told me, "Saint Jude is not greedy, like Saint Anthony! You can ask him for a favor, make him the simplest promise and he will grant it. Before Jones went to the Vietnam War, I asked St. Jude a favor concerning Jones' safe return and made him two promises while quoting a part of his prayer, 'come to my assistance in this great need that I may receive the consolation and succor of heaven in all my necessities, tabulations, and suffering.'"

Lee obtained from somewhere, a wallet size prayer to St. Jude, gave it to Jones, and told me that she made him swear on Lester's departed soul, that he would always carry it with him (which he still does). He also had to recite the prayer once a day while he was fighting in the war in Vietnam. On the third page of the St. Jude prayer, that Lee gave Jones in 1966 just before he left for the war in Vietnam, in Lee's distinctive script, still legible, is this message of her love, "Honey, I love you with all my heart! Always remember there is only one world for me and its your love. — Lee"

All during the time that Jones was doing his duty in Vietnam,

Lee wrote him faithfully everyday, and he her. During the war, Lee explained, that it was through her letters, although she had a lifelong disdain for writing, it did not matter when writing to Jones, because that was when she became alive. Mentioning that what she did during the day as it related to their baby, house-work, and every day necessities to keep her mind occupied, was done in remote. After she had contemplated her chores for the day, put the baby to bed, and the last television station had signed off for the night, was when Lee said that after taking her bath, changed into her nightgown, she would read the letter that she was sure to have received that day. Sitting propped up with pillows at her lap desk, reading Jones' always lengthy letter, it was as if he was right beside her there in their bed.

Lee would always smile as she remembered the letters from Vietnam, explaining that in every letter he would always include an imaginative narrative that would make her laugh. She knew that it was his way of taking her mind off of the danger he was in. As soon as she would finish reading the letter, Lee said that she would open the small drawer in her lap desk, take out a pen and paper, and answer her lover. Lee readily admitted that her letters were not as lengthy as Jones' — but he never complained, telling her, "As long as you write and love me, Honey, my world is complete!" Lee also, laughing, remembered how Jones would take each sentence of her letters replying with lengthily narra-tives of each. He told Lee in one of his letters once, "I write to you the way I do, because when I place pen to paper, you become alive to me for that moment, and I desire to keep you near just as long as I can for I love and miss you so, Honey!" Lee said that when she answered Jones' letter, she told him that it was the same for her when she wrote to him. She understood his love and longing for them to be together because it was also her wish, and not to worry — it would happen!

Lee mentioned this to me only once which she said was

included in one of her letters in a moment of desperation and it has always remained with me:

"Any women that has had to see their man go off to war, any war, and the possibility that he might be killed — for her, it's like the irrevocable entry into the pit of despair!"

When Lee told me the above in 1966, I made no comment, just listened in silence. Truthfully, I then, did not understand nor fully appreciate what she was feeling, but do now. To no longer, because of separation or death, have someone that matters, not near, is irrevocable despair, because you can not change the cause for the separation nor change death into life!

Lee, along with all of us that were writing Jones in Vietnam, always attempted to write him upbeat letters. Upbeat meaning that we discussed plans of what we were going to do together when he returned home — never any conversation about the possibility of him not returning home. Nothing about how the war was form this end only answered those few questions he now and then asked — an abundance of good news about individuals he knew (no mention of those we knew had been killed in Vietnam) — who was dating whom, engaged, married including pictures of the wedding when available. We also sent pictures of the new additions to our families. We also tried to let him know we were there for him and his family. Lee, concerning pictures, kept Jones pictorially informed of their sons activities, allowing him to see how well he was growing. During the summer months, when I was not available, Lee would take the baby in his carriage or her arms to the common and ask a total strangers to please take a picture of the two of them together with her camera to send to her husband in Vietnam. Her offer was never turned down!

During the war in Vietnam, Lee told me that she never found it difficult to write Jones upbeat letters, because that was always how she felt when writing to him — happy! Lee also confessed that she never harbored doubts that Jones would not return from that war in Vietnam, alive and to the safety of her arms. St. Jude would grant her favors to get the two promises she made him, and with pleading anguish in her voice, said, "It just has to be!" Lee also mentioned that if she did not think and feel that Jones would return alive, she would very quickly go completely out of her mind! Lee also held a fatalistic view about her own life. She thought that if Jones did not return from the war in Vietnam to her alive, she would die because he was her reason for living. I then, as I do now, believe she would have.

Contained in Lee's locked metal document box that Jones gave me several years ago, before I started this book about Lee's life, were two letters sent to their baby son, Robert, from his father in Vietnam along with instructions for Lee to read them to him. For some reason, known only to her, she saved these two letters out of all the others from Vietnam that she destroyed.

"22 December, 1966
Robert:
Well, this year, I will not have the joy and pleasure of seeing your face, this your very first Christmas!

I know that you know that I am far away from you in a stranger country than ours, for your mother tells me that you pick up the telephone headpiece to call me — telling me in your baby talk to hurry home. Well, my son, believe me, I am hurrying!

It is my wish that this Christmas of 1966 shall be the very last where any of us will be separated.

Now Robert, by being the first born that lived, and thereby the oldest, you must always lookout for any brothers or sisters you may have, and your mother — in all things! As you grow, I don't believe your responsibility as the oldest will be a problem for you, because your mother tells me in all her letters what a good and loving boy you are.

It is my Christmas wish for you that if you ever have to leave your family and home to fight in another war, do it as a man. Don't complain as so many so-called men I hear are doing there, while remembering that the country is worth saving — even with all its faults, and along with your mother who loves you! I can not tell you enough about the loving goodness of your mother, for every day that you live, you are the beneficiary of that love and goodness. Like today, for it is she, your mother, that has done everything in my absence, to make your Christmas a normal one. As normal as one can be without a father. You and I are blessed to have her in our lives, you as your mother, and I, as my wife!

So my son, keep calling for me on the telephone, and one day soon, you will look up — and there your loving and caring father will be! When that day arrives, we will remain together in love and joy, never to be separated again!

Much love,
Dad"

"January 1967
My Son:
This is coming to you from many, many miles away and a place, whose name, even I, can not pronounce!

Happy first birthday! May this be the last birthday that we will ever have to spend away from each other. May this day, your day, also be a happy one for you — and somehow, I know that it will be, for your mother will make it so! I look forward to your birthday pictures.

Even though I am not able to be there with you, I am happy just the same in the knowledge of what this day represents for your mother and I — that you have been the love and joy of our lives for one full year! May there be many more. My birthday present to you today is: may you always grow in love and happiness as you are today.

It is also my sincere wish, on this your first birthday, that when you become a man, you will never have to leave your loving family and home for the reason I had to — fighting in a war!

My son, always love and honor your mother for without her, none of us can make it! I love you Robert, and sincerely wish you, my little one, once again, a happy, happy birthday!

Love you,
Your Daddy"

I believe that Lee saved the above letters to their son, in the event that Jones was killed during that war in Vietnam. By saving the letters, and Jones was killed, Robert would always have something personal, and in his own words, from his father to remember him by.

The war in Vietnam came into Lee's home and the American public nightly through television. She had one Sunday night, a horrific and terrifying experience, when Jones just happened to be in Saigon. According to Lee, while Jones was fighting the war in Vietnam, periodically, he would be required to leave the bush and go to Saigon (never giving the reason why in his letters, or even today). While in Saigon, after conducting whatever business he was in the city for. He would go to the USO (United Service Organization) club in downtown Saigon, and call via the M.A.R.S. network Lee in the States. This particular Sunday (stateside), Jones reached Lee at 6 A.M., stateside time and they had a loving and joyful half-hour reunion via the telephone. During their conversation, Jones casually mentioned that he was staying in the living quarters (huts) at Saigon Airport for transit personal, and would be returning to the bush, first light, Monday (his time). On the Sunday nightly news, there was a reporter from one of the major television networks, who was -on-the-scene, with damaged, destroyed, burning huts in the background, with dead bodies laying about, wounded residents in the background, calling for help. He was saying, "That the Saigon Airport had sustained a 4.2 mortar attack and several living quarters within the transit personal compound had sustained numerous direct hits, resulting in many dead and wounded!"

Lee telephoned me, hysterically, "Saigon Airport has been attacked! Jones is there! He called me this morning from Saigon!" I told her, "I am coming," and hung up the telephone. Called my youngest sister, and told her to meet me at Lee's. When I arrived, I found Lee sitting on the sofa, tightly holding the frightened baby in her arms, with a dazed expression on her face, as I asked, "What happened?" Lee told me the story of Jones' call earlier that day, etc., as I attempted to reassure her, "He might not have been in his hut when the attack occurred, or for that matter, even on the base! You never know!" Then my sister arrived, and took the still frightened baby from Lee's arms, as she told her, "We both will stay over. I will take care of the baby, and I know this may sound stupid, but try and not to worry! Whatever happens, we will always be here for you and Robert!" Lee never said a word, and with the blank expression on her face, there was no way to determine if she even heard what my sister had told her! With the baby out of her arms, Lee remained on the sofa with both of her arms limply laying to her sides. She was staring straight ahead, not uttering a sound, which was the way my sister and I left her at 1:00 A.M., when we retired to our bedrooms for the night.

My sister and I, woke to the smell of bacon, eggs, pancakes, homemade biscuits, home-fries, coffee and tea. After washing and dressing, we joined Lee in the kitchen and found her preparing the breakfast whose smell awoken us. Greeting us with a smiling, cheerful, "Good Morning. I am fixing your breakfast, the table is already set in the eating room, so please take your places at the table. Jones is all right, he was not hurt or killed during the attack last night at Saigon Airport," then turned back to the food on the stove. Both my sister and I looked at each other silently, astonished at the amazing change that had come over Lee, as we took our places at the table.

After breakfast, as my sister cleaned up the kitchen and eating room, while Lee bathed, dressed, and fed the baby, while thanking us for coming when she panicked. Lee also told my sister and I, that we could return to our homes, "She was and would be alright! Jones was safe!" We suggested that one of us remain with her, just in case — for you never know! Lee gave us one of her Mona Lisa smiles, and thanked us for the offer, as she told us, "Believe me, it's not necessary. Jones is all right — I know it!" In unison, we said, "If you are sure, and that's what you want, then we will leave. But if you need us, just call!" Still smiling, Lee gave each of us, with the baby in her arms, a one arm hug and kiss on the cheek as she bid us farewell, "I know! Thanks again for being there when I needed you. I will never forget what you did for me last night — by coming and staying over. Your caring thoughtfulness was sincerely appreciated and I love you both!" We made our good-byes and left.

As my sister and I walked the lengthy front yard to the curb where our cars were parked, I asked her, "Do you think Lee is in denial?" My sister replied, "If ever there was a woman that is completely spiritually united with her man, it's Lee! If she says that Jones was not killed or hurt, then I believe she knows what she is talking about!" We reached our cars, said good-bye to each other, got in our cars and drove to our homes. Lee, with the baby in her arms, waved good-bye to us from her front door.

Lee and my sister were right! Three days after the attack upon Saigon Airport, Lee received a letter from Jones (dated the day of the attack — for he had heard of the V.C.'s actions when he reached his unit in the bush), explaining why he was not in his hut when the 4.2 mortar shells began to fall, with Lee immediately passing on her good news to me and my sister. What Jones wrote Lee was that after finishing his M.A.R.S. telephone call to her, he did return to his hut at Saigon Airport, and laid down on his cot to take a nap. He had not been asleep fifteen minutes when he had what he called a voice in his head experience. It told him to return to his unit in the bush — now! He said that he immediately sat up and got out of his cot, packed his gear, checked his weapons to assure that they were fully loaded, went to the flight line, and hopped a ride on a United States Air Force plane lying into the area where his outfit was deployed. Which was how he escaped the mortar attack on the Saigon Airport. How did Lee know this?

Lee often mentioned to me and other of her friends, how she thanked God and St. Jude that Jones was not wounded again in Vietnam, only contracted malaria and developed high blood pressure, and later learned that he was infected with agent orange. Lee said that she was happy, ready, and willing to nurse him back to health each time he was adversely affected by his afflictions. "Only once since returning from Vietnam has Jones been hospitalized because of his malaria when I could not break his fever. My nursing efforts are nothing and a small price to pay just to have him alive! All I asked of St. Jude was to return Jones to me alive, and he did! I will be eternally grateful to St. Jude as long as I live, and will pay homage to him at every opportunity."

> "Dost thou know the fate of soldiers? —
> They are but ambition's tools, to cut a
> way for her unlawful ends. — And when
> they are worn, hacked, hewn with con-
> stant service, thrown aside to rust in
> peace and rot in hospitals."
>
> *Thomas Southerne*

18.

APART

Apart from what Lee frequently told me in our many conversations about her never ending love for Jones and concerns about their children, our mutual friends, her fears of becoming disable — in what she called a "cold coma" — during our long friendship, I privately and silently made some observations about her's and Jones' long-loving healthy relationship that proved to be right on the mark! What I observed and remembered, in my opinion, demonstrated just how strong, deep, and secure their love was for each other despite the constant adversity that seemed to persistently pursue them throughout their marriage, above all, Lee's need to love and be loved by Jones.

In June of 1967, Lee received word from Jones in Vietnam that he would be rotated out of country that month. Lee, overjoyed, immediately telephoned all of us and you could hear the happiness in her voice coming through the telephone handset, along with the relief in telling the good news. "Jones is coming home this month! Talk to you later," then hung up. When I made my weekly visit, after learning of Jones' pending return, I found Lee literally floating on air and radiating happiness in her every word and gesture as she busied herself giving the house a top to bottom cleaning. She opened the closed rooms on the second floor that had been closed during Jones' absence. While making me welcome with my usual cup of coffee, Lee told me, "Isn't it wonderful! He' coming home! I knew he would! Saint Jude did not disappoint me and he granted me my favor." When Jones actually arrived home the first electric candle went on Jude's alter in the vestibule. I then knew what Lee's promise to Saint Jude was when Jones went to the war in Vietnam — return him safely and she would give him a continuous candle.

Later, during that same visit, over dinner that Lee prepared and served (when you visited Lee's home, no matter the hour, she feed you, and you had to eat), she became reflective. As we ate our meal, she told me, "Do you remember how I had often told you, that if Jones did not return from that war in Vietnam alive, I would die?" "Yes, I remember," I spoke softly. "Well, what I did not tell you then, was that is Jones was killed, then I was going to give our baby to my best friend in New York City to raise, then kill myself!" I stopped eating out of shock and horror at what Lee had considered during commenting, "Oh no! How could you ever think such a thing?" Continuing, Lee replied, "I would have, for without Jones, I have no life! Before he went to Vietnam, Jones had told me that, if he was killed over there, I was still young, attractive, and their son would need a father growing up. I might meet another man that I could love, and if that happened, remarry, for it would not in any way reflect negatively upon the love they had for each other when he was alive. I slapped his face (the first and only time), there in his den, just as hard as I could! Angrily, telling him, "Never! Don't you understand? You and only you are my life! Without you, believe me, Honey, life holds no meaning for me! If I could find a way, I would always keep you home and near me, because when you are away, my life is on hold until you return. Nothing holds any interest or meaning for me when you are not around, or I know that you are not coming to me. You are the only man that had ever laid on top of me, and no other man shall! You are the only man I can ever love! So don't you ever again, tell me that if something happens to you, to remarry, because I will not! I love you Honey! Only you!" Lee said by the time she finished her angry outburst, she was crying uncontrollably, and was sorry the she had slapped Jones in his face, telling him so. Adding, that she reacted the way she did because she was so mad by the very thought that he would ever think that she would allow another man to become interment with her — even if he was dead!

Lee said that she gently nudged Jones towards his chair and had him sit down, then sitting in his lap, she began to kiss him about the head, face, and lips, as she attempted to rub her red hand print off his cheek as she repeatedly told Jones, "I am so sorry, Honey for slapping you. I would never hurt you!" Lee said that Jones' arms went around her waist as he returned her kisses as he told her, "It's all right , Honey. You did not hurt me. I love you and do understand."

[I believe that what Lee convinced Jones of that night in his den before going to that war in Vietnam with her angry outburst for suggesting she remarry if he was killed, "For the love of a woman is a shoot, not a seed, and flourishes most vigorously when engrafted on the love which is rooted in the breast of another." — Arthur Wills Colton]

It was not until July of 1967 that Jones finally arrived home. On the way from the war, Jones' malaria, along with his Vietnam-acquired high blood pressure flared up, he was immediately hospitalized once the airplane landed at Travis AirForce Base in California. When asked, once June had passed, why no Jones? Lee would happily reply, "I don't care how long it takes him to get home, he's in the United States — and safe! If push comes to shove, then I will lock up the house, take the baby and Sooner II and go to him in California."

It did not come to that, for in the third week of July, Jones signed himself out of the hospital and arrived home. It was not until the end of August that Lee gave a Welcome-Home party for Jones that was well attended by I, and his many friends. We were so happy to see him return safely from the Vietnam War. When I first saw Jones talking to a group of his friends, the first thing that I noticed was how gray his hair had become (he had went to Vietnam with no gray in his hair), and how ill and grunt he looked. After our too quick exchange of greeting, to allow others their time with him, we made plans to get together just us two. It was for a long talk, which we later did, and again, as in after the Korean War, Jones never talked about what he had done or saw while fighting in the war, and I knew not to inquire. We had our long talk before Jones reported to his new duty station in New Jersey.

During Jones' Welcome Home party, Lee was elated just to watch him — no matter what she was doing or who she was talking to, she would consistently glace in his direction, happy to know that he was safe and near! When we had a few moments alone, without asking, Lee told me, "I know he doesn't look too good, but I don't care and am not worried. Just give me a few months. I will feed and gently love him back to the Jones we all knew before he went away. Just you watch, wait, and you will see!" And it was as Lee described. I learned from watching Lee lovingly nursing Jones back to his mental and physical health, that her total reason for being, was truly the love and welfare of her husband. As I observed Lee in her wifely duties of caring for Jones, I remembered, ["To pursue joy is to lose it. The only way to get it is to follow steadily the path of duty, without thinking of joy, and then, like sheep, it comes most surely unsought." — Andrew Cunningham Maclaren]

Lee had never liked the United States Army (nor any nations military), or Jones being in it, but understood after they returned to the States why Jones wanted to do his twenty years and a day in the army. He told Lee that once he retired, his retirement pay would pay the mortgage on their home, and according to Lee, it always did. She agreed to him doing the time without making his service a problem nor giving him grief about it because he was doing something she disliked. Problem, forcing him to chose between her or the Army. They had former military friends whose wives had forced them to chose — they got out of the service, and never stopped talking about why they left. Grief, always complaining about the substandard pay, twelve to sixteen hour days, six day work week, long and frequent absences from home — in the field training, weekend and holiday duty, etc. But when they shipped Jones to the war in Vietnam knowing that he was due to retire in a few months, Lee's dislike turned to disgust! Claiming that the army was attempting to kill Jones to keep from paying him his retirement pay! Until the day Jones actually retired from the United States Army, Lee's loathing for it and what it stood for intensified! What finally converted Lee into a hater of all things military the remaining years of her life was, "I discovered many years after the event the circumstances surrounding Jones' retirement form the Army — it almost didn't happen."

The revelation concerning Jones' retirement form the army came about when I innocently happened to ask Lee, "Aren't you now glad that Jones did his twenty years and a day?" Instantly, Lee's demeanor changed from pleasantness to anger, as she loudly replied, "No!" And this is the story she told me:

"No one (above all, the United States Army) can ever seem to understand, or for that matter, even care about the anguish and fear I lived through. The entire time Jones was fighting in the war, I was terrified, along with all of the other women of this country that had loved ones in Vietnam. I remembered the life I laid and hated it!

When Jones returns to the State, where does the Army assign him — to New Jersey! To a make-work job, when there was a position in the Fort for his skills, grade, and time in service right in the state we were then living in. He asked to be assigned there one month before leaving Vietnam.

Why New Jersey? The Army had family quarters there for Jones. The Army knew that he had a family and had been separated from them for more than fifteen months, but what they did not think Jones knew, but he did, had he brought his family to New Jersey and utilized the government family quarters, the US Army would have automatically extended his service by one year! Do you know what that would have meant? Jones would have been sent back to that Hell in Vietnam before his involuntary extended year was up!

From the time Jones submitted his retirement papers immediately upon reporting to New Jersey, he had nothing but problems, which was something that he never had before in any of his many past assignments.

Problem — the First Sergeant of his unit over R.H.I.P. (Rank Has Its Privileges), seventeen years in grade as a senior sergeant (more time in grade than his first sergeant) and Jones refused to perform duties beneath his rank. He was scheduled by the First Sergeant to be placed in charge of a detail preparing a barracks of men for a I.G. (Inspectors General) inspection and would not do it. Demanded and obtained private living quarters in the barracks (due to Jones by Army Regulations, his rank and time in grade and service). Refused to stand in any formation that the First Sergeant called (didn't have to, again by Army regulations — retirement papers submitted and over twenty years service). The First Sergeant never stopped through petty annoyances (calling Jones to his office — then telling him that he had forgotten what he wanted to see him about, not passing on information about the status of Jones' retirement to him — Jones had to do everything concerning his retirement himself) — basically attempting to make Jones' last days in the Army just as difficult as he could! Jones gave the First Sergeant as good as he got (telling him to his face that he was a brown nose and an ass kisser) and ostracized him as an individual that he would not speak to!

Problem — his female Major Boss, at Post Headquarters. Where Jones was assigned performing a make-work job, rewriting (making no changes), the Post Training Regulations until his retirement papers returned from Washington, DC — approved or disapproved. The Major objected to Jones' taking three day passes every week. He left the Post every Thursday evening after work, to travel home to be with his family. She called him on the carpet one Monday morning one month into his assignment to her G-3 Department, after Jones had returned from another three day pass and proceeded to chew him out! She ended the session with, "You will not take anymore three day passes unless approved by me! Do you hear me loud and clear, soldier?" Jones told the Major, very calmly, (even though she had insulted him by calling him 'soldier' when she should have called him Sergeant) "I don't need your approval to go on three day pass, Madam! I am retiring! Army Regulations allow me to go on pass without any restrictions," he quoted from memory, for the Major, the regulation, paragraph, year, and page number. Jones then told me that he saluted did an about face and left the Major's office. Needless to say, she became Jones' nemesis thereafter around Post Headquarters. She bad mouthed him to her boss, and anyone else that would listen to her claim that Sergeant Jones was very difficult to get alone with.

Problem — after taking his retirement medical examination, Jones was told later by a staff member of the Retirement Medical Examination Detachment (RMED), located in the Post Hospital that his examination records had been misplaced and that they were diligently looking for them. Jones panicked, for without submission of the results of the medical examination, his retirement paperwork could and would not be processed by DoA (Department of the Army) for evaluation concerning his request to retire. After being informed that his examination records had been misplaced, Jones said that he returned to the RMED at 0100 hours and quietly searched the office for his medical examination records, and after a hour and a half search found them under the desk blotter of the OIC (Officer in Charge). He took the records, left the hospital, and mailed them the next morning to DoA. Jones never heard another word form anyone in RMED concerning his misplaced records. It was then that Jones knew that someone (his First Sargeant, his boss — the female major or an unknown) was out to screw him by delaying submission of his retirement medical examination records and thereby his retirement.

Problem — one month before he was to retire, the Colonel in charge of the Headquarters Unit that Jones was assigned, called him to his Headquarters, a Monday, and told him he had some bad news to give him. Orders had been received over the weekend reassigning him back to the war in Vietnam. Shocked, but very calmly, Jones told the Colonel, "Sir, I believe there has been a mistake. I am retiring, and have been placed on Special Orders," quoting the number." The Colonel then verified what he had been told by Jones by telephoning DoA. Once confirmed, he told Jones," I am sorry, it does appear that a mistake has been made by someone in our Post Relocation Section. Disregard what I mentioned about being reassigned to Vietnam, and good luck in your retirement. Dismissed!"

Jones left the Colone's office in a cold sweat and, totally dejected — he could not believe what was happening to him! He had only been in the States for two months, and now the Army, his Army for over twenty years was attempting to send him back to that Hell in Vietnam! Had it not been for a Sergeant friend in the Post Communication Center giving him his Retirement Special Order Number as a paid favor, he would have been in thirty days, on his way back to that war in Vietnam!

Each time that Jones came home on his weekly three day passes, and told me of that weeks problems he sank into despair over the realization of what the United States Army really thought of his faithful and horrible service — they cared less! All they wanted were bodies to feed to that killing machine in Vietnam! "Done much, accomplished little," I thought each time that Jones would tell me of his problems at his retirement assignment. I would silently listen until he finished, then I would loving and gently hug and kiss Jones as I told him, "Honey, I love you and remember — in the end, you were always one step ahead of those ungrateful people! I, and others, and above all you, know that you are a good soldier. You have no reason to feel ashamed, angry yes, of the way you are being treated by those who are not fit to clean your boots! Soon, we will be free of them all!"

Jones took me and the baby to New Jersey for his last day in the United States Army. He had his retirement parade, and as I sat on the reviewing stand with our son in my lap, I did so with anger! Angry, as to how my husband's last days of service were maligned, as I watched the very impressive retirement ceremony — with Jones the only one retiring, standing in front of the assembled Post Headquarters Officers, taking the salute of the marching troops passing in review as their farewell to him.

After the retirement ceremony and parade was over, we immediately left for home. A month into his retirement, Jones learned that his female Major Boss had organized a retirement party for him at the officer's club. Driving home, Jones was more silent than usual, and I did not attempt to engage him in conversation, because I knew he was bitter and angry at the Army and himself. Bitter at the Army because they held his faithful and honorable service in such contempt. Angry at himself because he had sacrificed his youth and health for nothing!

Sitting beside him as he drove us home, periodically, I would lean over and kiss his cheek or I would gently rub his right thigh with by left hand. As I held the baby in my lap with my right arm around him, I told Jones, 'It's over, Honey! You made it! We are free. Your service was not a failure — you did much good when many ran from their responsibility to the nation, you stood and fought! Love you, Honey!' Jones would give me a half smile as he continued his silent drive home."

I listened in sadness to all Lee had to tell me about the events surrounding my friends retirement from the United States Army and thought to myself, "It's enough to drive one to drink!" I then asked Lee, "Had you ever had any problems with Jones adjusting to civilian life after he had retired from the Army?" Lee replied, laughing, "No, never! I give him plenty of TLC (Tender Loving Care) — I am always ready!" I loudly joined Lee in her laughter over her joyful reply to my question.

After I returned to my home, sitting all alone in my den, in the wee hours of the morning, thinking about the negative events of Jones' last days in the United States Army as told to me by Lee, I thought about the quotation, ["Ignorance, poverty, (Jones) and vanity make many soldiers." — Arthur Zimmer Mann]

It was Jones' ten year pursuit of a college degree, that Lee's eternal love and support for her husband, again, manifested itself in two situations that I still remember today.

The first manifestation was the results of the Vietnam GI Educational Bill passed by congress. It was not like the GI Bill of World War II (WW II) which paid tuition, books, and gave the former service member a living allowance. To qualify for the Vietnam GI Bill, nights, the former service member had to take at least four credit hours at an accredited school. In 1967, when Jones started his program, it cost $80 per credit hour, $320 of which the government would only give the student $40 a credit hour towards the tuition leaving a shortfall of $160! It has been claimed by some, that Congress wrote and enacted the Vietnam

G.I. Bill that way as their means of protesting the Vietnam War —
by not completely funding it! No books or living allowance as in
the WWII GI Bill. The shortfall for Jones had to be made up out
of his then small salary for ten years (to include the combat pay
that Lee had saved). Which meant that the standard of living of
the Jones family was just barely above the poverty line, caused by
the sums that had to be spent for his education. And it was Lee,
that for ten years, never owned a piece of new outer apparel
while making the clothing she had, last by repairing them when
she could.

I walked in on Lee one afternoon, sitting at the kitchen table,
with her sewing basket, darning the seat of a pair of her very
worn cotton panties. Embarrassingly I asked, "Do you really
have to do that? Throw them away and buy a new pair!" Lee told
me, "Yes, I have to darn them, because I can't afford to spend .98¢
on a new pair. With Jones in school and what he has to pay out of
pocket to acquire his education, money will be tight until he fin-
ishes. In order to stand any chance for advancement at the bank
— the Personal Officer told Jones when they took him on as a
Management trainee, "If you intended to make banking your
career, you will have to have a college degree." "I don't mind
what I now have to do (think before I spend our money), for this
is my way of helping out, and I know it will not always be this
way." And Lee was right. Three months after obtaining his college degree in 1977, Jones acquired a position at another bank,
increasing his annual income immediately by $5800! Thereafter,
the American Dream became a reality for Lee and the children.
There were no wants for Lee and the children — they became
upper middle class. For Jones nothing changed except that he
had more responsibility, he was the boss, and continued to drive
his junk cars. I, and all his friends used to continually tease him
about driving his junk cars with, "It's good that you take the train
in to work each day, for, if your boss at the bank ever saw what

you call a car, he would fire you on the spot for projecting a poor image of the bank." "That's the best an Officer of our Bank can afford?" Jones would always laugh loudly saying, "No he wouldn't! He hired me for what he knows I have in my brain about being a Boston Banker, and my ability as same, not the image I project. Boston Banker — you go to any other banker and ask him or her, How much is two and two? And you will receive the answer — four. Put that same question to a Boston Banker and you will receive the answer, How much do you want it to be?" Loud laughter. Ability — I can look at the totals of a column figures on a printout that contains an error and instantly tell the Department Head where and what it is! That's why my boss is not worried about my image. More laughter. It took Lee ten years to convince Jones that he should buy a new automobile, with him bemoaning the loss of his beloved junk cars! We all laughed when Jones starts to tell nostalgic stories about his former junk cars, interrupting him with, "They were nothing but rust-buckets!" Having the last word, Jones would counter, "Yes, but they ran."

Continuing that day in her kitchen, Lee mentioned how Jones needed and wanted his college education, and that was fine with her. Adding, that anything which makes him happy, makes her happy. I asked, "Does Jones know that you have been reduced to darning the seats of your worn-out panties because he is pursuing his college education?" Very sternly, with fire in her eyes, Lee replied, "No, he doesn't know, and don't you dare tell him! He has enough on his plate as it is: providing for us, his job, school, studying, maintaining our home, keeping his car running, and being there every time for me and our children — no matter what. I will manage." I didn't tell Jones, and he will learn for the first time when he reads this how Lee managed for ten years while he was pursuing his college degree.

The second manifestation was that with her very limited

financial resources due to making up the shortfall of the Vietnam GI Educational Bill to pay for Jones' college education, see managed to save money! Lee confided in me that for ten years she saved her nickels in the drawers of her dresser and when Jones graduated in 1977, purchased his class ring for $100! In the telling of the story, Lee mentioned that she knew that he wanted his class ring, but was willing to forgo it, because when he graduated, he could not in good conscience, just take $100 from the family budget for that purpose. Lee also, sadly, told how Jones could not attend his college graduation ceremony because they did not have the forty-two dollar for the gown rental, his picture in the class book, etc. While he was attending college, Jones did not realize that you had to pay a fee to have your picture placed in the class book (Lee didn't have to pay when she graduated from the University of Panama), gown rental, etc., nor did he in ten years ask anyone! He assumed in his innocence or stupidity, forgetting that this was America where only money matters — that the payments he made for his college education included the graduation ceremony. When I head, after the fact, the events surrounding Jones' non-attendance at his college graduation ceremony, (at the time, I assumed he just did not want to attend), I angrily asked Jones, "Your college graduation was a very important milestone in your life that you and Lee paid dearly for! Why didn't you ask me for the money? You knew I had it, and would have gladly given it to you! What's forty-two dollars compared to my life that you gave me 27 years ago when you took me out of that rice paddy in Korea!" In response to my angry question, I received this reply as Jones smiled sadly, "My friend, very early in my life, I have learned that if I don't have something — then I do without!" To which I had no counter remark, knowing that was actually the way Jones (to include Lee and the Children) lived and conducted his life, as long as I have known him!

In the two examples given above, I felt, as I observed Lee perform her willing deeds of love, that it reflected and demonstrated for me her very deep and abiding love for Jones, along with her determination to constantly do all that she could, to see him happy and at peace.

> "Our deed determine us, as much as we
> determine our deeds."
> *George Eliot*

19.

KAM

In October of 1968, Lee gave birth to her third (I counted all of Lee's and Jones children from live births, and not from only those that survived), child that she carried to term, a son — Kam. There was nothing unusual about her pregnancy that Lee or Jones mentioned. Nor that I or her friends could notice. Throughout, she was her normal, very active self, as she carried what appeared to be a basketball under her clothing as she went about her activates. But Kam was the heaviest of all her babies — weighing in at a healthy, amazing (for that time) birth weight of 9 3/4 pounds. When Lee brought the new addition to her family home, we all lovingly teased her with comments such as, "Where did you hide the rest of him while you were carrying him? How could such a thin person produce such a heavy baby? We now know where all that food you ate during your pregnancy went — to Kam!" Lee, laughing, would always reply to our loving teasing remarks with, "Go ahead, make fun! I don't care! My babies could weigh a ton, so long as they are healthy and Jones put them in me." Loud laughter!

Of all Lee's babies, Kam was the only one she breast fed, which she very soon had to stop. Lee gave as her reason for breast feeding (before it became fashionable again in the eighties), Kam was that for the first time in her marriage, she was totally, mentally at peace. Informing all that Jones had returned in one piece from that war in Vietnam, was out of that damn army, working at a job (Management Trainee in a bank) he liked with the possibility for advancement, and was going to college nights — to obtain his degree. She and Jones were at last starting their hopeful large family of five children and by breast feeding, she hoped that some of her happiness would pass through her milk to Kam. Because of Kam's large size, within a month, Lee had to stop breast feeding him — she could not produce milk fast enough to satisfy his hunger and had to place him on formula. Later, in talking about her failed attempt to breast feed Kam, Lee said that she had no regrets. She was just sorry that she could not continue to feed him that way. The breast feeding experience was rewarding in itself, Lee exclaimed, she was truly a woman and mother! Adding that every time she looked into Kam's chubby, healthy, and happy face as he suckled her breast, her happiness knew no bounds — life to life!

There was one unique feature of Kam's birth that we all happily never forgot — Kam was born on Lee's birthday. What are the chances of mothers giving birth on their birthday — one in millions! But Lee did it, and she, Jones, and I, along with their friends, thought it was just grand! We told her, "What a birthday present! You both will never be able to forget each others birthday. Now there will be two birthday celebrations in your home on the same day, and there were." Concerning birthdays in the Jones' household, to include mine, my families and Lee's and Jones friends, Lee took care of purchasing the presents (which Jones wrapped), cards, baking and decorating the birthday cake, except for hers and Kam's which Jones took care of. He performed what was normally Lee's tasks with regards to preparing for birthdays, except that Jones purchased their individual birthday cakes at the local bakery.

In addition to birthdays and Christmas, Lee made a big project of all holidays for her children and Jones. New Year's Eve —

she allowed all of the children to stay up late to watch Guy Lombardo on television and watch the ball drop at midnight in Times Square. Then they would all toast the New Year in with tonic in champagne glasses (neither Lee nor Jones drank and none of their children did either, at any time). Saint Valentine's Day — she baked Valentine cakes and cookies for the children to take to school for their parties, along with buying them Valentine cards to give to their classmates and siblings. On their Wedding Anniversary (2 April) — Lee and Jones exchanged presents with each other, sometimes including a small dinner in their home for a few select friends or dinner out at an expensive restaurant. On Easter Sunday — from the time the children could walk and sit in a chair at a table, the family went out for Easter dinner at a prominent restaurant. The children dressed in their new Easter clothing would eat out so Lee and Jones could teach them how to order a meal in a restaurant and learn the proper etiquette. I can attest that there were many lean years in the Jones' household while Jones was pursuing his college degree, but somehow I noticed that Lee always came up with the money to buy the children their Easter clothing even when she wore her same dress each year. Jones would also wear his same single breasted dark blue suit that he had obtained from a Salvation Army Thrift Store for five dollars in 1965 — when they had to bury Lee's father. Along with their new clothing, Lee made from scratch, Easter baskets for each of the children. Each basket would also contain a toy or some item that she knew they wanted and did not expect to get, because when they asked her, had not been encouraged by her reply of, "We will see." On Mothers Day — Lee received presents form all of her family, along with being taken out to dinner at a surprise restaurant. This day's activities were planned and organized by Jones and the children. On Memorial Day — they would visit the cemetery to plant flowers in the beginning, at their grandfather's grave. Lee told the children, "You can always take one day (hopefully more) from whatever type of life you may lead to remember those who have come and gone before you. On Father's Day — Jones received presents form the family and then was taken out to diner as a surprise. Independence Day — there was a cookout in the back yard around the above ground pool for family and friends. Lee and all of the children who she taught, could swim, but not Jones who was afraid of large bodies of water because he nearly drowned in a lake when he was seventeen years old. In every home they owned, there was an above ground swimming pool that Jones bought for Lee and the children because they all enjoyed swimming. There was also an ongoing joke about the Jones' family swimming pools that Jones always said at the beginning of each summer, "I will get the pool operating in the Spring and Winterize it in the Fall, but will absolutely do nothing else to maintain it! Use it and you take care of it," which Lee and the children did. On Halloween — each child dressed (into their middle teens) in their purchased or "made by mom" costumes, and were taken by their father around their neighborhood for Trick-or-Treating while Lee stayed home to give out treats to the other children that came by the house. Thanksgiving Day — Lee mailed out cards to all of her friends and, to the best of my knowledge, at that time she was the only person that I knew who did. Thanksgiving dinner was a formal event at Lee's and Jones' home, requiring suits and dresses (no pant suits were allowed for the ladies). Lee always made it a point to invite someone (a nun, someone living alone or recently widower, just arrived in the country, etc.), whom she knew would be alone for Thanksgiving Dinner. She also told her children to invite their friends who didn't have family or would be alone to come too. Lee would, before her family and guests sat down prepared trays of the meal for the children to take to her elderly friends. Everywhere Lee lived in the United States, as she moved to three different cities, and/or towns to four different homes she and Jones owned, she always had two or more such old people who she looked out for. She would do their shopping and sometimes cook for them, wash and iron their clothing, have the boys shovel snow and accept no payment and once she learned to drive, she would take them to their medical appointments. She did this in loving memory of Mrs. Jackson, who died in 1969, that had looked out for her when Jones was in Vietnam. After everyone had been seated at Lee's very heavily laden Thanksgiving table and the blessing was given by one of the children on a yearly rotation basis. It was a custom of Lee's that before the meal was eaten, each person had to publicly tell what they were thankful for that Thanksgiving Day. Lee often mentioned that of all the holidays Americans celebrated, she enjoyed and appreciated Thanksgiving Day the best because it was a family holiday (the Republics of Colombia and Panama had no such holiday). It made you pause and reflect, that no matter how difficult your life may be, you did have plenty to be thankful for — just living in America where you could celebrate the day unmolested.

* "Oh, my baby, I am so happy that you are here, Kam! Now I have two sons to love and care for. I will tell you a secret — when I married your father and he told me that he hoped that we would only have daughters and that was not a problem with me. For I wanted no sons! My reason, because of my oldest brothers brutal attack upon me the day that I buried our mother and the abusive way my father treated my mother as long as I can remember.

You make me so happy, even though you are heavy to pick up and carry around in my arms or on my hip (and you want to be carried all of the time).

* I am amazed Kam, how you are growing everyday to resemble my late father, you grandfather, (the Palmer side of the family), and I don't know if that is good or bad. You have your grandfather's forehead, eyebrows, eyes — darker than his, (his

were light gray) our nose, lips, chin and reddish brown hair. The only physical features you took from your father are his ears and long hands with those slender fingers and thumbs. Anyway, it's not important what or who you look like, but who you know yourself to be — your character as a man. I love my healthy, happy and fat baby that I have to use Q-Tips to clean between the wrinkles of the fat of your arms and legs!

But now that I have sons, I would not trade you for anything! Maybe, sometimes, God does know what's best for us."

With two sons just twenty-two months apart, Lee took to dressing them alike. Although Robert was the oldest, by the time Kam was walking, he was the same height as his older brother. People often mistook Robert and Kam for twins, I believe because of their identical clothing for they did not physically look alike. One child (Robert) thin and the other chubby (Kam), but both the same height. What outer garments Lee could not find in their individual sizes, and the same design, she sewed on her foot-peddled sewing machine after purchasing the material short and long sleeves shirts, vest, short and long trousers, and sport and suit coats. I once asked Lee, "Why do you dress the boys alike (although they always looked very smart in their matching apparel)?" To which she replied, "I don't know. I just like to."

* "As I stand in the sun porch, during what your father calls, 'Watching my brood,' you and your older brother happily playing together in our very large, paved backyard, my heart swells with happiness to see how good you play together. Sometimes you pull your older brother around the yard in the wagon — which you do with ease; other times your older brother pulls you — which takes some effort on his part because you are so heavy. He never stops until he had made the complete trip around the yard, as you did with him. Riding your three wheel bicycles — periodically changing positions and who would be in the lead.

that you don't want to see. Maybe that was what I was doing when it came to Kam as I observed him growing up. I also readily defer to Lee, the accuracy of her comments about her third son, because for me, her notes have demonstrated exactly the type of women she was, a very reflective and honest woman when it came to her feelings about her children.

* "You may never know it, but all of his children, it is you, Kam, that your father constantly worries about. He feels that you are too passive — claiming that you have no get-up-and-go and that you are always looking for the easy way out when you find yourself in an unpleasant or difficult (rather than stand, and tough it out) situation. Your father claims that if his observations of your behavior and actions through the years are correct, that's bad, for it means that you will develop a weak character — the inability to make a lasting commitment to anything or anyone! Commenting that you can not live in this world as a complete person, if there is nothing that you will not stand and fight for — your siblings, your faith, wife, children, honor, etc.

I don't see what your father does. When he periodically brings me his concerns about your supposedly passivity, Kam, I tell him that I just don't see it, and if it's there, you will grow out of it, or the people of this world will knock it out of you! I remind your father not to forget that it appears that you inherited the bulk of your genes form my mothers side of the family with their long history on my island home of inaction. Again, reminding your father that Auntie bore the family name of "Wooker" before she married her husband — nothing upset her when she was alive. She was patience — like all that carried the name "Wooker" and she lived a long, loving, and faithful life!

I also believe that I understand the foundation of your fathers concerns about you Kam. Whereas he had to fight all of his life to survive, he does not believe that anyone can make it in the world who is not willing to fight with his fist. I tell him there are many in this society and world who have passed through life without ever having a fist fight. These non-fighters, are not necessarily, passive — they have found other ways to resolve the conflicts they encounter, as you will, Kam. Your father makes no comment to my logic, as I gently kiss the lingering concern from his face and tell him with my lips next to his, "Kam will be all right, honey. Don't worry."

It doesn't matter to me at all who's right in the matter of passivity, you are ours and I will always love and care for you — no matter what! Love you son.

* You came to me, Kam, telling me that you don't understand your father's attitude sometimes in the way he approaches problems and there solutions, giving as an example that he only sees black and white. What can I tell you? It's true, that's the way he is for reasons based upon his life experience (thank God that you and your siblings will not have to relive those experiences), that he and others were forced to live — that you will never be able to comprehend no matter how hard you would attempt to understand what this country and the world was like before you entered it. It was the people like your father who fought — sometimes with his fist, and suffered reprisals to change it, and he has been forever marked by those past experiences — How could it be otherwise?

As I have told you before, don't be so quick to condemn your father for the way he is, for each of us finds our own way to live in this hostile country successfully, and your father has found his by allowing no room for gray.

As I have also mentioned, all of his life your father has worked for substandard wages, unknowingly — been taken advantage of, lied to , abused, cheated by those in positions of responsibility and trust, but he never once compromised his integrity — because he saw no gray. He smiles when he shaves the beard off of his face each morning because he knows who he is as a man, and is at peace with himself.

As I have also told you, if as a man, you can live your life and truthfully say that you have never compromised (with many suggesting, after the fact, that your father should have to make it), your integrity that will speak volumes about they type of person and man you are. Your father can say this. However, there is a price to be paid for seeing only black or white and your father has paid that price without complaint.

I tell you this not because I am your mother, and love you dearly Kam, but your father is truly a good man — to us all!

* You complain that every time something goes amiss at school, your father is there the next day to straighten out whatever the problem is, with the Sisters, lay teachers or the parents of your classmates, and you often become embarrassed because he often raises his voice in anger — Shouts!.

Often when your father has to go to your school, he is angry and you should be thankful, Kam, that he raise his voice and not his fist — which he is capable of doing when he is mad. You must remember that you are in a private school, and the rules apply to everyone. What angers your father is that when the school does not enforce their own rules regarding standards. Mainly when it involves your wealthy classmates — by promoting them to the next higher grade when they did not meet the academic standards for promotion just because their father and mother have money! He lets those involved know that their actions were not right — for it was against their own rules relating to the quality education they claim they are selling. Asking, "What were they going to do to assure that another infringement of the rules did not occur again?"

Your father has a saying that he often repeats whenever he is confronted with infringement of the rules at your school, "All paper money in this country is green and black, and when I pay the price asked, my children will receive the same value for my money as everyone else! A paid for non-diluted quality education."

When your father shows up at your school, what he is doing, son, is to demand that your school abides by their rules, and defending your (and other non-wealthy students) rights to equal treatment under those rules. You have no reason to be embarrassed son, but proud that he really cares enough to make the case for you. Your father and I love you dearly.

I have told you all of what I have placed on paper here for you upset me when you complain about your father, when all he is doing is being a father: loving and defending his children, as he often quotes Oliver Wendell Holmes, "The place for a man who is complete in all parts is in the fight."

* I have become very concerned now that you are a teenager, Kam, over a behaviorally characteristic that I have noticed and has been brought to my attention by the parents of some of your former friends and classmates, that I have sternly taken you to task for — you are deliberately using people! It's wrong and I don't like it!

I don't know what's the matter with you. You are bright, get along with your siblings, everyone likes you, yet you go out of your way to have others do your bidding. Then, after you obtain whatever it was you wanted — you cast the person aside. You no longer take their telephone calls, speak to them in public, brush them off when they show up at the house unexpectedly. You are too busy to talk or hang-out with them.

Well, I have read the riot act to you, and you had better heed what I told you. None of that people using behavior here — I will not have your younger siblings believing your way, because they both look up to you and hold you in high esteem, is the right way to treat people. I will not set back with my mouth closed with as much love as I have for you, and raise a user without attempting to correct you. I have told you to change your behavior with regards to using your friends.

I have also informed you that you had better pray to God that your father does not learn or suspect what you have been doing, for he would come down on you like a ton of bricks! Preserving your behavior as a problem that he must solve and I can reasonably be assured that you would not like his solution whatever it would be!

You have a bright future ahead of you, son, it is yours to mess up.

Oh, my child, I love you so! You have no idea how you worry me. I am even too frightened to place my anguished thoughts on paper for fear that they will become reality. I pray to Saint Jude every night that you do not grow into the beast that was my oldest brother, that you know absolutely nothing about!"

There were a number of Lee's notes pertaining to Kam on subjects that I was not able to determine exactly where they fit into his development, because all of Lee's notes were undated, so I am including them here.

* "Your father has accused me, Kam, of preferring you above your siblings. Hold you in more esteem. I angrily denied his accusation. He made me very angry by this claim and I told him so in very understandable heated English mixed with Spanish that I love all of our children the same and made no differentiation between any of them. Your father's only reply was that he was articulating his observations as he numerated them for me. I listened in silence until he had finished and then told him that he was only observing the normal differences of our children that I was responding to and not preference for Kam.

Several months have passed since your father made his accusation concerning you, Kam, and I return to it because in our long loving marriage he has never accused me of anything before which gave me reason to pause. Maybe he sees something I don't.

With a cooler head, I have thought about what your father had to say about my actions as they concern you Kam. I started by readily admitting that I never wanted sons. I also, from the time I became aware of the differences between male and female, I held very strong negative opinions of all males until I met your father. He changed my opinion because when I immediately laid eyes upon him, I knew that I could love him and he would love me back — I had found my soul mate. Since I have sons, I now realize that you are everything that I wanted in a man child: tall, handsome, bright, mannerly, clean of body, particular about your clothing, neat with your personal effects, and very loving to me. It appears that with your birth you have fulfilled a suppressed desire that I never knew that I had about what I wanted my son to be like if I had a man child.

I now also realize form your father's comments that I have deliberately overlooked or discounted those traits of your personality that I do not like. You are not responsible with your money, you appear to be a user of people, you are always the last child to offer your father assistance when he needs help, and are always looking for the easy way out when you are confronted with a difficult situation.

I love you Kam — more than you will be ever able to understand, but you also worry me more now that I realize my eyes have been closed to your bad ways after being forced by your father's accusation to really look and see who you are. I have also in the past ignored what I was doing to you by not admitting to myself that there were things needing addressing.

Now I have to find a way to tell your father about what I have learned about myself as it pertains to my special (not preferential) love for you, Kam, and how in the past, it has affected my actions towards you.

* I believe, Kam, that you are afraid of your father. If I am right, that makes no sense. No one loves you, and your siblings, more than your father. He's always there for you. When you were an alter boy for four years, after arriving home from work at 2:00

A.M. who would get up at five every morning to drive you to your six o'clock mass? He never asked anything of you that you could not successfully accomplish. Who in this family is the most proud and vocal over all your accomplishments? If I am right, I don't understand your fear.

Thank God your father does not see what I do (you hide your fear well) and I will never tell him. It would break his heart to know that one of his children is afraid of him when none of his behavior is conducive to that type of reaction from any of his children.

I have told you, Kam, all that I have written here and more, that no one will love you more than your father. I don't know what's the matter with you — you have what many would kill for, and yet you may destroy your relationship with your father if he ever becomes aware of your fear, by not recognizing the fact that your fear is groundless. Oh love of my heart and life, what can I do, or say, to open your eyes to just how very, very important it is to us all, that your father is the loving and caring person he is.

* It was no one's fault, Kam, that your brother, Robert died, but die he did. Now you are the oldest son, with the accompanying responsibilities. It greatly distresses me when you come complaining to me about how you had to go foot-to-toe with your father for four hours on that project of building rooms in the basement, and I told you, "That's the duty of the oldest son, among other things is to help and learn from your father. God forbid if your father dies before you become an adult, you would become the man of the house doing what he does." I also told you that as long as I an alive, you shall not be allowed to avoid your responsibilities towards your father and family as the oldest son. You sadden and disappoint me, Kam."

During Kam's entire high school years, I, along with other friends of Lee and Jones, were constantly invited and attended some function in the school's auditorium, where he and the other six bright members of his class were to receive some type of school, municipality, and state appreciation or national awards for their individual scholastic achievements. No one, in my opinion, each time we attended what came to be called in the Jones' household and their circle of friends as "Kam's award nights," could have been happier and prouder over her son's academic achievements than Lee. After the ceremony at the school, we would all return to Lee's and Jones' home, for homemade cake that Lee had baked for the occasion, and coffee and tea, along with picture taking, which was the routine for all the children when their accomplishments were publically recognized. Jones framed every award his and Lee's children received and hung them on the walls of their bedrooms.

* "When you entered your first year of high school, Kam, you did so, with a continuous education history of 'A's' and 'A +'s', with mathematics being your best subject. During the first, second, and third quarters, your grades in mathematics began to fall (only subject) to A, A-, and a B, as reflected on your quarterly progress reports. You, along with your siblings, all know that it is to your father that you must answer to about your education. When he asked you each quarter about your unacceptable Math grades as compared to those you brought to high school, in my presence, you told him, "The Math was difficult." Your father accepted your assessment, with his often quoted comment about learning, "You do not unlearn what has already been learned," and try to bring your Math grades up to the level that he knows you can perform at.

When your third quarter progress report came in with a 'B' in Math, again, in my presence, your father pulled the plug on you. He removed your radio, television, and hi-fi sets from your bedroom, as he told you, very annoyed, "No telephone privileges or CYO dances until you bring your math grades back up to where it was when you entered High School, A+, by the end of the fourth quarter and keep it there! If you fail to apply yourself, and perform at the level that I know you can, then I will pull you out of that private school and place you in public school. You picked that school. The best in the state that you chose to attend for your high school education. If you are unwilling to apply yourself to it's standards, then I am equally unwilling to continue to pay for a below-standard performance from you."

After the above conversation with your father, you came to me in the kitchen when I was alone, very angry with your father for what he had done with the items in your bedroom and told you, while telling me, "I do not like being threatened, and that's just what Dad has done to me!"

I made it abundantly clear to you, Kam, that your father did not threaten you, but did make you a promise! Knowing your father, and you should also know him by now, he stands for no foolishness when it comes to his children's education. If you have any problems in your Math Class or need additional help, you know that all you have to do is to tell us, and we will take care of the problem and provide the additional help. If you do not straighten yourself out, he will keep his promise and you will end up in a public high school. I also told you that you were playing around with your future by not doing the very best you can while you are in school, not 50% or even 75%, but 101%.

You then left the kitchen, angry with me, after I told you that I agreed with all that your father had done and said to you concerning your present and future education. You have to learn, son, that life is about taking responsibility for one's actions, which includes your education.

One month into your total grounding by your father, during one night's pillow-talk, I attempted to get your father to lift his edict concerning you and your math grades. Explaining that you had learned your lesson. Very sternly, he told me, "No! You keep out of it! Kam has to learn now that his education is not a plaything, but his key to his future." I never mentioned it again.

* In the eleventh grade, your father went to Parent's Night Kam, to pick up your report card, as he always does for you and your siblings, to meet your teachers and to hear from them how you are progressing in your subjects, as an adjunct to what is reflected in your grades. When it was his turn to meet your Trig teacher, he was told by him, "Kam is lazy. He is just coasting on his ongoing A+ grade. I have repeatedly attempted to get Kam interested in more advanced and theoretical mathematics that he can do, and he tells me, "No thanks!" Your Trig teacher also told your father that he hated to see your exceptional mathematical abilities go to waste and that he had told you this.

After completing his visit at your school, your father arrived home, furious (your Trig teacher did not know, as you do Kam, that the word "Lazy" is your father's red button word) that you would allow yourself to be thought of as lazy in relation to your education. It took all of my persuasive powers to keep your father form placing you in a public high school the next day. I made the point that your Trig teacher's remarks was just one teachers opinion. No other teacher throughout your education up to now, has ever held that opinion of you.

Oh, Kam, I just don't know about you! What are you doing? Are you attempting to get back at your father because he made you bring up your grades in Math? I hope not, for it's not him that you are hurting, he has his education, but yourself. I love and worry about you — all the time.

* In the eleventh grade, when you telephoned me at home, asking to bring to your all boys high school, a freshly laundered, white shirt, because the one you had on was messed up — my heart skipped a beat Kam, as I asked you, "What happened?" You told me that you were sitting at your desk arm-chair going over your assignment book before the class started, when you felt your chair pulled from behind and the next thing you knew, you were flat on your back on the floor, and five of your classmates,

after removing the desk arm-chair, were kicking and stomping you about the face and body. You also mentioned that something was wrong with your right hand.

During the entire time that I listened to you, Kam, I could feel my heart slowing down and I thought that I was going to pass out. When you finished, I quickly pulled myself together and told you, "I am coming with your father! Take it easy. I love you!"

I telephoned your father in the city and told him that you had been attacked in school and was injured. He borrowed a car from the Banks motor pool and made the fifty-two mile trip home, in record time. Before your father arrived, I hid they key to where he kept his pistol and ammunition locked up — for I knew he would be determined to kill someone because they attacked and injured one of our children!

Once your father arrived home, after giving me a fleeting kiss, without saying a word, he immediately went to where he kept the key to his pistol should have been. Not finding it, he turned to me and looking at me with his eyes that were slits in his face, and very softly — which meant danger, told me, "Give me my key, now!" I went to your father and put both of my arms around his upper body and embraced him just as tightly as I could and told him, "No! That's not the way! No matter how many of them you may kill, we loose you! Kam ,along with the rest of us need you here — not locked up in some prison for the rest of your life! We love you, Honey! Think about it! You will find a way to get back at them for what has been done to our son." Your father looked at me silently, holding him tightly in my embrace with his red blotched, angry face for a few minutes — then told me, "Let's go!"

When we arrived at your school, we found you standing alone at the administrative desk in the front hall — your face swollen, cut , bloody, with your dry blood covering your once white shirt, tie, and trousers. Your badly swollen right arm was hanging limply at your side as if it was not a part of your body. I went to you crying as I engulfed you in my arms, with your father angrily telling the woman behind the desk, "Get the Headmaster, now! He kept us waiting an hour." When he arrived, saying nothing to you, Kam, he escorted us to his office and offered us chairs, to which we declined in unison. The headmaster then sat behind his massive, impressive, ornamented, red wood desk, with your father telling him, "I am not interested in the 'why', only that those responsible be expelled from school, and I don't care how wealthy their parents may be!" The Headmaster replied, "I will investigate and get back to you Mr. Jones." Your father lost it, shouting at the top of his voice, "What the Hell is there to investigate? Look at Kam (which he would not do)! How do you think that happened to him? I will tell you how it happened! Inside your school there is violence that has never been allowed in any Catholic School!" The Headmaster turned red in the face and did not reply to your father's outburst. I gently took your father by the arm and told him, "Let's go Honey."

We left the high school, took you to the hospital, made a report by telephone to the police about the attack on you. You were treated in the Emergency Room and they discovered that your right hand was broken. On the way home from the hospital, with your hand in a plaster cast up to your elbow, you told us that you could not think of anything that would provoke such an attack. As far as you knew, until today, you got along with all of your classmates and the other members of the student body.

A week later, the Headmaster telephoned your father at his office in the bank and told him that he was not going to expel the five boys that Kam claimed attacked him. No one in the classroom at that time saw anything and it was Kam's word against the five he accused of attacking him and the other twenty members of his class. He also knew that Kam's right hand was broken, but he could and would not play God! Your father angrily asked the Headmaster, "How do you think Kam acquired his broken hand?" No answer. Then the Headmaster was told, "Neither you, nor your school, or those five students that attacked my son, I promise you, will get away with what you allowed to happen by your inaction! I will not let the attack on my son go unrevenged and unpunished — no matter how long it may take me to get to you all!" Then hung up his phone.

It took your father over two months to find a lawyer who would take your case, Kam, because it was the top Catholic School in the State, and the other attorneys were afraid to touch the case — we a no-body against the largest church in the state! We won, and the Judge told the Headmaster to expel the five boys who attacked you, along with the school, and the parents of the five students, each having to pay triple damages for the bodily injuries you suffered, Kam.

Your father also told me that the judge told the Headmaster of your school in open court that cases like the attack on you, Kam, should always be taken care of by the school and not by the courts. Adding that if there was ever another attack upon Kam, he personally would close his school down — not withstanding it being a private catholic school.

I did not attend the trial because I could not bear to look at the mothers of your attackers without hating them for giving life and raising those evil beasts! They then turned them loose upon society. All of the above to arrive here.

The night after the day of the trial and dinner, you had returned to your upper bedroom with your father following you because of your almost total silence during dinner, and told me this story when he returned to our bedroom. He found you sitting at your desk doing your homework with your left hand, because your right hand was still in a cast, and asked if you were all right. You nodded. He, then, sat on your bed with you turning in your chair to face him, told you, "Kam, you do not have to stay in that evil school. You are bright and a good student, and can go to any school in the country. You pick the school and I will gladly pay for it!" You smiled at your father as you told him, "Thanks, Dad. I am attending the school that I want to. I an not running, because I know that everyone in my school are my enemies — except one, my Spanish teacher. I will conduct myself accordingly, believe nothing they say outside of what's being taught and never turn my back to them. No matter who does not like me being a student in the school, which I know now includes the Headmaster. I am staying. I will not allow them to run me out of the school that I qualified to attend, can do the work, and for which you pay full tuition." Your father said that he told you 'good' and got up from your bed and left your bedroom.

After hearing your father's story, I have never been so proud of you, Kam! You are right not to run (although I don't want you hurt). Your right to live free and unmolested in the United State of America, had been paid for by your father, and many that went before him."

When it came time for Kam to apply for admission to college, he had already received, based on his SAT scores, three unsolicited, full four year scholarships to MIT, Princeton, and the University of Florida. Shocking Lee and Jones, by announcing that he did not want to attend any college in the State of Massachusetts where they were then living. He was going to apply for admittance to the United States Military Academy, West Point, New York."

After Kam's announcement that he was going to seek admittance to West Point (WP), Lee said that she held her tongue in disbelief, and was sorry that she had not shared with her children, her negative opinions about all things military. After her initial shock, Lee said that she remembered that all of their children had been raised to make lawful choices, and she and their father would support them — even if they did not understand their reason behind the choice, turning down MIT for WP.

During their pillow-talk the night Kam announced that he was going to apply to West Point (WP), Lee later told me that Jones was appalled by Kam's decision, telling Lee, "What's the matter with him? Doesn't he listen or see what the Army has done to my body and mind? I felt that I had to go into the Army because I believed that was the only way that I could get out of the abject poverty that I was born and grew up in! Kam does not have to go to WP to improve his lot in life. He's not poor and has a first class education as demonstrated by the number of colleges and universities — final count of full four scholarships offered him — eight. Anyway, I will help him submit his paperwork, but the more I think about it, Kam will not be accepted at WP! We need not worry that all of our sacrifices to date could be wiped out by a nine cent bullet! The Republicans are in power in Washington, DC with the election of Reagan and I am on record as a very vocal, lifelong Liberal — I write letters, and belong to organizations that the muttly crew around Reagan hold in disdain, like the ACLU, DNP, UL and etc. Once they start processing Kam's paperwork that information of my liberal activities will surface, and the "Powers that Be," will assume that he is made from the same cloth, and that will be the end of his application to WP. Look what Reagan has done to the nation's courts to include the Supreme Court packed it with judges that believe Government owes it citizens nothing (except to take their money via taxes, while reducing it on the wealthy!)" Reagan won the election by repeating that lie, with the American voters never stopping to ask the question, if the government owes its citizens nothing, then why do I allow my money to be taken in taxes?

Jones was wrong. Kam received a Presidential appointment to the West Point Military Academy, New York, from President

Ronald Reagan. Lee often, perplexingly, commented that she had no idea how Kam's name came to the attention of Reagan.

* "We visit you as often as we are allowed and Kam, you really look good — the military life appears to agree with you. You look so sharp in every uniform that we see you in.

You have no idea how proud your siblings are of you! Not only them, but also all of our friends, above all, our Mailman! When he delivers our mail, he always rings the doorbell to ask about you. He believes that you are truly an exceptional young man, exclaiming that in the twenty-odd years he has been walking this mail route, you are the only son of his customers that has ever went to West Point!

* We attended your Family Night, Kam, and everyone of your instructors who we met, including the Commandant of the West Point Academy, told us that you are brilliant. If you make the Army your career, you will become a General, because you are General material.

* Your father remained silent, Kam, when our friends are expressing joy over how well you are doing at the Point, and how they tell everyone in their family they know someone who is attending West point.

Your father has confessed to me that he has willingly conceded to himself, that your enrollment at West Point appears to have been the right choice for you to have made for yourself (for you have taken to that highly regimented life-style, like a duck to water), even with his concerns for you life, because "armies exist to fight." He only hopes that you stick-out (30 years), your chosen career, but he doubts that you will. He believes that you will find something to complain about, and point-in-time, get out. Army life is hard your father claims, even for West Point Officers!

* You broke your father's heart, Kam, when you told us during our last visit, "That you wanted none of your family there for your "500 Night" dinner! How dare you! You are what you are

today because of your father and family, even if you are not willing to admit it, by telling your father during our last visit, "you
have gotten where you are by your own efforts." Your father
looked at you sadly, smiled, and said nothing. You have no right
to hurt him, for he lives only for me and you, children. I warn
you, if you ever hurt your father again, I promise you, I shall give
you back double the hurt you inflict upon him!

If you don't want us to attend any of your functions, then
don't tell us about them, for we have no other way of knowing.

I, unsuccessfully, attempted to convince your father to take
us to the "500 Night" ceremonies, notwithstanding your desire
not to have us there because of what you told us, (not to come)
was wrong! He said, "No! We will not go anyplace were we are
not wanted."

I am so angry at you, Kam! As sure as there is a God in heav-
en, you shall pay for denying your family! We have done nothing
to justify this type of treatment from you. Your poor siblings!
They can not be made to understand why their brother (who they
dearly love and look up to), does not want them at his "500
Night" dinner. They miss you, Kam! Your siblings always enjoy
making the motor trip to West Point — as they make their list of
things to tell you that has been happening in their lives, since you
have been away.

I have put all of the above in a letter, that your father does not
know that I have mailed to you, because he repeatedly tells me,
"Leave him be! It's Kam's life, and he has the right to live it anyway he likes — even if it means excluding his family." I shall
never forgive you, Kam, for the needless anguish that you have
caused your siblings, father, and me!"

According to Lee, Kam did not seriously date until he
entered West Point Military Academy, New York, at seventeen
years of age. During high school, Kam attended the weekly
Friday night, chaperoned by the parents of the parish, CYO

dances at the Parish Community Center (CC). Lee had learned to drive by then and she, along with Jones, used to alternate driving Kam to and from the CC — with him, over time, telling his parents, that there were four girls that he alternated dancing with (Lee and her daughter taught the boys to dance), during the four-hour dance period, 7:00 through 11:00 P.M.

* "We finally had the pleasure of meeting, and having Lola as our house guest! We all like her! Same background as us — trying to make it in this land of the Big P.X. (Silvia would bust his gut laughing to hear me using this phase), but of a different faith.

As your father and I have repeatedly told you, Kam, and your younger siblings, never let your religion stand in the way of what you perceive as your happiness. Life is too short.

We are very happy for you, son, for it appears that you have met someone you enjoy being with, and maybe in love with — and she with you.

* I receive weekly telephone calls from Lola's mother and she will never know how she drives me up the wall every time she calls me, "Mother Lee!" Your father tells me not to say anything about my feelings to her that she's just attempting to be friendly.

I listen to your father, because I don't want to make problems for you with Lola or her family, for you have frequently been their house guest, (Long Island, NY is closer then MA when you only have a one day pass) but I make you a promise — if our families ever become one, the first thing I am going to tell that woman is to stop calling me "Mother Lee!"

You will never see this.

* You graduated and you and Lola walked through that giant West Point Ring — becoming engaged.

I have never been more proud and very happy for you both! I love you both and wish you every happiness in your planned life together.

* My God, what happened? The engagement is off, you and

Lola have split up! It's lasted all of eight months, and what you both nurtured for four years while you were attending West Point, all went for naught!

I hope you know what you are doing, Kam, for Lola was a nice young woman, because I sure don't! You have not bothered to explain your reasons for your actions concerning Lola, to your father or me, maybe believing that you are a man and don't have to explain your actions to anyone.

* Lola's mother has telephoned me very upset (she has reason to be, for she truly loves you, Kam), asking me for information about your breakup with Lola and I truthfully could tell her that I had none. I was as much in the dark as she was. Lola's mother told me that Lola has also told no one, not even her twin sister nor her father who she is very close to — the reason for the breakup.

* Lola telephoned your father at his office in the bank, crying hysterically — ranting on about you, Kam, which he could make no sense of. Your father told me one thing came through loud and clear during Lola's overwrought telephone conversation, "She now hates you!"

Oh, my son, what have you done that has turned Lola's love to hate?

* Kam, you have informed me that you have met at your new duty station, a female US Army Officer from Western Massachusetts who you are in love with and are bring her home for us to meet Sheri.

It didn't take you long to get over Lola!

* Sheri is very attractive, and all can see she's head-over-heels in love with you, Kam. From just this first meeting, I believe that Sheri loves you, Kam, more than you love her.

Sheri is a homebody and I like that about her. We both laugh together (when you are not around, Kam), as she tells me, "You are everything she dreamed about growing up, that the man she could love and marry would be like. All she now wants out of life is to marry you, take care of you, and have as many babies as you want — she will always be ready! (I hear myself in her remarks). Sheri, is such a loving, trusting, and pleasant young woman, and in these times — the eighties, I never thought there were any left like her. You are lucky, Kam. I hope you don't turn Sheri's love to hate, a s you did with Lola, Kam.

* So you and Sheri are engaged, Kam. I am sorry if we appear to be reserved over your happy announcement, but 'once burnt, twice shy.'

* We had the in-law dinner here, and Sheri's mother and I could grow to be friends, because she desires for her daughter the same thing, divorced Catholic, not withstanding, as I do for my children that they be happy.

Sheri's mother told your father and I in the presence of her former husband (from whom Sheri received her good looks), sitting around the cleared dining room table, when you both went for a walk, to allow us to plan the wedding. Who would pay for what? Your father has already told me that he believes that Sheri's father and mother should pay for it all — it's their daughter (even if they are living below the poverty line!) I replied, "Yes, that's true, but you are our son."

Sheri's mother mentioned during our conversation, "Their were members on both sides of Sheri's family that were violently opposed to her marrying Kam. I told those in opposition that at least Kam is not like all of Sheri's former boyfriends throughout high school and college that would repeatedly knock her to the ground when they were displeased and proceed to kick her about the body! Why did they do this to my only child? Because they knew that there was no man in the home to defend her," looking sadly at her former husband sitting across the table (who embarrassedly hung his head). I told all that opposed the marriage of Kam and Sheri that they did not have attended their wedding, but I liked Kam and he was the best thing that had ever happen to my daughter!"

Oh, Kam, poor Sheri! I hope that you do not ever give Sheri's mother reason to regret her assessment of you as a man.

It was finally agreed that your father would pay 3/4 and Sheri's family (somehow), would pay the other 1/4 , towards the cost of Sheri's and your wedding.

* Your father is frantic about Sheri being out of the country on a military assignment, months before your wedding date, and you bringing another young woman, Lisa, home for us to meet and to be our weekend house guest!

What's the matter with you, Kam? What are you doing? It's apparent to us all, that you and Lisa have a personal relationship. What are you doing is wrong, with Sheri out of the country (even if she was in the country)! It took all of my will power to keep your father form telling you both to your faces, that your relationship, by any standard, was a flat out insult to Sheri, along with being beneath contempt!

I was only able to restrain your father by reminding him that we do not insult guests in our home, and that this was still your home, "Home was were you went and they had to let you in." My son. Oh, my son!

* Sheri telephoned from overseas today, Kam, asking if we knew where you were? We had to truthfully and sorrowfully (because we could hear the anxiety and pain in her voice), answer, no.

* Sheri returned safely form her overseas military assignment, and now your engagement, Kam, along with the wedding has been canceled, and Sheri had purchased her wedding dress before being sent overseas (at great expense to both families). And how did we get the news? Not from you, Kam, but form Sheri and her mother!

* Sheri's entire family is angry with you, Kam, and they have

a right to be! If what Sheri's mother told me is true (as with Lola, you have told us nothing), that another woman, Lisa, came between you and her daughter. Then you are to be blamed for allowing it to happen! If I could reach you, I would shake you just as hard as I could for embarrassing our family. We thought we had a man, but you are just another male. You have put our faces in the dirt!

I am your mother, and love you more than you can ever know — but Kam, you are no good, and are going to pay for what you have done to Lola and Sheri, as surely as their is a God in heaven. I may not be alive to see it, but pay you will!

* Lisa, another female US Army officer, has made herself right at home, and appears (as with all your woman whom I have met) to be genuinely happy and in love with you. With Lisa, I am unable to read your love for her, Kam.

Your father likes Lisa a lot, now that you both are planning your wedding, (claiming, that she has a first class mind) although they agree on nothing political — he being a Liberal, she a Reagan Conservative, "God bless me, and the Hell with you!"

* So Kam, Lisa and your wedding plans are proceeding smoothly. Why am I not surprised? You both are only concerned with your own self gratification — refusing to recognize that your actions affects others.

*I understand Kam, that you and Lisa are planning a very expensive wedding, which you are paying for yourselves. Lisa comes from money, her father being some type of medical professional. I also understand that he is opposed to his daughter marrying you, Kam.

Your father told you, Kam, in my presence, that you were not going to take him down that path again, as you did with Sheri concerning defraying some of the expense of your wedding to Lisa (although he loaned you $2,500). He was out-of-pocket, a very large sum that he can not replace (your planned wedding to

Sheri) and you were not an only child — your younger sibling might need help when it came time for his wedding. You messed him up once — not again! I also told you that I agreed 100% with your fathers decision! What you did to Sheri and her family, was wrong!

* Your wedding, Kam, including the reception, went off without a hitch, and was the most expensive (held in a castle) that we and your friends ever attended. But why am I not over-whelmed with joy, the way any other mother normally is at the marriage of her first child? The answer, because I know, Kam, that your marriage to Lisa is based upon the misery of two other women. Another damper on my emotions at your wedding, Kam, was your total lack of sensitivity in choosing the month when we experienced an horrific tragedy with one of your sib-lings! Not only the month of the tragedy, but two days after that horrible event! Are you able to imagine or even understand, what your father and I were thinking and feeling amongst the gaiety? I think not. You put us through Hell!"

The month that Kam married Lisa, was the fourth anniver-sary of a horrible event in Lee's family, that came very close to destroying her family forever. Jones had one foot over the cliff of loosing his mind.

* "Kam, we had a monumental tragedy in our family, and you were not there for us! Not there for your father, who came very close to loosing his mind; your youngest sibling, who kept asking, "When is Kam coming home?" and me — attempting to deal with my and everyone else's grief! You ran! You never wrote or telephoned, and I was paying your telephone bill, to ask about any of us. You also had your grief, but you could leave where it happened, and that was some relief for you — but we had to stay, and be reminded of the tragedy everyday!

To think that I gave birth to you, loved, and nurtured you into adulthood (with your father's help), for you to turn your back to me when I fell in need of your support — just your voice on the telephone, a few lines in a letter, and your present — a visit now and then, that's all I was looking for from you!

I now pray to Saint Jude every night, to ask God take me first, before your father, in order that I may not grow old and fall into your uncaring hands.

* It's been over a year since our tragedy and you came home, Kam, for your first visit. I could not believe my ears, sitting on the sofa in the Sitting Room beside your only remaining sibling, your father and I across from you on the other sofa, as you told us, "Someone should stay with you both in your old age, and it should be your youngest sibling!" I could feel because we always sat with our bodies touching, your father's body trembling with rage, as he told you, Kam, "You are the oldest, and you are attempting to pass on your responsibilities to slowly become the head of the family as we age, to the youngest! Kam, you haven't learned a thing about being a man! Don't worry about your mother and I. Believe me, we will manage without you for any type of non-financial support I once thought I could depend on you for. I also, never want you to mention this topic to me again!" Do you understand? You nodded your head. Your father excused himself in his anger for his den.

I sat there in shocked silence, as I looked at you, and saw the ghost of my late older brother — who you never knew existed! I became afraid."

Lisa had resigned her United States Army Commission, a year before she and Kam married. After their wedding and honeymoon, Lisa traveled with Kam to Germany, then to Belgium, where she became pregnant — three years into their marriage.

* "Kam, you have asked that your father and I come to Brussels for the birth of your first child — our first grandchild. We are so happy for you both and ourselves — we are going to be grandparents!

* I have agreed to come, Kam (for you know that your father will not fly) although I have hesitations about making this trip. When I tell your father about my uncertainity, he replies, "You have to go, because Kam and Lisa asked us to be there for them during the birth of this, their first child." I know your father is right, but my uneasiness will not go away!

* I returned form Belgium a week early because my son disrespected me in his home! I promise you, that I will never forgive you for turning what should have been a joyful event into a nightmare! You have truly broken my heart, Kam for the last time!

Your father kept asking me What happened? And I tell him that I don't and will not talk about it because I am so hurt, except to say, "I always refused to see who Kam really was and what he was about in our lives."

* Your father is worried about me, Kam, as I hug and kiss him about the lips, face, and hairless chest while lying in bed and telling him, "I love you , Honey and I will be just fine" He tells me, as he holds me tightly in his embrace close to his body, "I am sorry, Honey, that I insisted that you go when you were uneasy about going." I squeezed him back, "It's not your fault, for I agreed to go and know that had I told you differently, it would have still been all right with you."

* I telephoned you, Kam, in Brussels (from your fathers den, with the door closed) to tell you just what I thought of you! When I hung up and returned to my bed as your father took me in his arms, as he attempted to kiss away the tears, he asked, "What did you say to Kam?" I replied, "Nothing that I want you to know, Honey. Okay? How could I have been so blind all of these years." I continued to cry softly and safely in those arms that has been my refuge every day since I have been married.

After I had cried myself out, in the quiet of the night, laying awake against your father's warm, sleeping body, listening to his quite breathing, I now know what has been my continues fear, form your fifth birthday onwards — Kam, that you would grow up to be like my late older brother! My fear has become a reality."

Eleven months and three days shy of her thirty-second wedding anniversary, after cutting short her trip to Brussels to be there for the birth of Kam's and Lisa's first child, and her grandson, Trott, Lee suddenly, in less then twenty hours, died! Lee's death came after four months earlier, receiving a clean bill of health from a completely physical examination conducted by her long time health care giver!

"It is probable that God punishes the wrong wish as truly as he does the actual performance; for what is performance but a wish perfected with power; and what is a wish but a desire waiting opportunity of action; a desire sticking in the birth, and miscarrying for lack of strength and favorable circumstances to bring it into the world."

Robert South

20.

JUDY

In August of 1969, Lee gave birth to her fourth child prematurely, a daughter (at three pounds), that Jones named "Judy". Lee later said that both she and her Obstetrician miscounted; for when they thought that she was only one month into her pregnancy — it was actually three months (she did not show). Believing that she was only one month pregnant, Lee said that she never reduced or varied her routine and her Obstetrician told her that her very active routine was what caused the premature birth of Judy.

* "O' Baby, you are early and so very tiny, Judy! But thank God, everything is in place, and it appears that you have no medical problems.

"Your father is elated! He, at last, has his daughter, and I finally feel that I am now a complete woman and wife to him because I have been able to make his girl. You can never know how happy your father is, and in his happiness — all in my world is at peace. During the birth of each of your brothers, although he was overjoyed with each, and loves them dearly, but I could always (no matter how he tried to hide his disappointment), see in his eyes his yearning for you, Honey.

"I only live Baby, to love, care, and see your father happy! With your birth, Judy, I have made him happy beyond his wildest dreams!

"When your father came to see me in my hospital room after your easy delivery, he held me tightly in his arms — sitting on the side of the bed, and kissed me over and over, as he repeated, "She's beautiful! Thank you, Honey! Thank you for everything! I love you!"

* "I am so happy over your birth, Judy, that when you marry, I shall give you every note that I may write about you because I just know that they will only be happy ones. I want you to have my notes, for I always want you to remember as you start your family, how very, very, happy you made your father and I, by being our daughter. I love you child.

* "After seven days, I have been discharged from the hospital, but you have to remain Judy, until you weigh five and a half pounds. You will never know how it broke my heart to leave you at the hospital — but I will be back tomorrow, and everyday thereafter, until we can take you home to stay! See you tomorrow, Baby.

* "We have settled into our new routine, Judy, until we can bring you home. Your father drops me and your siblings off at your hospital room, then continues on to the bank.

"During my stay at the hospital, I daily receive instructions and training from your doctors and nurses on how to care for a premature baby. While with you, I also do everything for you as if you were home; feed you with an eye droppers, bath you using cotton balls, change the diaper that the doctors and nurses keep you tightly wrapped in — they say its an attempt to make you believe that you are still in my belly, and hold you in the bend of my arm for hours on end — just lovingly watching you making funny faces as you sleep, while I tell you of my love.

"Periodically, during each visit, the nurses will scrub and gown up your siblings and bring them into your room with the incubator to view their sister. If I have you in my arms, they will allow them to very carefully, hold you. Inevitably, your brothers always say the same thing each time they hold their baby sister, 'Mom, she looks like a small doll!'

* "I am not worried about you making it, Judy, for your doctors and nurses assure me, and I can see it for myself because each time I visit you — the first thing I look at is your Weight Chart to see how much weight you have gained since my last visit. You are doing just fine! Your care givers have also told me, that for some unknown reason, statistically, more female premature babies survive to live productive lives than males do.

* "There are some strange things connected to your care and stay in the hospital that I shall mention here, and never again, that has given your father and I reason for pause — but immediately push it out of our minds, because you are alright. Before arriving at the hospital and your room each day, we first must, call ahead and say that we are coming, with your father performing the same task before he leaves the bank to pick us up. "When we arrive, we do not go through the main hospital building to reach your room, but to what appears to be a high (ten feet?) bricked walled, private (our automobile the only one parked there), courtyard where you father parks the car. After getting out of the car, we walk a short distance to a heavy looking, windowless, wooden door with your father ringing the bell next to it, which is then opened by one of your nurses.

"We ride the elevator to the third floor, and walk down the corridor pass with seven closed doors with large brass numbers screwed to each door — when we reach your door, it has no number! But you can still see the screw holes where the brass number has been removed!

"I speak of "your room," but in reality it's an adjoining room: a typical hospital room with you in your incubator, and another beautifully furnished (that I would love to have in my home), sitting room — with connecting doors, containing a sofa, three easy chairs, television, radio, toys for your siblings to play with (different toys each day), hard cover books in a small glass door bookcase, magazines rack containing several of the latest magazines and the daily newspapers, and two vases on end tables with fresh flowers that are changed everyday! In your hospital room, there are always two doctors and nurses on duty — twenty four hours each and every day!

"In the over three months that we daily visited you, Baby in the hospital, we meet your permanent team of four doctors (my original Obstetrician was not among them), and four nurses that were taking care of you, and during that entire time, there was no type of rapport ever developed between your care givers and us — although your father and I tried! They all, the doctors and the nurses, were always very polite to us, and your siblings, along with being very professional in the care they gave you. There just was never any personal comments about themselves, their jobs, family, children, Pets, etc.. It was as if your care givers had been told not to attempt to know us! This same atmosphere existed in the evening when your father replaced me. As you grow, you will come to learn your father is able to talk to anyone and will, about any topic under the sun, but was unable to do that with any of your care givers! Your father would return to do the hospital alone, after taking me and your siblings home, so we could all have dinner — to spend his four hours with you — performing the same tasks as I, during my daytime visits. Over time, your father and I stopped trying to communicate on a personal level, with your care givers.

"When your father and I saw early on what we felt (your father had told me that Lester was in a ward with several other premature babies in their incubators) was your perceived exceptional treatment, we knew that it had to be paid for. He casually mentioned over coffee one morning, to his friend the Personal Officer at the bank, 'How much of my daughter's bill will I be responsible for once she is released from her lengthy stay in the hospital?' Receiving he said the reply, 'Nothing! Our health plan allows the hospital and doctors to do whatever they think is best for the patient, and we will pay the bill. You have nothing to worry about — you and the members of your family are completely covered, to include whatever is done for your daughter while she is hospitalized.' And we were.

* "The best part of my daily hospital visits with you, Judy, was when I would be holding you in the bend of arm or rendering some type of care to you, and you would open those large eyes (which you did not do often, during the first few months after your birth), and look at me. My heart would swell with happiness as I would tell you, smiling, 'Hi! You have decided to look at your mother. You are something, Baby. Your mother loves you.' And during the too brief encounter with your eyes opened, it seemed that you understood who I was, and all the love I have to give you.

"Then, too quickly, you would close your eyes, leaving me alone, to return to your world of darkness! I would be so sad and lonely until your returned to me an my world of light. I would sit patiently beside your incubator, gently rocking you in the bend of my arm, waiting for that joyful moment when you would open your eyes. God, how I love and need you Baby to complete my world!

* "We brought you home on the 16th of December 1969, enabling you to spend your first Christmas at home, Judy.

"There was a small group of our friends to greet you, and make you welcome Baby, and they all were so taken with your very small size, and your large, wide, very dark eyes. Your eyes remain open longer now, and as you were passed, wrapped in your pink baby blanket with its hood, from person to person. Everyone that held you, had a good laugh over how you made a different face for each person — they claiming, 'That was your way of saying hello!' What a happy day!"

As Judy grew, she was lovely as Houri! With Lee's reddish hair (that grew very straight and past her waist by the time she was ten years of age), and ears. Jones' forehead, very dark brown eyes (in some light — appearing to be black), his straight nose, full lips, pointed chin, and long facial structure. Lee used to often, laughingly, tease Jones, as Judy grew into a beautiful, tall (as tall as her father), thin, healthy young lady, to wit, "There is no doubt in anyone's mind when they look at our daughter and you together — who her father is!" Jones would embarrassingly smile, give Lee a hug and kiss, as he held her in his arms, "Yes, I know. I like the idea that Judy looks so much like me. What I am surprised at, is that I could produce a carbon copy of myself — only female! Maybe it's because I wanted her so badly." Lee, Jones, and any others present after hearing a commonly shared known fact, would all laugh over their love-play about Judy's almost identical appearance of her father.

When Judy was nine months old, she turned blue while laying in her playpen. She was rushed to the Pediatric Clinic at the hospital and upon her arrival was immediately given oxygen.

Judy's pediatrician was summoned, arrived, made his examination and returned to us in the waiting room (I was in the home when this happened, and accompanied her parents to the hospital — driving, while Jones breathed into his daughter's mouth), telling us, "She will be alright for now." Then asked Lee and Jones, "What type of heat do you have in your home?" They replied, "Gas" The pediatrician then proceeded to explain that Judy had underdeveloped lungs, that was not apparent at the time of her birth. The only solution for her condition was for Lee and Jones to purchase a totally electrified house and failure to do so would result in Judy not living to see her first birthday. Lee screamed, "No! Not again!," and fainted.

Lee was immediately rushed to the Emergency Room (ER) by us in the waiting room, revived, with Jones assuring her, "Please don't worry, Honey! I will not allow it (another of our children to die) to happen to us again for the need of a house! I will find the electrified house we need. I promise you, Honey! Judy's pediatrician said before he left the ER that if we find the house that is needed for Judy, and she reached her eighteenth birthday, she would have no more problems with her lungs." But what Jones did not tell Lee but did me, that day in the ER, after watching him hovering over her laying on a hospital dolly, was that he was furious with Judy's birth doctor. To include those that took care of Judy for over three months when she was hospitalized until her weight was five and a half pounds, for not detecting her lung condition! Telling me later, "She could have died, and we would have never known why! Can you imagine what that would have done to Lee? Well, they are not going to kill my daughter because of their negligence! I hate doctors! They bury their mistakes." Today (in 1996), the treatment for premature babies with underdeveloped lungs, like Judy's is that doctors fill the tiny, collapsed air sacs with an oxygen-rich liquid that enables the lungs to expand. Over time, the liquid evaporates.

In record time, Jones did as he promised Lee — he found one of the seven electrified houses in their city of ninety thousand that was for sale — inspected it alone, and made a down payment. Went to his employer, The Shawmut National Bank of Boston, told his boss about his situation involving Judy's health and the solution, and was told, "Don't worry about it. Bring all your paperwork on the new house to us, and we will find a way to finance it for you." And they did. What was amazing, Jones told me concerning the transaction surrounding the purchase of their third home, was that it cost 40K, and his annual salary was only 13K!

Lee and Jones quickly (the house was empty), moved into their new home with their children, and Judy grew and thrived in continuous good health. Many years later, Lee, swearing me to secrecy to never tell Jones while she was alive, confessed to me, "It broke my heart to leave our second home, because it was my dream house! We had put so much love and labor into it. Especially the blacktop yard, and the large flower garden in the front that Jones trimmed with red bricks and painted white for me — and the many different rose bushes I had planted. In the back as you know, there was my vegetable garden, where I grow my herbs, peppers, strawberries (that I canned for you and Jones), and the vegetables that we ate. This house, ten rooms, sits on the entire lot — no land for any type of garden! My second home was actually like what I pictured in my mind growing up — that my home would be like when I thought about the type of house that I would like to grow old in. But my dream house was worth less than Judy's life!

"The time Jones was looking for this electrified house, I was worried sick Lee said, remembering that Judy was three months shy of her first birthday! What if Jones was unable to find a house in time? I could hardly get through each day without the thoughts of: What if he doesn't succeed in his search? Judy will die! What will we do? If something happens to Judy, I will lose her father — he will go out of his mind, she is, after me, all he ever wanted out of life! Jones has told me many, many times since Judy's birth, 'My life is complete — I could ask for nothing more.' Well, Jones did as he promised me, when we heard about the conditions of our daughters lungs. I will, also, as long as I live, never doubt him again, in anything he says he will do. Not only did he save our daughter's life by finding this house in record time, but also our lives as a family. I tell you this, and would never mention it to anyone else — truthfully, I do not understand how Jones manages to be the person he is, with all that has happened in his past life and since we have been married. I wouldn't be able to take it! I would loose my mind! All I know for sure is that I love him more than life itself, and thank

God everyday for sending him to me to love, care, and have his children. I love my man!"

When Lee finished her secret confession, my eyes were moist, for I knew that I had experienced a woman speaking from the very depths of her soul about the love she felt for her husband. I have kept Lee's confessed secret thoughts about the move to their third home these many years, and revile them only now, in order when I die, that beautiful, profound shared moment of Lee's love for Jones, will not be lost forever.

* "Oh, Judy, you are so funny! The moment your eyes open, your mouth opens at the same time and you scream to let us know that you are awake. We all come running — and there you are, laying in your crib, not smiling, just making those funny faces that you do, as you look at each of us leaning over the crib rails. We laugh. It's as if by your scream, you are saying, 'My eyes have no business to be opening, I was not ready yet!'

"You know what? Sooner II is the only member of the family that does not become concerned by your screams — she remains under your crib, looking out at us surrounding it. The dog has an expression on her face that seems to say, 'What are you running for, everything is alright — I am here.'

"Ever since we brought you home from the hospital, Baby, Sooner II spends all of her free time in your bedroom under your crib. Before you came, Honey, the dog used to sleep on the floor at the foot of our bed, now it's in your room, under your crib. Wherever I take you Judy, throughout the house, the dog follows. She knows that you are special. Dogs are wise beyond our understanding. I love you so child!

* "Your father is so concerned, because you will not make 'baby-talk,' even though we and our friends all try to get you to. I tell your father, 'Don't worry, Judy will talk when she is good and ready. Don't rush her, for you maybe sorry! For once Judy starts to talk, like you, she may not know when to stop!' Your father smiling, kisses me on the lips, as he tells me, 'You think you are so funny!'

* "Sometimes I will miss your father, Judy, and without calling for him, I will go looking. I often find him standing beside your crib with his hands behind his back — just smiling down at you sleeping, and I will swear, that you can actually see the happiness radiating from his body! I quietly remove myself from the area in order not to intrude upon your father's private moments with you — and loudly call to him. Oh, Baby, words can never express how very, very much your father loves you!

"In the quiet of the night, in our bed, your father's happiness, Judy, sometimes will overwhelm him, and he will take me tightly in his arms, as he repeatedly, softly kiss me on the lips, while telling me, "Oh," Honey! Honey! Honey! Look what we made!' I will hold him very gently, as I return his kisses as I tell him, 'Yes, Honey. We did good!'

* "Your siblings have taken to you, Judy with great joy. They are so happy to have a baby sister. When you are in your playpen, they remain near, talking to you, sharing their toys with you, feeding you whatever they may be eating — when they think I am not looking, and sometimes, just leaning over the sides of your crib or playpen as they smile and make funny sounds for you. Your brothers love their sister.

* "You play with your dolls, Judy, and all things 'girlish,' but you appear happiest when you are with your father, helping him repair some household appliance in his basement work area or working with him on his junk car in the garage. So far, it appears you are the only child that has inherited your fathers mechanical skills, and he willingly allows you to help him. Afterwards, happily telling me, that he only has to show you mechanically once what to do and you have it!

"Baby, you are also the only one of his children that he allows to use his tools! He says, that he sends your brothers to his work area in the basement for a tool, and repeatedly, they come back with the wrong item. But not you. Even with never being shown or told the identity of a particulate tool, he can send you to the basement — and you always bring him the right item the first time! You are something, Baby. Even I don't know your father's tools.

* "I watch your father with you under one arm like a football, running around the large backyard of our fourth home, with your brothers chasing him — and you, loudly laughing, Judy, with your arms flying as you shout, 'Run! Run faster, they will catch us!' My heart swells with happiness to be among my healthy and fun-loving brood.

"Oh, Baby, you are the sunlight of our home and family, that I thank God for every day.

"I must confess, I do worry. I often think that your father and brothers are a little too rough with you (they are ten times heavier than you), but I keep those thoughts to myself because I know they are only treating you like 'one of the boys, I sometimes believe, that they forget that you are a girl even with your ponytail or two pigtails down your back.'

"You never get hurt or complain when you are knocked about by them — for you give as good as you get when playing basketball, baseball, street hockey, water and regular volleyball with your father and brothers.

"For your father, he throws you high (I think too high — all I can think of is: What if he misses you when you are coming down?) into the air because you are so small and thin. He catches you in his arms — then squeezes you tightly in a chest embrace as he kisses you all over your face and body, as he loudly proclaims, 'Look everyone! My bundle of joy just fell from Heaven!' Squealing with delight, as you loudly and joyfully tell your father, 'Do it again Daddy!'

* "Judy, you are a risk taker, like your father, and that concerns

me, for I believe you should have something in your life that you are afraid of!

"When we were clearing the many trees from our very large backyard of our fourth home, and your father asked your older brothers to go up the tree with him to keep the electric cord to his saw free as he cut off the branches before falling the tree. They declined, telling him, 'No thanks! We might fall and get hurt!' Your father told them, 'Okay, I will just have to watch the cord myself as I saw.' Then you, Baby, only eight years of age, told your father, 'I will go with you Daddy.' He climbed up the tree, then hoisted his saw up, then you, with ropes that he tied around your waist and under your arms that he had placed on you before he went up. Once up, your father tied you to the trunk of the tree, straddling a branch, while you kept the electric cord free as he operated his saw. My heart was in my mouth Baby, the entire time you were up those trees.

That was the way all the many trees were removed from our backyard — you and your father in the trees doing the cutting, with your brothers and I remaining safely on the ground.

"Your brothers saw the possible danger in what was asked of them, but not you! You were not afraid, and went up those trees happily with your father."

Throughout Judy's elementary school education until high school (she attended an all girls high school — as her brothers an all boys), she was always attending a school with one or more of her brothers. According to Lee, like her father, Judy was always hungry! So Lee said, that when she was making their school lunches, that she always gave Judy a larger lunch in her lunch box than the boys. It was not until they were all in high school, separated in their individual schools, that Lee came to learn how Judy would eat her large lunch, then go to one or more of her brothers and they would give her part of their lunches. Judy would and did eat anything, all the time, and not gain any additional weight — again, like her father.

Judy had offhandedly mentioned to her mother how her brothers had fed their lunches to her when she was hungry, after eating her own in elementary school. Lee said that she later asked each of the boys, "Why did you feed your lunch to your sister? You know that all you had to do was to tell me that she was still hungry and I would have put more in her lunch box." Lee told me that the reply she received from each of their son's was, "Mom, you and Dad have raised us to share and take care of each other, above all, our only sister! So we do. Anyway, she's our sister, if she asks — she can have!" Lee told how she gave each of her sons a hug as she told them, "You are right. You did the right thing. May you always look out for and take care of your sister — she is the sunlight of this house, and lives in the klowledge that you will look out for and take care of her."

* "You are not as bright or swift in your studies as your brothers, Judy, which you make up for in your doggedness! Surprisingly, you have no problem with mathematics, only with science, history and biology. After dinner, we all, while sitting around the table, pitch in to help you with your homework. Your father takes history, your brothers and I, science and biology. But it is Kam, who is the best at enabling you to understand a theory, concept, formula, etc. I watch your face as he's explaining something to you, and I marvel at your intense attentiveness. It's amazing and pleasant to watch for I am reassured that you will always be safe in the bosom of your family, because your brothers have gained at an early age a sense of love, responsibility, and support for their sister. That's good, and I thank God!

* "You sometimes rant and rage at your brothers, and to me about them over some minor disagreement. You claim that they always want to boss you around — tell you what you can and can't do, etc. I take you in my arms, Judy, and tell you, that your

brothers are not trying to boss you around only attempting to take care of you — they love you and don't want to see you get hurt. You also know, Baby, not like your brothers, you have no fear, believing that you can do anything. Well, you can't! And some of things that your brothers stop you from doing are dangerous — like riding on the handlebars of your girlfriend's bicycle!

"What I did not tell you, Baby, as I held you loving in my arms close to my heart, was that you will never know how lucky you are to have loving and caring brothers! I was not so lucky growing up. I had a verbal and physical abrasive older brother.

* "Judy, you win awards in penmanship, art, spelling, and mathematics — which your father framed and hangs on your bedroom walls. I am not worried about you, Baby, you will make it! When your father and I have gone to out reward (hopefully), and you need a little help, we will rest in peace, because we know that we would have left you in the good hands of your brothers — who dearly love their sister!

* "I can still remember that Christmas in 1979, when you were ten years of age, Judy. You wanted as your expensive present, every child, ever Christmas, was allowed one expensive gift, from your father and I, a pair of fine crafted, tan, leather knee high boots that cost $179. Your father told you, 'No way! The limit is $150 for each of you.' You made no complaint, Baby, and we continued on our mall hopping.

"Christmas morning, as you opened your presents, you opened one that had no 'From' name tag on it. It contained your $179 boots! Your father and I were shocked, and looked at each other with our mouths open as we mentally asked each other, 'Who?' You were elated! Screaming your joy, as you happily turned to your brothers with a boot in each hand, and told them, 'Thank you!'

"Afterwards, and when your brothers had left the living

room where the Christmas Tree was and we had opened our presents, I asked you Judy, 'How did you know your boots were from your brothers — there was no tag on the box?' You replied, 'I just knew. They love me, and will do anything to see me happy — and I am happy with my boots! I never asked them for my boots!'

"I later spoke to your brothers when you were not around and they told me the same thing that you did — you had not asked them to get your boots. That's good, because you all have been taught, not to ask each other, your friends, or friends of the family for gifts — what you receive should be freely given as their choice. They told me that they loved you, even if you are always screaming about something and turn everything on at full volume, and that you could have anything you wanted, as long as we did not object. 'Dad did not say, 'No', only that it was too expensive for his children's Christmas budget. We each took money from our saving accounts to give our sister her boots.'

"I gave each of your brothers a kiss on the cheeks, along with a tight hug, as I told them, 'Your are truly good brothers to your sister! Your father and I are very proud of you — never change your caring and loving relationship that you have with your sister because she lives in that assurance.

* "As you grow old, Judy, it is apparent to all your pride in Kam's every accomplishment. You have often told me, confidentially how bright Kam is and he knows everything! I smile as I tell you, 'Yes, Baby, Kam is very quick and bright, but does not know everything. A lot, yes, but not everything. Like you, he also is learning. Baby, we all have gifts that we were born with to give the world: Kam, his brightness; you, your doggedness, happiness, your love of family, your genuine kindness to people, and your love of all animals especially dogs and horses! Baby, you are a good daughter and person, and I would not have you change for the world! I love you, and always will, just the way you are!"

LEE

For me, it was a joy to be in the Jones' household when Judy was a teenager, she would have her television and radio on at full volume in her bedroom on the second floor. She would be on the first floor, performing some task in the eating area, sitting room, living room or in the kitchen with her mother. The televisions and radios in these areas also on full volume! Judy, would be happily dancing around with a walkmen on her head, doing whatever was beneath her hands. If you think that Judy was not listening to each of her noise makers — make the mistake and attempt to turn the volume down ,or turn them off, and you would immediately receive a loud reaction from Judy, "Hey! Leave that alone, I am listening to that!" Jokingly, I once asked Lee, "Do you really believe that she is listening to all that she has on?" Lee smiled, softly laughed, and told me, "I really don't care is she is listening or not. It makes her happy, and that's all that matters to me."

When Judy turned thirteen, Sooner II was still alive. Judy grew up loving and caring for that old dog with her father. She taught the dog to follow her when she played any one of three songs on her tape player. It was the most hilarious scene you could imagine, to see Judy sitting on the floor in the sitting room, with an arm around Sooner II's neck, singing loudly (and she could not carry a tune even if it was on a platter), one of the songs that she has taught the dog — the dog's head back, howling. Judy was a spontaneous type of person, she could be reading, watching television, listening to the radio, talking, dancing, performing some task for her father or mother, when out of the blue, she would call to the dog, "Come baby! Come to the one that loves you! Come sing with me!" Sooner II would come running, her tail going a mile a minute!

Judy's godmother was Lee's best friend from the Republic de Panama, who had married before her in Panama, then came to the United States of America with her husband. Judy's

302

godparents, who I had met on numerous occasions when they came to visits their goddaughter, lived in Brooklyn, New York, and owned a dry goods store there. Very quickly, the godparents undertook the responsibility for Judy's clothing and jewelry. I was made to understand by Lee, that Spanish Girls grew up with an abundance of gold jewelry (when possible), without explaining why — and I did not know enough to ask. The godparents had no children, and all the clothing and jewelry that they gave their goddaughter, came from the top, upscale shops of New York City. What they did not bring during their frequent visits, was shipped to Judy. There was never a week that went by, that when I visited Lee's and Jones home, that Judy did not have some new finery or jewelry to saw and model for me that her godparents had sent her from New York City. Even as a child, Judy looked stunning in everything she wore — tall, thin, long straight reddish hair, large dark eyes, and clear facial skin. The joy of being in Judy's company, was that she appeared not to know what a fashion plate she was and didn't seem to care! As I watched her grow into a very beautiful young woman, the most important things in her life I observed — in this order, were, "When is Dad coming home? Where's Mom?" and "Where and what are my brothers doing?" Judy was a very happy, laughing, dancing, singing, loud like her father, animal lover, fun loving, personable, and a joy to behold in her happiness with life. Judy, truly, as Lee often said, as she watched her only daughter with pride and love, "Was the sunshine of the house and family."

* "Oh, Judy, I am amazed and so very happy over how tall and healthy you are growing! You did give us a very bad scare when you were nine months old. I don't even want to think about that time!

"In my happiness over your healthy progress, I just had to stop, and place my happiness on paper for you to let you know how very, very much you are loved by us all — but above all your father! You will never know, even if you live to be a hundred, how very important you will always be to his well being.

"I often watch the interaction between you two, and have come to understand that the rules you play by — only you two can understand. You, Judy, shouting at your father because he will not allow you to do something that you want to, like talk to your friends on the telephone before finishing your homework — the house rule is that no telephone use, until one's homework is finished. You continue to shout your case as your father calmly continues to read his book sitting on the sofa in the sitting room — telling you, 'Let me know when you are finished.'

"You browbeat your father for another ten minutes, attempting to have your way, I am in the kitchen, which is off the sitting room, washing the dinner dishes, when I hear you tell him, 'I am finished! Now what do you have to say, Dad?' I know what is coming, so I stop washing the dishes, wipe my hands on a dish towel, as I silently come to the kitchen doorway to watch. Your father looks up form his book and over his eyeglasses, 'The answer is still no — homework first! I love you, Baby!' and went back to his book.

"Your face is red with anger. I sometimes think that you are about to burst you are so mad; as you remained standing in front of your father (who is not even looking at you) for a few moments then you jump in your father's lap, bury your head in his face and neck, as both of your arms go around his upper body, as you tell him, 'I love you so much Daddy!' His book pushed aside by your jump, he makes you comfortable in his lap, as he continually, gently, rubs and pats you on your back while softly repeating, 'I know Honey! I know Honey!' You lay in your father's arms with a serene expression on your face that is only there in moments after your anger with your father has subsided. After a few minutes, you get out his lap as you tell him, 'I am going to do my homework now.' He replies, 'Okay,' and returns to his book.

"When I am sure that you are in your bedroom with your door closed Judy, with my hand over my mouth to keep from laughing at your failed attempt to get your way — I leave the kitchen and join your father in the sitting room. I remove my hand, and softly begin to laugh standing in front of your father, as I tell him, 'That child is something else! One minute, she is so angry with you, she could have bust her gut! The next moment, loving you up!' Your father smiles at me over his book as he tells me, 'I know Honey. What can I say? That's just the way she is! I really don't care how often or loudly she shouts or becomes angry with me, she knows I love her just the way she is! She's ours and is here — which is enough for me.'

"Your father loves you, Baby.

* "Your father told me today, Judy, that he asked you to promise him, that you would never cut your hair as long as he was alive, and you agreed. That was nice. You are a good daughter, Baby.

* "I became very annoyed with you today, Judy! Ever since you have had the ability to look over my stove in the kitchen, I have allowed you to use it — supervised, until you become a teenager it to bake your cookies and cakes for your brothers, father, me, friends of the family, your friends, and to take to school. But today you baked a three layer cake to take to school, then walked out of my kitchen and left it in a mess! You did not, and that was our agreement when I allowed you the freedom of my kitchen, clean up after yourself! You know that I do not like a dirty kitchen!

"If you ever again, do what you did today — leave my kitchen in a mess, you will loose the right to use my kitchen — forever!

"I have told you all of the above, Judy, and am putting what

I have told you on paper, to remind myself that I have warned you. I don't like being annoyed with you, Baby."

From a very early age, Judy was again, like her father a Liberal. When she heard, read, or saw on television some tragedy, her immediate response would be, "How can they be helped? Who is helping them? Can we help?" Judy was not like her mother, brothers, nor I, whom were all conservatives. Upon being exposed to the same information as Judy, our immediate response would be, 'What did they do to get themselves in their present situation?' Sadly, we conservatives, as a general rule, only recognized the unseen hand in economic and not in people's lives. During the eighties, when President Ronald Reagan, and all those millions and I was one of his supporters, that supported his mean spirited domestic policies, a results of which has sit us back as a people fifty years! Jones and I had many, heated, long discussions about Reagan's mean spirited policies (blaming the victim) that affected real people — never agreeing! At the end of each such discussion, Jones would always ask me, this same question, while at the same time providing the answer, "My friend, do you know what the different between a liberal and a conservative is? A liberal wants to help, and a conservative wants to know why!"

I was advisedly affected by one of President Reagan's mean spirited policies. The means testing of a disabled veterans benefits (during WW II, Reagan never saw combat stayed in the states making training films). Veterans had to pay for the service received at a Veterans Hospital (because of Reagan's budget defect) for wounds received during combat if their means test demonstrated that they could afford to pay. That was not the contract that this nation made with its disabled veterans; if you are wounded or injured in service to the nation, you will be medically taken care of — free, during your lifetime. Reagan changed the contract without any national debate on the subject! It's an insult! There was no means testing on the 5th of July, 1950, when I was hit eight times by North Korean small arms rounds in the legs, arms and chest, that has prevented me from living a normal life ever since! Jones warned me, quoting Reagan's record as Governor of California and that he was an empty vessel — waiting to be filled by the moneyed interest if this country. But I would not listen and voted for him anyway, to my detriment.

* "I am so proud of you, Judy! When your co-workers at your after high school job at the teen shop in the mall were making insulting, intolerant remarks about some young Spanish teenage girls customers behind their backs as they shopped — you told me how it made you very angry!

"After the Spanish customers had made their purchases and left the shop, you said that you gave your co-workers a piece of your mind! Telling them, you would not work with, or call them friends who were public bigots! What you felt and thought about someone different than yourself, was your business, but keep it to yourself, for the Spanish speaking people had as much right to live in this country as them, for their great grandparents came from another country to America! My mother is Spanish! My mother has never been on welfare! My father is married to my mother! My father works, lives at home that we own, takes care of all of us, has never done or sold drugs, does not drink and has never hit my mother!

"You told me how your co-workers quickly, embarrassingly, apologized, assuring you that it would never happen again, and that they were sorry for the things that they had said about the Spanish girls, not knowing that you were part Spanish. You said that you told them, 'Me being part Spanish, makes no difference — you should not say or think those things about anyone different than yourselves, we are all people!'

"Sadly, Baby, your co-workers were showing you what type of conversations goes on in their homes concerning those different than themselves. Their parents refuse to acknowledge the undisputed fact, that there are more European Americans on welfare, than Spanish Americans or Spanish speaking people living in the country!

"We have raised you right. Love you, Baby, and never tolerate a bigot in silence!"

On an extremely, bitterly cold Saturday morning in February of 1988, Judy, who was six months into her eighteenth year of life, accompanied by her boyfriend — Tony — went in his car to the parking lot of the dance hall where they had been dancing the previous night, to retrieve her 1978 Mercury Monarch. Judy had purchased her car with her savings to take her back and forth to work in the mall. The Mercury would not start the night before due to the bitterly cold weather. With Tony sitting in his parked car — engine running, heater on full blast, behind Judy's Mercury, Tony later said that he offered to start Judy's car for her. But she refused his offer, telling him, no thanks, I know how to start it, and his view blocked by the raised hood of her car, he waited. The Mercury started and Tony said that he waited for Judy to close the hood of her car — when he saw both of Judy's legs fly above the Mercury's open hood! The headlines of the area's local paper screamed in bold black type:

GIRL STRANGLED IN FREAK ACCIDENT

Scarf dragged victim into car engine yesterday morning (Judy was wearing a twelve foot multi-colored scarf knotted around her neck)

TEEN KILLED IN FREAK ACCIDENT

FREAK MISHAP KILLS WOMAN, 18

When Jones telephoned me and told me of Judy's death, I screamed, "No!" and abruptly hung up on him in shock! I immediately got into my car and speedily drove to Lee's and Jones' home. As I drove, I could not believe that once again, Lee and Jones were confronting, yet another, horrific tragedy. Another of their children was dead! I was beginning to believe that God has no power — only the Devil!

After Judy's burial, I practically lived in Lee's and Jones' home! To help in their hour of need, the two people that I dearly loved and cared for whom had cried themselves dry and were going around in a shell shock like trance. Often, the only help that I could give them was no more than I was there when they wanted to talk about some past event in Judy's life, always beginning the conversation with, "Do you remember the time...?" My heart ached for them! The sunlight went out with Judy's death for that entire family! None of them were ever the same again. They laughed less, they smiled only with their lips, and their eyes appeared to have a veil over them, disbelief that Judy could have died so violently! Lee often said that the Devil wanted to make sure he killed her, because she was too happy to live in this world!

Today, nine years after the death of his daughter, Jones still blames himself for Judy's death, for it was he, who taught her how to start her Mercury in bitterly cold weather — had judy not known how to start her Mercury. Jones says that he would have had to start it for her. Jones, also condemns himself for not being vigilant enough with Judy — remembering what her doctor had said when she was nine months old about her making it to eighteen years of age. Meaning that only with regards to her lungs, but Jones said that over the years, he developed the mind-set concerning Judy's well-being, that once she turned eighteen, he was home free! He now say's that he was wrong, because he forgot Tony Danza's comment about children, "When we were kids, you made a mistake, you ended up with a bloody nose. Now you make a mistake and you could end up dead. So you have to be real vigilant with your kids!"

Today, Jones still says, that every Saturday morning, from 6am (the time Judy left her home with Tony) through 11am (when she was pronounced brain dead) the entire sequences of events surrounding his daughter's death — still replays in his head like a motion picture film.

It was Lee who was totally devastated by Judy's death, for not only her only daughter, but her best friend! When Lee begins to call off the names of the daughters in their upper middle class neighborhood, who are on hard drugs, have babies out of wedlock — claiming that they don't need a man to raise their child, (forgeting, that it took the father to put it inside of her), smoke, get sloppy drunk, steal from the mall stores/shops and think it's funny because they are not caught and if they are caught, freed with no charges being pressed because of where they live and are out and out teenage prostitutes! I say nothing, as Lee continues, "Judy had none of societies social ills, yet she is dead, and the daughters of those that do live!" Then Lee would put her red with a rage-bloated face close to mine, with tears running down her cheeks, and ask me screaming, in an angry and grief stricken voice, "Why me daughter? Oh God, please someone, tell me why my Baby?" When I hear the anguish question of why, from Lee, my shared grief overcomes me, and I am crying with her.

When I have been able to control my tears, I tell Lee, "I don't know why Judy had to die, when all those that knew and loved her, knew that she should have been, somehow, allowed to live by God, or whatever force is out there. For in her too short eighteen years, Judy had never harmed any animal, man, woman or child! Living is the only answer to our shared sorrow and pain over the death of Judy, I tell Lee. Maybe, before each of us join in her journey of no return, we will come to understand the why of her brutal and violent death." I sure hope so.

When I once a month visit Judy's grave, I always find one or more single long stem red rose — her favorite flower, laying at the base of her monument, left there by those who had preceded me. I go alone because I inevitably cry. I can still see Judy and

Sooner II sitting on the floor of the sitting room of her home, loudly singing! I am ready to swear, that sometimes, as I silently stand before her grave, that I can actually hear her, and that also dead, old dog singing together!

I think as I stand before her grave, there she lies — tombstone still sturdy, the inscription still legible, "A feeling of sadness come o'er me that my soul cannot resist," and specifically, '1969-1988.' With tears running down my cheeks, I think, here buried and helpless, lies all the love that could not be bestowed. I have held in retrospect, in a sort of wonderment, that very young, dead Judy. Tall, thin, beautiful, with her long straight reddish hair flowing from her head as she ran to greet me whenever I came to visit, unworldy, full only of love for family and life, like a flower blossom that never had the opportunity to completely open. Pity, that I could not breathe back into her some of the life she once gave us.

* "It has been five years since you died Judy, and it had taken that long for me to be able to pen my good-bye to you, Baby.

"For ever two years, I spiritually and mentally lost your father due to your death — he withdrew so deeply within himself, that I thought he would never be able to return to us from the dark recesses of his mind that he had ran to hide!

"But I gave him no peace! I argued with him, 'It's no one's fault but the Devil's that Judy is dead — above all, not yours!' Smoothed your father with love — 'When he would go into the darkened cellar, to keep me from seeing him cry, because he knew that it upset me. I would pretend that I did not know what he was doing, and when he would finally come upstairs, I would go to him, and gently take him in my arms and softly kiss him about the lips and face as I told him, 'It will be alright, in time, Honey. I will always love and take care of you!' And I would feel his hot, silent tears on my face, as I would hold him that much closer to my heart. Kept him near, wherever I was, he had to be 'No more projects that would take him out of my sight!" Anytime

I left the house for any reason, 'I demanded (would not accept from him, 'I don't feel like going out) that he accompanied me!' Never let your father forget that we needed him here with us, because I and your brothers loved him, and hiding in the recesses of his mind, would not bring you back to life, Baby.'

When your father finally worked his way (with a lot of support from his many friends at E.G. and G.) back to us through the shock of your death, Baby, he is a changed man! It's as if a light has been turned off inside of him. I also pretend, when we go out, that I do not see him longingly watching other fathers with daughters about your age as he silently bemorns our lost. When I catch him watching the permanent hole in the center of my chest — that has been there since you died, Baby, fills up and for a few moments, I am unable to speak as my heart goes out to your father in his lost. I even suggested that we adopt a baby girl, and your father said no, because he claimed that if we did, "Everytime I would look at the baby, I would think, that no matter what we did, we would only be raising her to become a teenager, and then killed!" I left it alone.

"Your face, Baby, was so distorted by the violent method of your death (they had to cut your beautiful long hair to untangle you from the cars engine), that the only thing that looked like my lovely Baby who I loved and nurtured to a beautiful young woman, were your hands folded across your waist, holding your Rosary — laying there so cold and still in your casket!

"Tony was never the same after witnessing your death, Baby. He blamed himself, for not even going to the front of your car to see what had happened, but rather, running for help — that took all of fifteen minutes, according to the Police. His parents, friends, teachers, priest, professional medical trauma councilors, and us did all we could to save him by repeatedly telling him, that he was in no way responsible for Judy's death, because the moment her legs flew over that raised car hood, Judy's neck was broken! But we lost. Two years after you died, Tony's parents had to commit him to a out of state private mental institution, where he remains as I pen my good-bye to you Baby. We all pray, that somehow, someday, he will return to us, for he is a good boy.

"In the past, before your death, Baby, everything, the good and the bad, to include the horrible things that have repeatedly happen to us as a family, seemed to just a part of life, the future would always be better, and our tragedies just a temporary setback on the road to happiness. On February 6, 1988, I found that I was holding fast to a lie! Judy, you are dead, and my grief is constant and permanent!

"There are those that are worried about my anger, and tell me that I should let it go, your death." I don't need anyone to tell me about my enormous anger! You are dead Baby, and I am not supposed to feel anger?

"I do all the things I did when you were alive, Baby, but the passage of time has not helped! I am in pain all of the time. My grief is always there.

"When I sleep, I dream of you, Baby! Bad dreams. Sad dreams. Happy dreams, which make me feel good all over. After such a happy dream, I wake up and my suffering and pain begins anew!

"Good-bye my Baby. I miss you so! It's not fair! I will always love you, and never forget the happiness that you brought into my life! There is no God!"

> "Never fear spoiling children by making them happy. Happiness is the atmosphere in which good affections grow — the wholesome warmth necessary to make the heart-blood circulate healthy and freely."

> *Thomas Bray*

21.

HUGO

In April of 1971, Lee's fifth and last child was born. A son, after a very difficult pregnancy and delivery, that Jones named Hugo. Sometime after Lee returned home with the new addition to her family was when she and Jones told me the story of Hugo's birth. The birth of Hugo, came very close to Lee loosing her life, along with that of the baby's. This is the story they told me:

Hugo was an eleven month baby! This only occurs, with the baby surviving, one in one hundred thousand births (1971 figures). Lee told how she and her United States Navy Lieutenant Obstetrician got the count right, how many months she was actually pregnant, but when the seventh and eighth months passed with no signs that the baby was going to be born, they became very anxious.

From the eighth month onwards, Lee said that she began to experience constant, debilitating pain at the bottom of her enlarged belly and between her legs — so bad that she could hardly walk! Jones related how he took an extended leave of absence form the bank in order to take care of Lee and the other three children. When Lee's pain became unbearable, Jones said that the only way he could relieve it, was to submerge her in a bathtub of hot water — just as hot as she could stand, to soak until the water cooled, while he gently rubbed her enlarged belly with both of his hands.

Ninth, tenth months passed into the eleventh month, and still the baby would not come! Lee recounts how she came close to loosing her mind, attempting to bear the pain that was constantly beneath her large belly and between her legs! Being driven to the hospital everyday — (very slowly, because every jolt sent a spasm of pain through her body). Not being able to do anything for herself or family, except to lay in bed — exhausted!

Lee's Navy Obstetrician wanted to place her on painkillers, with she and Jones vehemently opposing! Their reasoning — no one had any idea what the painkillers would do to their baby, and as long as there was a chance for him or her to be born healthy; they wanted to so nothing that might endanger its chances by use of the painkillers.

It was halfway through the eleventh month, during their daily visit to the hospital — after talking it over the night before about the baby Lee was carrying it was killing her, they decided to abort the baby! It was during that visit, Lee and Jones asked her Obstetrician to abort the baby! He responded, "Believe me, I know that Lee is going through Hell, for I suffer with her, because I am unable to bring the baby or ease her pain. I can not abort the baby, because I can see the top of it head each time that I examine Lee. The baby was in the proper position to be delivered, and why it would not come, I have no idea. Every test that I have had Lee take, all have come back normal! I have been reading every medical textbook that I can lay my hands on about Delayed Pregnancy. Acquiring no information on Lee's situation. I have been telephoning around the country, talking to prominent Obstetricians (in and out of the military), about Lee's case with none of them being able to give me a reason why this is happening to her! But what I am going to do, today, is to admit Lee to the hospital and induce labor, if that fails, then I will surgically deliver the baby." Lee and Jones immediately agreed — that meant the pain would stop!

Lee continued by telling how after her labor was induced, Hugo completed his entry into the world, ending her exhaustion. When Jones came to see Lee in her hospital room after viewing their baby through the Baby Viewing Room Glass, he told her how there was a large sign, with bold red lettering at the head of Hugo's crib: Miracle Baby — 11 months! That was when Lee said that Jones told her, "No more children! I almost lost you, and I will not see you suffering like that again for want of another! We now have four children, and what you went through to bring this one into the world, maybe a warning to us to stop!

[Several years later, Jones told me and Lee, that the reason he was afraid to have anymore children, was because of the aftereffects that Agent Orange was having on those that fought in the Vietnam War. Everyone that he knew who were in Vietnam with him and had children since they returned — all of their children have been born with some type of birth defect. One former comrade — had four children, since he returned from Vietnam; one with six toes on each foot, another with only four toes on each foot, a son with no testicles, and a daughter born blind. When he realized from reading the American Legion's magazine articles on Agent Orange and birth defects, he stopped having anymore children — angry with his government and what they had done to him and his children! It was to late for those children already born.

The information about the aftereffects of Agent Orange, was just beginning to be published in the American Legion's magazine (the United States Government claimed that there were no after effects — which they knew was a lie), when Lee was carrying Hugo, and during all of her pain and difficulties with Hugo, Jones said that he was constantly hunted by the thought of the possibility that he might be the unwittingly cause of Lee's pain and suffering, because he knew, for over the year that he that he was in Vietnam, that he had operated in Agent Orange deforest areas! He also, now, wonders if that might not be the reason Judy came early and her lungs underdeveloped.]

Lee said as Jones held her gently in his arms, as he kissed her lips while stroking her face and hair with his hand, as she sadly told him, "Okay. But I am so sad, for I promised you, when you told me that you wanted children, that I would always be ready and have as many as you want." Jones said, "Yes, I remember. But do you also remember what I told you Honey, concerning children? I will always love and care for you, with or without children!" Lee told him, "Okay" again, as Jones continued to hold her close to his chest. With his arms around her upper body, he gently rocked her back and forth while sitting on the side of the hospital bed, that day of the birth of their last child!

[In the eighties, after bring tested by the Veterans Administration, Jones has been informed that he was exposed and his system infected with Agent Orange from fighting the war in Vietnam.]

Lee told how, that before she left the hospital with Hugo to come home, she had her tubes tied because she also believed that she could not live through another episode of pain like she experienced while carrying him!

* "Oh Hugo, at last, you are here — safely and apparently healthy! When they laid you on my belly, I could not believe that I was looking at my baby — your hair had grown to where it covered all of your face, your skin was peeling from your body, and your fingernails were so long, that even before the doctor cut the cord that still connected us, the delivery nurses were cutting your fingernails — one to each hand.

"You almost didn't make it You almost killed me (along with yourself) with pain by taking eleven months to decide to join your loving mother in her world! Carrying you past term was so painful, that your father and I asked my doctor to abort you in your eleventh month! He wouldn't. Labor was induced — and happily, here you are Honey!

"Not only are you special, Hugo, I like your name — it's Spanish, because you are a eleventh month baby, but you are the last child your father and I will ever have! Do you know what that means? Every time that we look at you, silently we think, 'There stands our very last child, there will never be anymore!' You gave your mother a bad time getting here, but I tell you, Love, that, in no way diminishes my love for you!

* "Already, everyone comments how much you look like your father, even though he denies it — saying that you look like me. You do have my reddish hair, very light brown eyes, my ears, and facial features, but there is just something about you that makes everyone to include myself, think when they look at you, "There goes your father!' No matter. I lone you, Honey!

With the addition of Hugo to the family, Lee and Jones took him home to their third house that allowed for the continuation of the practice for allowing each of their children to have a bedroom for themselves. And it was in this third home of theirs that Hugo spent his formative years. When they moved in 1978 to their fourth home in another town, at the end of the moving day, Hugo asked, "Mom, when are we going home?" From Hugo's question, we all come to realize that it was the third home where he had his first memories of his life — and that would always remain "Home" to him!

* "You are such a good baby, Hugo! Chubby, happy, and so easy to please. I don't know what it is, but I always want to be in your company or have you in my arms. I love you so, baby!

* "We had a frightful experience when you were three months old Hugo. Your father has a rule of making everyone's medical appointments. We had just returned home from your three month checkup, when we noticed that your face was a bright red and you were burning up with fever! We speedily

returned with you to the hospital. You were immediately admitted, and placed in an oxygen tent!

"You remained hospitalized for ten days, and to this day, neither your Navy Pediatrician, other General Physicians nor the specialists that were called in to examine you were able to determine what was wrong worth you! Your medical record still reads, "Hospitalized for unknown causes."

"After that hospitalization, you grew with no major health problems requiring you to ever again to be hospitalized — thank God! I note your only hospitalization, for I am still baffled by it. Love you dearly, Hugo!

* "With your other siblings, Hugo, when they were babies, if I was late in their feeding — they would loudly let me know about it! Not you. You lay or stand in your crib, eyes open, smiling, waiting, knowing that your Mom was on her way to feed her lovely, chubby, happy baby! Whenever I found you like that — waiting — I can not control my happiness, and rain kisses all over your chubby face and body as you squealed with delight!

"You will never know the joy that I take in caring for you, as I did with all your siblings — but with you, it's a special joy! I guess it's because I know that you are my last baby, and I want to savor every moment of this last experience! I love you so, Hugo!

* "Your siblings have you spoiled already, Hugh, especially your older brother, Robert. He sits with a smile on his face, as he watches you when you are out of your playpen crawling around on the floor, or in your walker — learning to walk, always ready to catch you to keep you from falling and hurting yourself. If I have to attend another of your siblings, I can easily ask Robert to watch you until I return or continue to feed you, etc. Your oldest brother dearly loves you, Hugo, and Robert's love for his baby brother swells in my heart with joy!

* "Hugo, you are the only one of our children, that from the very first day of his life has been driven (never been in a carriage)

everywhere he has been taken, and as a result of that — you have an endearing love for cars!

"Until you came into the family, Hugo, we had with your siblings a rotation system, as to which of them would sit in the passenger seat of the VW bus, now they all say when it's their turn, 'Let Hugo sit in front!' Your siblings all know how you delight in seeing the many cars coming towards you on the other side of the street or highway! Hugo, you truly have good siblings. You are blessed beyond words.

* "Anytime I or your father go out, or our friends visit, we (they) bring something inexpensive for each of you. But you, Hugo, always receive a ten cent Matchbox Car. You have quite a collection of Matchbox Cars on display in their plastic display cases hanging on your bedroom walls.

"Not only do you display your Matchbox Cars, but you also play with them, and because of that, one weekend, your father built for you, without our knowledge, for he kept us all out of the cellar, "Hugo's Village" on a large wooden table that he constructed for that purpose. Your village came complete with many roads, houses, school, lake, hospital with a heliport, church, stores along main street, and one hill and mountain for you to play with your cars.

"You were never again so happy as when he finished, and called for us to come down into the cellar for he had something for Hugo. He really did a beautiful job, and you played and cared for your village well into your late teens. Your father loves you, Honey and takes great pleasure in doing things for his children. We are very lucky, that he is the way he is! Our children happy — then he is.

* "Keeping with your love of cars, Hugo, on your fourth Christmas, you received from your father and I, as your expensive present, a battery powered car that you could drive on the sidewalk.

"I write about your car because I originally was opposed to you getting it— for it was truly expensive, but your father insisted that he wanted you to have it! After I saw how much enjoyment you got from your car, I told your father that he was right to insist that you have it.

"Because you and your sister always play and do everything together, the day after Christmas because she asked for a car like her brothers, your father had to go and get her a foot peddle (she was to old for the battery power type of cars), white car (your's is black and red), in order that you both may go on what you call 'trips' back and forth on the sidewalk in front of our house.

"I love you so, Hugo! You are such a loving child. I am glad that it's you who is to be my last child!"

As with his sister, every school Hugo attended until high school, there were one or more of his siblings. With Judy, from Hugo's first grade onward, taking complete (never asked or told to) responibility to see that he had all of his outwear, lunch box, school books, etc. for whom she called her baby when school was over and time to return home, whom she called: "Her Baby!" As Hugo grew, he always remained for his sister, her baby! Being his sister's baby, often annoyed Hugo as a teenager (with many of us thinking that Judy sometimes just called hugo, her baby to annoy him) as he would loudly tell her, "I am not your baby, only Mom's and Dad's! And stop calling me your baby!" Judy would shyly smile at her baby brother, as she told him, "Yes, you are and will always be! For I am two years older than you — the only girl in the family and you are the last child, thereby, making you my baby!" All present for hearing Judy's perception of how she perceived the situation with her younger brother, would laugh loudly! Annoying Hugo that much more because he could not refute anything that Judy had said.

* "I have told you this Hugo, please don't be annoyed with your sister because she calls you her baby. She loves you, and

that's her way of expressing it. And if you will think about it, God forbid, is If should die before you are able to take care of yourself, it is your sister who would have to do all of the womanly things for you, your father and your brothers.

"Be thankful Hugo, that you have a sister. Sisters are a blessing no matter how much they may now and then annoy you, because they are in most families — the sunlight of the family! I have often wished that I had a sister — and I know, in some-things, I treat your sister more as my sister then my daughter.

"Never forget that Judy is the glue that will hold this family together — if something should happen to me, and only she can do it!

* "You are very good about doing your homework, Hugo. You never ask to do anything until you have finished.

"You are a Peaks and Valleys type of student — but that's okay, they are all passing grades! One thing I love about you — when I or your father are going over your school progress reports, and either of us tell you that you should attempt to do better in a particular subject, you tell us 'Okay!' And without ever having to repeat ourselves, you show improvement. Your father says that you will grow to be the man of the family, because already, at a very early age, understand the connection between doing what you say you will and can do! Love you, Hugo!

* "From the time you entered elementary school Hugh, you immediately linked up with the other rough and rowdy boys in your class. The Sisters and Lay Teachers are always complaining to me and the parents of your playmates that all of you play too rough with each other! They are afraid that you just might hurt each other! But you never do.

* "I have always worried about the friends your siblings choose to make, but not about yours. You and your rowdy friends seem to have a levelheadedness about you — you all seem to know just how far to go with each other, which is why

you don't hurt each other in your roughhousing play.

"Now that you are in high school, you have done the same thing as you did in elementary school, teamed up with the other three rough members of your class! But this is different, because I can see each of you are male bonding. I have met the parents of your three new friends as we drop you off at school in the morning and pick you up in the afternoon after class, and they all enthusiastically approve of the new friends you each have made! The reason for their approval, they claim that you four are exactly alike! Peaks and valleys students. Play rough. Do what you say you will do. Easy to get along with, and above all, very easy to love!

"As I pull into the driveway of your high school to pick you up in the afternoon, my heart swells with happiness to see you four standing together in your school's forest green blazers and/or sweaters, talking and laughing among yourselves, each looking so manly, healthy, happy, loved, and cared for. Hugo, it looks like you have made three friends for life! You truly, are enjoying your high school years, and that makes me happy!"

Hugo and his sister were very close because there was only two years between them. When Hugo came into Judy's life, she immediately proclaimed to all, that Hugo was her baby and belong to her! This announcement laid too many an amusing situation involving Judy attempting to care for what she called her baby!

* "Your sister is so funny! You are a solid, chubby, heavy baby, Hugo, and your sister is very thin and a lightweight when compared to you although, like her father, she eats all the time! The entire family will be in the living or sitting rooms reading, talking, watching television, playing some game, etc. And your sister will pick you up from crawling around on the floor, by placing both of her arms around your chest, as I ask her, "Why are you picking up your brother, Honey?" Receiving in reply, "I am going to sit my baby in my lap." I say nothing, just smile, as I wait for your sister to accomplish her task.

"I watch from the sofa, as your sister sitting on the floor, with great difficulty, arrange your solid — heavy body in her lap. Judy places both her arms around your ample waist, as she looks around your solid body at me with a smile of sheer delight, and a twinkle in her eyes and satisfaction in her voice, as she calls to me, 'Look Mom! I am holding my baby on my lap!'

"Hugo, you sit comfortably in your sister's lap, not attempting to get off. In a few minutes, your sister releases her arms from around your waist, Hugo, throw herself backwards on the floor (you have not moved) and with panic in her voice, screams, 'Mom! Someone! Help me! Get him off — he's crushing me!' I (or whoever is closest) quickly, laughing, rush to remove you from your sister's lap.

"Your sister never learned that you were just too heavy to be sitting in her lap, and continued that practice as long as you were a baby — always, with the same results. She calling for someone to remove you from her lap!

* "After your older brother Robert died, Hugo, you and your sister became even closer — never out of each other's sight when at home. Your closeness does not mean that you did not have your normal disagreements — you do!

"I never worry about you helping your sister, because I watch you two together. No matter how annoyed you get with her when she is doing "Her Thine," when she asks you for help, you never hesitate to give it Hugo, and Judy to you. You watch out for each other, and that's good!

"You have seemed to come to understand, at a very early age, Hugo, that your sister is secure in her love of family, and that now and then — when she does Ding-Bat things, it's just out of being happy and a part of who she is. You must never forget what your sister sometimes mentions when she becomes overwhelmed with some situations that involves only you boys and your father, 'It's not easy being the only girl, not counting Mom, in a household with four boys!' As you, yourself, have often told me, concerning your sister, 'She's ours and we love her!'

"I love you, Hugo

* "I will never forget that day we buried your sister Hugo. You came into your father's den that night where we were attempting to give each other comfort — just by being in the same room, and asked him hurt and annoyed, 'Dad, how could you have allowed this to happen?'

I was shocked by your question! "Your father was not angry, shocked, or annoyed by your question — he merely handed you a pad of paper and a ball point pen form his desk, which you took, as he told you, 'Write down every conceivable cause you can think of that your sister could die from. I am sure having her neck broken because her twelve foot scarf got caught in her automobile's engine will not be on your list!'

"You thought for a few moments — gave the paper and pen back to your father who was still sitting at his desk, as you told him, 'You are right. I am sorry, Dad!' Your father told you that it was alright for he understood what you were feeling and going through. Your sister's death, just makes no sense! You left the den and returned to your upper bedroom.

"Oh Hugo, my heart goes out to you in this, your hour of sorrow. So young and having to be confronted so soon in your life with the death of your sister!

"I guess, Hugo that in the end, that is what life is all about — there is no promise as to how long a life each of us will have. And for us, all that is left of our once large, happy brood, Hugh, is you, your father, Kam and I.

"Your father and I had just mentioned to each other before you entered the den, how, with the death of Judy, all of our hopes, dreams, and labor with regards to have many children, has run through our fingers — like sand!

* "My blood ran cold, Hugo, when you came to me in the

kitchen and told me of your fear that when your time comes, there will be no one to recognize your milestones of life: completion of high school, college, law school, marriage, children, etc.

"I cried as I held you in my arms, as I attempted to reassure you by holding you tight in my arms, that there would be someone, (I knew what you meant by "no one" — no brother) when you reached each of your milestones in life, even if it turned out to be only your father or I! I released you from my embraced and held on to both of your shoulders — as I sternly looked into your face with my tear-filled eyes and asked you, 'Do you understand me?' You told me, 'Okay, Mom,' and left the kitchen.

"Oh Hugo, my baby, I don't believe that I reassured you, and would do anything to lift that sense of foreboding that you are living with. You feel that your remaining brother, Kam, will not be there for you, when your time comes. Oh God, I pray everyday Hugo, that you are wrong!

"I love you so, and my heart goes out to you son, because you are truly our good child. You care and think about your father and I. You sincerely, deserve better than what you are getting out of life, one horrific tragedy after another!"

The work ethic was the corner stone of the foundation on which Lee and Jones raised their children—all honest work was honorable! From the age of eight, each child received a weekly allowance in order to teach them how to manage their money, of three dollars from their father for performing some assigned task around the house. Some of the children's allowance tasks consisted of: daily emptying the wastepaper baskets in each room into the trash can, bringing in the daily and Sunday newspaper, taking the dog out — twice a day, drying the meals dishes (before Lee received her dish washer) — Lee has no problem washing dishes but disliked drying them, help wash the cars, cut the grass, rake the leaves in the fall, and only the boys — shovel the snow with their father during the winter. When Lee's and Jones' children turned fifteen years of age, it was required that they must obtain some type of job, amount of the pay — not a consideration for not working, during school summer vacation.

* "Oh Hugo, you are only fourteen, and want to get a job for the summer!

"I have attempted, unsuccessfully, to convince you to wait until you are fifteen like your brothers and sister. Telling you that you did not have to work, and that you are only going to be fourteen this one time in your life and to savor the moment. But you are adamant, and your father approves.

"During our nightly pillow talk, your father tells me that what you are doing is a good thing, and that the work ethics we have taught the children has also taken hold in you. Your desire to work is as normal as breathing and walking.

"I realize that what your father tells me is correct. I also know that my publicly expressed concerns over you going to work early, Hugo, is no more than my desire to keep my last child close for another year.

"Hugo, you will never see this or hear the words from my mouth, so I can trust it to paper — out all of my children, you are the only one who, when entering my presence, I smile inside! I don't know why or what my inside smile means, but I do."

Hugo's character, if it had to be defined by one word, could only be described as reflective. He was noticeably different than his siblings: Robert — serious, Kam — bright, and Judy — happy.

Lee once related to me, the story of how she once asked Hugo about not having to get on his case about the same things as she did with his brothers and sister (picking up and cleaning their rooms, returning borrowed items, performing their allowance task, etc.). The reply she received, "I watch what gets my brothers and sister into trouble with you and Dad, and then I don't do it!"

* "Now that you are driving, in college, working after your classes at a bank, I have to tell you how happy and proud I am of you, Hugo. You never forget your mother and the little things that matter to her.

"The thing that will forever endear me to you, Hugo, is that once or twice a week you bring me ice cream, even though there is always some in the freezer. It's not the actual ice cream, but the realization that you think enough about me to bring what you call my surprise.

"I will take your love and thoughtfulness to the grave with me, Hugo.

* "All my friends tell me how fortunate I am to have as a teenager and college student, a son who will readily drive me around and enjoy doing it, as you do, Hugo!

"I tell my friends, it's because we both love to drive! But, I also know it's your way without words of taking care of me. If Mom wants something, Mom gets it, to include being driven about when she desires.

You are so good to me, Hugo, and I will always love you for your caring ways.

* "I, along with everyone else that knows the story, still laugh over the time your father asked you, Hugo 'Where do you plan to go to college?' You told him, 'I am no fool! I am not going to leave home like Kam did! Some college nearby.'

"Both your father and I told you that Kam had the right to choose the college he did. With you replying, 'Yes, that's true, but he left his family!'

"I then understood that Kam's going away to West Point only reinforced your fear that there would be no one here to celebrate your milestones of life.

"Oh, my poor child!"

Ever since he could talk, and you asked Hugo what did he want to be when he grew up, he would reply, "A Lawyer!" He completed his undergraduate studies at a college near his home — receiving a BS in Accounting, borrowed the money on his signature, and immediately entered Law School, while remaining living at home.

* "You married another law student in your first year of law school Hugo! Why couldn't you and she wait until you both had finished? My God!

* "Anyway, it's done Hugo. Even I, along with everyone else, can see that you both are in love! I also know that love is blind. I sincerely pray and hope that you both will always be happy and in love with each other — you have a hard road ahead of you!

* "Your father Hugo is very upset about your law school debt, your wife's undergraduate, law school, and personal debts and her parents hostility to the marriage. I tell him, you both will be all right and to remember when we married, we had all of seven cents between us!

* "One thing your marriage did for your father and I Hugo was to open our eyes to the fact, that all those that have children and call themselves parents are not! We innocently, believed that no parent would teach hate to their children, only tolerance. The way your wife's parents behaved, Hugo, because their daughter married, and her husband happen to be you, is beneath contempt! Your wife's parents comments about you, Hugo, was mind-boggling, coming from two people whom have Masters Degrees, and exemplified the fact that no amount of education will eradicate race hate! They didn't even know you!

"Your father and I now know that what was once said and done in public in this country, about people of another race, is now said and done in the privacy of the home — where their children hear!

"With regards to the relationships between the peoples that make up this nation, nothing changes in the United States of America and the hate between the races. I now know, why your father never wanted to live in this country, once we met, fell in love in love and married!

"America is an evil place!"

> "To be able under all circumstances to practice five things constitutes perfect virtue: these five are gravity, generosity of soul, sincerity, earnestness, and kindness." (This is Hugo)
>
> *Confucius*

22.

DEATHBLOW

The circumstance surrounding the death of Lee, as told to me
by Jones, and that I witnessed.

[At 2:02 A.M., in the month of April, Lee got out her bed and
went to the bathroom and threw up in the toilet bowl the restaurant meal that she had consumed the night before of baked scrod,
string beans, mashed potatoes, white bread, lime Jell-O and tea.
When she returned to her bed and told Jones what had just happened, he told Lee that she possibly had eaten a bad piece of
scrod. Later that same night, around 3am, Lee had to leave her
bed again, and return to the bathroom to throw up! From 3am
onward, Lee remained in that state until Jones was able to convince her that she should allow him to take her to the hospital —
she was afraid of hospitals and doctors in this country. Jones took
Lee to the Emergency Room in the hospital of their managed care
health plan that was 52 miles from their home passing four other
hospital emergency rooms during their trip to the health plans
hospital.

They arrived at the hospital Emergency Room (ER) at 8:30
A.M. with the ER personnel immediately prepping Lee — running
a series of blood tests, x-rays, EKGs, with all the tests immediately being returned and appearing normal! The ER doctor said that
Lee's EKG looked as if she may have suffered some type of heart
attack, but he wasn't sure, based upon all the returned normal test

results. He then asked Lee, "When was the last time you had an EKG?" He was informed there, in October and December of 1994. The ER doctor said that he would obtain her past EKGs of October and December, and compare with those that he had. If there was a variance, that would confirm although it has not shown up in the tests that have been run — his tentative diagnosis that Lee may have suffered some type of heart attack, and he would then know how to treat her. The ER doctor also stated that he would not be able to obtain Lee's previous EKG's until Monday morning. Today, in this country, the weekend is the worst time to attempt to be serviced at any of the this nations hospitals, because to save money, they close everything down except the ER support services (X-Ray, Laboratory, etc.). In the meantime, the ER doctor continued, he was going to admit Lee to the hospital for observations, just in case she had suffered some type of heart attack, and if it reoccurs, for she seems fine now, she would be in the hospital, and in a better position to treat her.

The ER doctor then informed Lee and Jones that the reason he keeps mentioning may have suffered a heart attack was because Lee has experienced none of the telltale signs normally associated with a heart attack patient: acute pain in the chest, shortness of breath, and numbness on either her right or left sides — all she was experiencing was vomiting. The ER nurses had two intravenous bags going into Lee's arms. Whatever type of medication that was going into Lee, it quickly made her color return and she asked that the dolly be rolled up — in order that she could sit up, and that she be given a pillow for her head — which was done. Lee told the ER doctor and Jones, smiling, that she felt so good! No more pain from her constant vomiting or anywhere else in her body. Lee's positive comments about her physical state were made around 11:30am or noon.

Lee repeatedly from that time on told the ER doctor and Jones how good she felt and began to plead with Jones, "Please go home, Honey! Get something to eat. They normally went out for breakfast every Saturday morning. You know you what will happen if you don't eat — you will be sick! I feel fine. Everything is good with me!" Jones told Lee, "No, he wanted to stay there with her until he was absolutely sure she was alright, had been admitted, and settled in her hospital room." Lee, adamantly insisted that Jones go and not come back later that day, but tomorrow. Sunday, when he returned bring her some night-clothes, toilettes, her knitting, and what she needed to take care of her hair.

Jones said that he reluctantly agreed, because he could see that Lee was becoming upset because he had not eaten — and they both knew what the results of that could be. He reluctantly agreed to do as Lee asked — leave her and return Sunday with the items she requested. He left Lee, still on her dolly, after kissing her about the lips and face while holding her smiling face in both his hands as he softly told her, "Don't let anything happen to you, Honey, while I am gone. You know, that you are my reason for being, and I can't make it without you, Honey!" Lee, smiling, kissed Jones' back on his lips, as she also told him softly, "I know, Honey. I love you too, and nothing is going to happen to me. I feel just fine! I will see you tomorrow. Be careful driving home and get something to eat!" Little did he know then, that was to be the last words Jones would ever hear Lee speak, as she smilingly waved and throw him kisses as he left the ER for home.

When he arrived home, after stopping at McDonald's to eat a Big Breakfast, Jones telephoned Kam and his family in Brussels, Belgium, Hugo and his wife at their Saturday Law school classes, and me at my home to inform us of Lee's hospitalization and to share the little accompanying information he had as to what was wrong with her; with me at once leaving my home to drive to his. Approximately at 4:00 P.M., Jones received in my presence a telephone call from the female doctor of his managed health care plan that was on call for the weekend, who told him from her home — with her children playing in the background, very distressed, "I didn't want to call you, but no one at the hospital wanted to! I hate to have to tell you this — but we are loosing your wife! I am told (I am at home), your wife had a heart attack while still in the Emergency Room, and in administering some type of medication that was supposed to dissolve the blood clot in her heart, it threw her into a massive stroke! The stroke was such, that many blood vessels had burst in her brain, leaking blood into her skull — putting pressure on your wife's brain. The doctors at the hospital wanted permission from you, to drill a hole into your wife's skull to relieve the pressure on her brain. They had already helicoptered a neurosurgeon in from Maine to perform the operation." Jones told the doctor on the other end of the telephone line, No! Don't do anything to my wife until I can see her! I am on my way!

As we were about to make our speedy departure for the hospital, I told Jones, we will go in my car. Before we could get out of the front door, the telephone rang again, it was the neurosurgeon, whom Jones had never met, with Jones telling me to listen in on the other extension, because those damned doctor's have messed Lee up! The doctor from Maine immediately attempted to convince Jones to allow him to drill into Lee's skull to relieve the pressure on her brain. Telling Jones, "If I do not relieve the pressure on your wife's brain, she will die!" Jones angrily told the doctor, "I will not give you permission to drill into my wife's skull, or to do anything to her — until I first see her!" The doctor on the other end of the telephone, equally angry, told Jones, "I don't need your permission! This is a dire life emergency!" Receiving, in voice so soft, it was as if he was shouting, this reply from Jones, "You drill a hole into my wife's skull without my permission, and I guarantee you that I will find you — and you will not live to drill another!" They hung up on each other.

Jones and I made the mad rush in my car to the hospital in record time, as I telephoned via my car phone, Hugo and his wife at their Law School, telling him that his mother had taken an unexpected turn for the worse and to meet us at the hospital. Which they later did.

Lee was still laying on the dolly in the Emergency Room (ER) and the first thing that Jones and I notice, was that an area of her head had already been shaved where the neurosurgeon intended to drill his pencil size hole. Surrounding Lee, unconscious, with a horrible expression of shock and bewilderment on her face, as if she was silently pleading, "What's happening to me?" was the neurosurgeon, two other doctor's (one female, the other male) and two ER nurses. Lee was experiencing spasm that were effecting her right arm and hand — causing her hand to raise to her face as if she was about to claw her cheek! Jones immediately took Lee's right wrist and forcibly held her arm to her side, as he leaned over her while repeating, "I am now here, Honey. I love you Honey! Everything will be all right!"

Bending to kiss Lee's lips, Jones discovered that she had almost bitten her tongue in half and her mouth was full with blood! Angrily, he shouted at those surrounding Lee's dolly, "What the Hell is the matter with you people! To leave her like this! Give me something to clean my wife's mouth out now! While telling me to hold her right arm down — which I did. As Jones gently began to clean the blood from Lee's mouth, he began to softly cry (and I too), as he began to mournfully mouth the words, "Oh Honey! My Baby! What have they done to you? I should have never left you!" As Jones continued his cleaning of Lee's mouth, the neurosurgeon began anew to tell us, what he wanted to do, and why it should be done immediately. Along with the consequence, if he was not allows to relieve the pressure on Lee's brain — she would die! At that time, Hugo, his wife, and Lee's and Jones' surrogate son, a friend of Hugo's from high school whom Lee and Jones loved and claimed as their own, arrived. Upon seeing the condition that Lee was in, they hugged each other in a circle and began to softly cry over what was surely her pending death!

I was still forcibly holding Lee's right arm down on the dolly, to keep her from clawing her right cheek, when Jones raised from finishing cleaning the blood out of Lee's mouth. Turning his red, bloated, dry eyed, angry face to the neurosurgeon, as he asked him, "Why should I believe anything you tell me? How do I know, that you only want to drill into my wife's head to collect your fee? When I left my wife at 1pm, she was conscious, feeling great, looking forward to seeing each other tomorrow, and there was no mention of a heart attack — had there been, I would never have left her, nor that she was in danger of dying! I return four hours later, and she's literally a vegetable! (Shouting) Look at her! I don't believe Jones noticed, but I did. The neurosurgeon turned his glance away from Lee laying on the dolly. What did you people do to her?"

The doctor from Maine, equally anger told us all that they were dedicated medical professionals, and they wanted to assure us that everything they had done and were doing was within proper medical procedures to attempt to save Lee's life and he resented Jones remark about "fee!" Jones lost it — becoming extremely angry, shouting at the neurosurgeon, "Who the Hell do you think you are? Don't you dare lecture me about dedication, unless you have survived two wars, the rigors of several POW camps for two years and eight months, and been wounded three times!" The neurosurgeon hung his head and thereafter remained silent — realizing that he had unintentionally pushed Jones' red button.

With the ten of us standing around Lee laying on the dolly, the female doctor began to tell Jones that before they administered the anti-clotting drug to Lee that caused the stroke they had

338

explained to his wife the drug's risk (could cause a stroke) and obtained her signature on the consent form. Jones angrily told the doctor, "Let me tell you something Lady — that's a lie! My wife would and has never in all of the thirty-one years that we have been married, ever, signed anything until I have read it first, amd told her it was okay to sign! If she was having a heart attack as you claim, then how could she possibly sign a consent form, or for that matter, understood what you were talking about regarding stroke? You are lying! Lee has always been deathly afraid of having a stroke, and if she had understood what you were telling her, while having what you claim was a heart attack there is noway she would have allowed you to give her that anti-clotting drug, because she was petrified of being kept alive in a coma caused by a stroke! My wife addressed her fear of stroke by asking her God in her daily prays not to give her a stroke — placing her in what she called a cold coma. At the same time, making me swear on the graves of our dead children, that if she was ever in a coma, that I would not allow the doctors to keep her alive in that state!" Still speaking to the female doctor, Jones asked her, "Why didn't someone call me once my wife's so-called heart attack began, and before administering the anti-clotting drug?" Receiving the reply that it is the normal practice of the hospital, that when a patient is coherent, they get the permission from them rather then the next of kin. Jones told the doctor, "Well, had you telephoned me, I would not have allowed you to administer the drug if it could possibly cause a stroke! Had you heeded my instructions — Lee would not be laying here about to die as a vegetable!" No one made any comment to Jones' angry pronouncement, because the truth of his words were before all of our eyes — to see for ourselves — for Lee was dying.

Calmly, with a look of resignation on his face, Jones told the neurosurgeon and the other two doctors, "My wife is in the very cold coma she dreaded. Do nothing more for her. Let her die."

None of the medical personnel present, made any protest to Jones' request. Then turning to Hugo and his surrogate son, he told them, "Do you see what I am doing for your mother? Well remember, if I should end up like her, you are to do the same for me — do you hear me!" Still crying softly, they both in unison replied, "We will Dad!"

We accompanied Lee after she had been transferred from her dolly to a hospital bed with wheels, to a Continuances Care Unit (CCU). Upon arrival at the CCU, we were asked to wait, while behind a bed screen, they bathed Lee, fixed her hair — combed her hair over that portion of the skull that had been shaved, had fresh nightclothes put on, and connected monitors for her brain, heart, and lungs. While we waited to be allowed behind the screen, someone asked the head of the CCU, a female doctor, approximately how long would Lee live with her brain swelling? We all attentively listened to the reply, "There is no telling. She looks to weigh about 130 pounds, and she could last thirteen days, three months — they had no way of knowing, for every person is different." When we were allowed behind the screen that was around Lee's bed, she looked at peace — the spasms of her right arm had stopped. We silently, crying, continued our death vigil around Lee's bed — some standing, some sitting in chairs. A few minutes after 10 P.M., all the lines on the monitors went flat — Lee was gone. With tears in our eyes, we each bent to kiss Lee's slightly smiling, still warm lips — she knew that she had been released from her dreaded cold coma.]

After Lee's death and burial, Jones went into deep mourning and claims that will remain his condition throughout whatever time he has left, until he joins his wife in her journey of no return. Jones has experienced all the stages of grief over Lee's sudden death: Denial, anger, depression, and acceptance. Outwardly, everyone is amazed at how Jones appears to be living a normal limited life without Lee. But I, and those who really know Jones

— realize that it's only an act! Once again, a light has been turned off inside of him, in the past, over time, Lee was able to turn back on. This time, Lee is not here. I worry about Jones, because he has just taken too many of life's blows, and for the first time in forty-seven years, I see fear in his eyes — the other half of his soul is gone — Lee.

Jones told me this once, right after Lee's death, when we went the only time together, to the cemetery to visit her grave:

"I now know, that it would have been better had I never came out alive from the POW camps in China and North Korea, but I was determined that I was not going to die there! I would survive!

"Had I not been so determined, and perished then, my life would have been over and I would not now be experiencing what it is to die alone — in pieces!

"Nothing has ever worked out for me!"

> "We die. That may be the meaning of life. But we do language. That may be the meaning of our lives."
>
> *Toni Morrison*

EPILOGUE

With the death of Lee, I can now put pen to paper about my long held beliefs that I never mentioned to her or Jones about the adverse conditions they constantly lived under during their entire time in the United States of America, in my opinion, would have never had happened, had they been able to remain in the Republic de Panama. They possibly would not have had an additional two of their children die! As destiny had brought them out of their perspective countries of birth, to meet, fall in love, and marry in Panama, that was where they were to remain! Through no fault of theirs, they could not stay in Panama, and had to leave — thereby changing their destinies forever, resulting in disastrous and horrible consequences.

While carrying Lester, Lee experienced something called toxemia of pregnancy, experienced by one in two hundred women — cc 1963, — excess water, preventing the baby from turning in the fifth month, in order that his or hers insides could fall into place. The then standard treatment for this condition was to hospitalize the pregnant women and drain the excess water out of her. Why Lee's European American, United States Army Major, Obstetrician, did not hospitalize her in the fifth month of the pregnancy to drain the excess water out of her — begs an answer, even today. Once told of the circumstance surrounding Lester's premature birth and death in three days, Lee, Jones and I, are convinced, that had Lee's Obstetrician been a Panamanian, she would have been hospitalized and the excess water drained from her, and just possibly would have experienced the normal nine month birth of Lester!

Had Lee and Jones been living in the Republic de Panama, when it was discovered that Robert had an untreatable hole behind his heart — Auntie or someone, would have known of a "Holy Women," that they could have gone to and asked that she pray for Robert! Instead, we their friends, had to stand by along with Lee and Jones, and just watch Robert waste away, because their and our prayers were not enough to save him. For the doubters, I must confess, that I am a Roman Catholic and do believe in the power of prayer. Praying to my God, in that rice paddy that afternoon in 1950, wounded, just knowing that I was going to die — that he would not allow me to die that day, and he sent me Jones. Prayers, are answered, when done by a holy person (which I am not), whom are not necessarily or often a Pope or Priest. They are, such silent and unidentifiable holy persons amongst us.

Had Judy grown up in Panama City, Republic de Panama, she would have had no need to own an automobile to take her to and from her pace of employment. The public buses ran twenty-four hours, nor to wear a twelve foot multicolored scarf to keep out the cold. I continue to believe that it is not unreasonable to hypothesize that Judy possibly would be alive today and not rotting in her grave, had she been born, raised, schooled, and lived in Panama!

I believe what I have written about Lee's and Jones' life, their love, and deceased children, I did so, remembering Dick Morris' often quoted remark, "Truth is what which cannot be proven false."

In this narrative about Lee, I have also attempted to follow the advice of William Gass, "When we remember a life, we must remember to remember the life lived, not the life remembered."

It has been said that a man's life can be understood only at the moment of his death, and so too, maybe, with the love Lee and Jones felt and gave to each other. Their life together, I believe, was a testimony that one can endure life's horrific trials, if one is continually, uncompromisingly loved!

Now that Lee is gone, "We are two old men — one, European-American, the other, African-American, growing old alone, each with his memory of one woman, who we both loved." — Unknown

Unlike Jones, my love for Lee was not the love of passion nor self-possession, but the love of knowing. I had been able to live my life with the knowledge that Lee was the best part of it! Until that day arrives for me to also make that journey of no return, that Lester, Robert, Judy, and Lee are presently on, — I will continue to miss Lee with the hopelessness that she is no longer here, and I still need her to make my life whole!

> I tell my grief about which neither my
> hand nor my heart can write without
> remembering what the Apostle Paul says
> about not grieving for such things, and
> the words of IDRISI.

> "Call me again the day that is past."

F
Her lee
HERMEN OTTERMAN J.
  Lee.

31630

	DATE DUE		